McGRAW-HILL PUBLICATIONS IN INDUSTRIAL ARTS

Chris H. Groneman, *Consulting Editor*

BOOKS IN SERIES

Industrial Arts Drawing and Blueprint Reading—Coover

General Metals—Feirer

General Shop—Groneman and Feirer

General Woodworking—Groneman

Printing: A Practical Introduction to the Graphic Arts—
Jackson

(Other Books in Process)

Printing:

A PRACTICAL INTRODUCTION TO THE GRAPHIC ARTS

HARTLEY E. JACKSON

Late Head of the Printing Laboratory
San Jose State College
San Jose, California

Prepared for publication by
M. Ardelle Cleverdon

WEBSTER DIVISION, McGRAW-HILL BOOK COMPANY
St. Louis • New York • San Francisco • Dallas • Toronto • London

THE MAPLE PRESS COMPANY, YORK, PA.

Preface

This book is for the beginning student in the graphic arts. By following its simple, step-by-step instructions the beginner may advance as rapidly as his ability permits. The lessons cover carefully selected and graded projects in the basic processes of printing (type case, hand composition, and press work), bookbinding, linoleum block, silk screen, and photography. Cross references within the text aid the student in relating the activities of allied units. The nearly 300 carefully selected and prepared illustrations assist the student to understand the text and the various steps in the activities of each unit. Because of the self-instruction character of this book, the instructor may spend most of his time supervising the actual work done by his students and is free to give individual attention when needed.

Many of the individual projects are basic jobs that may be done or repeated with different copy or modified details. This flexibility permits and encourages the student to use his or her own originality and initiative. Most of the 80 units are designed for single-period classes. The number of units completed by a student depends on his or her aptitude and application and the number of hours and days the course is scheduled.

This book includes most of the topics recommended for graphic-arts instruction in the popular publication *A Guide to Improving Instruction in Industrial Arts.* Because of the wide variety of projects offered, the instructor can plan programs of interest to the beginners, to those students who may have had some graphic-arts instruction, and to those students with special interests.

Discussion Topics at the end of each unit provide a review of the important points covered within the unit. A few brief paragraphs about some phase of the printing industry are found after most units. This material is intended to supplement the instructional material within the units and to introduce the student to the history, production, and various occupations of the printing industry.

The equipment needed for the projects is of nominal cost. Suggestions are given for making some of the equipment that might easily be made in the school or home workshop.

THE PUBLISHERS

v

Acknowledgments

Grateful acknowledgment is extended to the many students of the author who have tried his plans in their teaching procedures and to Mr. Claude H. Eads, Director of the Printing Division of the University Press at the University of Texas, Austin, Texas, for his criticisms, suggestions, and editorial assistance. Acknowledgment is also given here to the kind and generous assistance given by John A. Backus, formerly Manager of the Department of Education, American Type Founders, Inc., Elizabeth, N.J.; F. W. Christoffel, Grover Cleveland Junior High School, Elizabeth, N.J.; John Emmel, Connelly Vocational High School, Pittsburgh, Pa.; J. Ely Van Hart, Supervisor of Industrial Arts, Elizabeth, N.J.; Fred J. Hartman, Educational Director of the International Graphic Arts Education Association, Washington, D.C.; Allan Kellock, Text-Film Department, McGraw-Hill Book Company, Inc., New York; Nils and Marie Ostberg, Jamaica, New York; John T. Porter, Manager of the Educational Services Department, American Type Founders, Inc., Elizabeth, N.J.; Scott Williams, Zundelowitz Junior High School, Wichita Falls, Texas; Anthony T. Stavaski, Associate Professor in Industrial Arts, State Teachers College, California, Pa.; John A. Woolley, Washington Park High School, Racine, Wis.

Acknowledgment is also given here to the following students of the College Station Public Schools, College Station, Texas, who posed for the pictures on the section-opening pages: Ann Elizabeth Cleland, Mary Varvel, Marcy Goode, Fred Brison, Jr., Johnny Turner, Lyman Joe Hardeman, and Bill Breazeale.

The following companies and institutions are here acknowledged for their generous assistance in providing not only technical advice and information but also illustration material: American Type Founders, Inc., Elizabeth, N.J.; Ansco, Binghamton, N.Y.; Bostitch, Westerly, R.I.; The Challenge Machinery Company, Grand Haven, Mich.; The Chandler & Price Company, Cleveland, Ohio; Eastman Kodak Company, Rochester, N.Y.; General Electric Company, Instrument Department, West Lynn, Mass.; The Goss Printing Press Company, Chicago, Ill.; Colton Press, Inc., New York, N.Y.; Graphic Arts Research Foundation, Inc., Cambridge, Mass.; Hallmark Cards, New York, N.Y.; The Haloid Company, Rochester, N.Y.; Hamilton Manufacturing Company, Two Rivers, Wis.; The W. O. Hickok Manufacturing Company, Harrisburg, Pa.; Intertype Corporation, Brooklyn, N.Y.; Lanston Monotype Machine Company, Philadelphia, Pa.; New York Herald Tribune, Inc., New York, N.Y.; The New York Times, New York, N.Y.; Mergenthaler Linotype Company, Brooklyn, N.Y.; The Pierpont Morgan Library, New York, N.Y.; The Reader's Digest, Pleasantville, N.Y.; Russell Ernest Baum, Inc., Philadelphia, Pa.; The Smyth Manufacturing Company, Hartford, Conn.; Southern Bleachery and Print Works, Inc., Taylor, S.C.; West Virginia Pulp and Paper Company, New York, N.Y.; Weston Electrical Instrument Corporation, Newark, N.J.

THE PUBLISHERS

Contents

Fred learns to set type by hand.

Section *I.* THE TYPE CASE

Unit 1. Introduction to the Type Case

To set type, you must first learn where to find the different letters of the alphabet in the type case. The case is divided into small compartments, or boxes. Each letter has its own box (see Fig. 1-1).

Throughout this course you will be using a *California job case*. This kind of type case is generally used in newspaper and commercial composing rooms in the United States. It holds, in a single compact unit, all the characters and symbols used in ordinary typesetting.

In this and the next eight units you will learn the California job case, a few letters at a time.

Procedure

1. Take the type case assigned to you and place it carefully on top of your case stand.

2. Examine the case. The case is divided into three equal parts, or sections. The right-hand section contains the *capitals.* The other two sections contain the small letters (called *lower-case letters*), the *figures,* and the *punctuation marks.* Figure 1-1 will help you to locate the position of the letters, spaces, quads, and so on, as they are mentioned.

Notice that some of the boxes are larger than others, especially in the lower-case section. The largest boxes hold the more frequently used letters, such as e, t, a, o, i, and h. The smallest boxes hold the less frequently used letters, such as k, z, x, and q.

The *spaces* used between words to separate them and the *quads* used to fill out lines are also found in the lower-case section. The large box in the lower right-hand corner of the left-hand section is for the 3-em spaces, which are the more frequently used spaces. Another box in a similar position in the middle section contains quads. You will learn more about spaces and quads in Unit 3.

3. Put one of the 3-em spaces alongside a type letter. You will see that

Fig. 1-1. California job case.

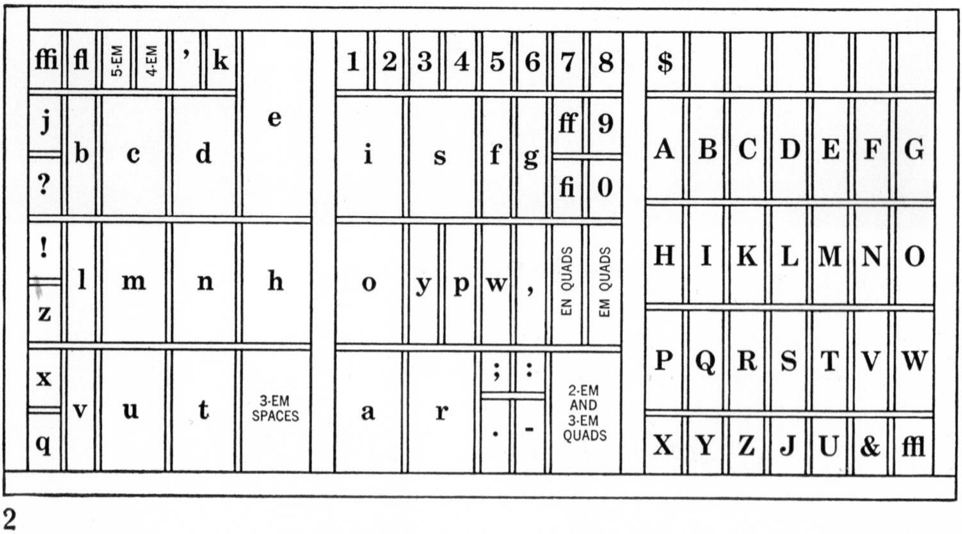

the space is not so high as the letter, and, therefore, it will not make a mark on the paper when it is used in a printed line of type.

Unlike typewriting, every type line must be filled from end to end, either with letters and spaces or with quads.

4. Draw an outline of the case shown in Fig. 1-1 on a card. Print your name in the upper right-hand corner of the card. You will fill in the spaces for each letter, figure, space, and so on, as you learn its location during the next few lessons.

5. Return your case to its proper place before you leave the class.

Discussion Topics

1. What kind of type case are you using?
2. Is type metal as hard as iron? Can you scratch it with your thumbnail?
3. Why do most printing plants use the same kind of type case?
4. Is the type in your case larger or smaller than the type used to print this question?

THE PRINTERS' SYSTEM OF MEASUREMENT

A composing stick is a metal frame in which type is set by hand. The composing stick that you will be using in the next unit is divided into picas. A pica is about one-sixth of an inch, that is, 6 picas make about 1 inch. The pica is divided into points. A point is one-twelfth of a pica, that is, 12 points equal 1 pica. Therefore, 72 points (6 times 12) make about 1 inch.

In general, picas are used to measure lengths, and points are used to measure thicknesses. Type sizes are usually given in points. In Fig. 1-2 a pica gauge is being used to measure a letter. What size is the type in your case? Look at some of the other cases in the case rack. You may find such sizes as 18 point, 24 point, 48 point, and perhaps 72 point.

FIG. 1-2. Measuring a piece of type with a pica gauge. The piece of type shown is 5 picas, or 60 points, high. Therefore, it is 60-point type.

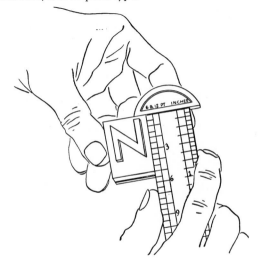

Unit 2. Location of Capital Letters.   Use of
Composing Stick.   Setting Your Name

In this unit you will learn the names of the parts of a typical letter (Fig. 2-1), the location of the capital letters, and how to use a composing stick.

CAPITAL LETTERS

You do not have to wait until you have learned where all the letters in the type case are before you set type. You can begin by setting the capital letters.

Procedure

1. Place the type case on your type stand. Along the top of the right-hand section is a row of small boxes. These boxes contain the dollar symbol ($) and other extras. Skip this row for the present. At the left end of the next row you will find the first capital letter, A.

2. Pick up a capital letter A and examine it. On one end is the letter itself, called the *face,* and on the other end are the two *feet* on which the letter stands in the type line (Fig. 2-1). On one side, near the bottom, there are one or more deep grooves. These grooves are

FIG. 2-1. A piece of type. How many nicks, or grooves, does the type in your case have?

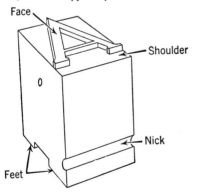

called the *nicks.* When type is being set, the nicks show whether or not the letters are right side up.

3. Letter a neat capital A in the proper space on your case diagram.

4. Pick up a letter from each box along the row to the right of the letter A. You will find B, C, D, E, F, and G. Return each letter to its correct box. Continue in this way along each row. You will find that the letters go on in alphabetical order in the next three rows, *with two exceptions.* Capitals J and U are not in the usual alphabetical order but are found in the bottom row after capital Z. This unusual order came about nearly five hundred years ago when the alphabet had only 24 capital letters. At that time capital I was used for both I and J, and capital V was used for both V and U. When capitals J and U were introduced, about two hundred years ago, the printers did not wish to change the order of the letters in the type case as they knew them. As a result, they placed the two new letters after Z, where you now find them.

5. Fill out the rest of the capitals on your case diagram. Letter neat, clear letters in the spaces. You will refer to them many times in the next few weeks.

6. Ask the instructor to check your diagram after you have filled in all the capital letters.

USE OF COMPOSING STICK

The composing stick that you will use in this course is called a *graduated* stick

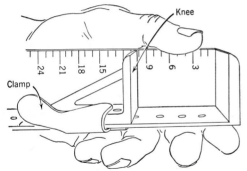

FIG. 2-2. Composing stick.

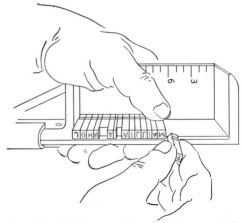

FIG. 2-3. Hold composing stick in your left hand and use your right hand to place the type in the stick. The thumb of the left hand holds the last letter in the line.

(Fig. 2-2). By means of the holes in its frame and the movable part known as the *knee,* this composing stick can be set to any width in picas. The knee is held in the desired position by the *clamp.* Ask the instructor to show you how to set your stick. Now you are ready to set your name.

Procedure

1. Hold the stick in your left hand as shown in Figs. 2-2 and 2-3.

2. Pick up the first letter of your name and place it face up in the left-hand corner of the stick with the nicks facing the open side.

3. Hold the letter in place with your left thumb (Fig. 2-3).

4. Follow with the rest of the letters in your first name.

5. Place a 3-em space after your first name and continue with the setting of your last name.

6. When complete, check each letter to see that the nicks on each letter are the same and facing the open side of the stick.

7. Fill out the line with quads and spaces. Figure 1-1, page 2, will help you find the necessary quads and spaces. Make the line snug but not tight.

8. Lay a piece of soft paper on the letters in the stick and press it down firmly with your right thumb. The impression of the type in the paper will show you what you have set.

9. Return the letters, spaces, and quads to their proper boxes.

10. Set other lines if you have time.

11. Return the type case to its proper place before you leave the class.

Discussion Topics

1. Why not set everything in capital letters? Why use lower-case letters at all?

2. It is not possible to set type with the left hand. Why?

3. Why do you think the tool used for setting type is called a stick?

4. What is the movable part of a stick called? What holds it in place?

The Composing Stick and Its Care

A composing stick is always held in the left hand as shown in Fig. 2-3, and the type is placed in it with the right hand. Place your stick in your left hand and examine the graduations on your stick and those shown in Fig. 2-2. You will notice that every third pica graduation is indicated by a longer line than those used to mark the other pica divisions. These longer marks will help you to count the pica divisions quickly. For example, four of these longer marks indicate 12 picas and six of them make 18 picas.

Nongraduated composing sticks are set to different measures by using pica spaces, known as *pica quads,* with which you will become familiar in the next unit. The pica quads are exactly 12 points, or 1 pica, square. To set a non-graduated stick, you place the required number of pica quads in the stick with the nicks to the right or left next to the end and move the knee of the stick up to them. A piece of newspaper is placed between the knee and the end quad for what is called *squeeze.*

Some things to remember when you are using a composing stick:

1. Do not drop your stick. If you drop your stick, you may bend the end of the frame and make the stick inaccurate.

2. Never pull a proof of type lines while they are in the composing stick.

3. Remove all type lines from your stick at the end of the class.

4. Always hang your stick up in its proper place when you are finished with it.

Unit 3. Location of Spaces and Quads, Figures, Periods, and Commas Setting Your Name and Address

Spaces are used between words to separate them, and *quads* are used to fill out short lines, as, for example, at the ends of paragraphs, in an address, or in poetry. Before you can set your address, you will need to know where to find the figures, periods, and commas as well as the spaces and the quads.

Spaces and Quads

In the lower right-hand corner of the center section of your type case is the big box that contains two sizes of quads. Just above this box and next to the wide bar that separates the lower case from the capitals, you will find the *em quads.* You will notice that the ends of the em quads are perfectly square.

The em quads are used at the beginning of paragraphs to give the first line of the paragraph the desired indention. The em quad is the unit by which all other quads and the spaces in your case are measured (Fig. 3-1).

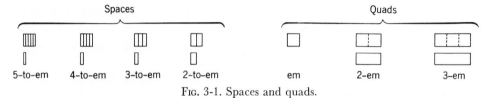

Fig. 3-1. Spaces and quads.

Procedure

1. Take two em quads and place them beside the next largest quad taken from the box below. Since this quad is as wide as the two em quads together, it is called a *2-em quad.*

2. Take three em quads and place them beside the largest quad taken from the box below. Since this quad is as wide as the three quads together, it is called a *3-em quad.*

3. Take three spaces from the big box at the lower right-hand corner of the left-hand section. Set these together and place an em quad with them. The three spaces together are the same width as the em quad. These spaces are called *3-to-em spaces* or, more briefly, *3-em spaces.* Each space is one-third of an em.

4. Take two of the spaces from the box at the left of the em-quad box and place an em quad with them. Since two of these spaces together are the same size as an em, they are called *2-to-em,* or *2-em, spaces.* Printers often call the 2-em spaces *en* quads, but this sounds too much like *em* quads and may lead to confusion. It is much better to say "2-to-em space" or "2-em space."

5. Take four spaces from the box that is fourth from the left in the top row of the left-hand section and check them with an em quad. Since four of these spaces together make an em quad, they are called *4-to-em spaces* or *4-em spaces.*

6. Take five spaces from the box that is to the left of the 4-to-em spaces and check them with an em quad. Since five of these spaces together make an em, they are called *5-to-em spaces* or *5-em spaces.*

7. Mark all the spaces and quads on your case diagram. Write or letter their names carefully in full as follows: "3-to-em spaces," "em quads," and so on.

The em and multiples of the em are called *quads,* and the divisions of the em are called *spaces* (Fig. 3-1).

FIGURES

The figures are easily learned. They are found in the top row of boxes of the center section of the case and in the two boxes below the right-hand end of this row.

Procedure

1. Pick up a figure from the first box at the left of the top row of the center section. It is figure 1. Figures 2, 3, 4, 5, 6, 7, and 8 follow in order in the boxes across this row from left to right. Figure 9 is in the box directly below figure 8. Zero (0) is directly below figure 9.

2. Examine a figure from each box to be sure that the figures are in their proper boxes.

3. Add the figures to your case diagram.

PERIODS AND COMMAS

The periods are in the box in the center of the bottom row of the center section—two boxes to the left of the big quad box. The comma box is just to the left of the 2-to-em-space, or en quad, box.

Procedure

1. Pick up and examine a period.
2. Pick up and examine a comma. Could the comma be used for any other mark of punctuation?
3. Mark the period and the comma on your case diagram.

Setting Your Name and Address

Now that you know where to find the capital letters, figures, periods, and commas as well as the spaces and quads, you are ready to set your name and address.

Procedure

1. Set your composing stick at 18 picas.
2. Ask the instructor for two 6-point *slugs* and two 2-point *leads* (rhymes with "sleds") to fit your stick as you have set it. Slugs are metal strips 6 points and sometimes 12 points thick, and leads are metal strips 1, 2, and 3 points thick. The word "lead" alone usually means a 2-point lead and is used in this sense throughout this book. Leads and slugs are used for spacing between lines.

Always have a slug in the stick before you start to set type.

3. Set your name in capital letters in the first line. Use 3-em spaces between names and before and after each initial. Be sure you use a period after each initial. Fill out the line with spaces and quads.

4. Place a lead in the stick in front of the type line.
5. Set your street address in the second line. Fill out the line with spaces and quads.
6. Place a second lead in the stick.
7. Set your city and state in the third line. Use commas where needed. Fill out the line evenly with spaces and quads.
8. Place the second slug after the last line of type.
9. Use a piece of soft paper to make a pressure proof with your thumb.
10. Return each letter, figure, period, and comma to its proper box in the type case. This is called *distributing type*. A more detailed description of this operation is given in Unit 16, "Distribution of Type," pages 40–41.
11. Return the leads and slugs to their proper places.
12. Put the type case away.

Discussion Topics

1. Why do we need more than one size of space?
2. Does it make any difference if the em quad in your case is turned halfway around?
3. Why are spaces made lower than type letters?
4. How many leads, piled one on top of the other, are as thick as a slug?

Type and Its Care

The type metal used for most hand-set type is an alloy of lead with antimony, tin, and sometimes copper. The type is made by pumping this alloy, when hot, into an adjustable steel box called a *mold*. The end of this box is covered with a piece of brass in which is cut a sunken letter. This is called a *matrix*. Such type is called *foundry type* because it is cast in a type foundry. Other metal types are cast by typesetting machines.

Type letters can be damaged by dropping them on the floor, by scratch-ing them with a rough cloth or metal tools, or by applying too much pressure on them in printing.

The ink on type should be washed off carefully with a commercial type cleaner and a soft cloth after pulling a proof or at the end of a press run. If ink dries on type, it is hard to remove.

Unit 4. Spacing of Lines. Removing Type from Stick and Tying

In this unit you will be setting a name and address that you may use later on in the course (Unit 42) to print some personal stationery. You may wish to set your own, your mother's, or someone else's name and address. In Unit 34 you will have another opportunity to set type for personal stationery that will be printed in Unit 47.

When we read a book, we do not usually notice the spaces between words, but sometimes the words seem to run to-gether. This is because the spaces be-tween the words are too small. It is, therefore, important to space each line correctly.

Since only a few lines can be set in a composing stick at one time, it is also necessary to learn how to remove the lines as they are set and to tie them securely before they are stored on a *gal-ley*. A galley is a metal tray with a rim on two sides and across one end as shown in Fig. 4-1. It is used for holding and storing type.

SPACING OF LINES

The right space between words set in lower-case letters is about as thick as the lower-case f, or a 3-to-em space. Words set in capitals need more space between them; a space about as wide as the capital F, or a 2-to-em space, is about right.

All the spaces in a line should *appear* equal. This means that some of the spaces can be thinner than the others. For example, the space used after a comma or a period should be smaller than the space between the words in the same line in order to appear the same.

Procedure

1. Set your composing stick at 18 picas and put a slug in it.

2. Set your name, including your middle initial with a period, in capi-tals.

Fig. 4-1. A galley. What is it used for?

Rim

Open end

Head end

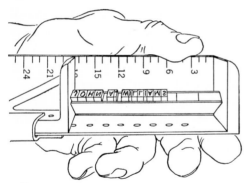

Fig. 4-2. Testing the justification of a line.

3. Put a 2-to-em space before the initial and a 3-to-em space after it. When you print the name, it will look as though the spaces are the same. Why?

4. Add the quads and spaces at the right-hand end of the line until the line is tight.

5. Push the line forward between the jaws of the stick as shown in Fig. 4-2. The line should not fall back, but it should slide forward and backward freely. Test all your lines from now on by pushing each one forward and by moving it forward and backward to prove to yourself that it slides freely.

Justification is the word that describes what you have done in steps 4 and 5. To *justify* a line means to fill it out correctly so that it will pass these tests. All composing sticks are made a little wider than exact picas to allow for the *squeeze* that results when lines are properly justified. Slugs and leads are cut to exact pica measure and fit easily into the stick.

When you justify a type line that is filled out with quads and spaces:

a. Always lift out the end quad while you are inserting the spaces between words.

b. Always place the spaces next to the type—not at the end of a line or between quads.

6. Put a lead in your stick after your name and finish setting your address. Put a lead after each line as you finish setting it. Justify each line carefully.

7. Put a slug after the last line.

Now you are ready to learn how to remove the type from your composing stick.

REMOVING TYPE FROM STICK AND TYING

Removing a *type form* (lines of type) from a composing stick (or *dumping type,* as it is sometimes called), placing it on a galley, and tying up the type form with string is a very important operation. During this course, you may need to tie and untie type forms many times in one class period.

First examine Fig. 4-3 carefully. It shows you how to place your stick on your galley. Then study Fig. 4-4, which shows you how to place your fingers around the type form as you remove it from the composing stick.

Fig. 4-3. Placing a composing stick full of type on a galley.

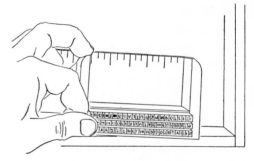

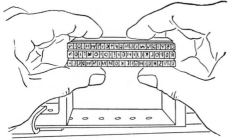

Fig. 4-4. Removing, or lifting, the type form from the stick and placing it on the galley. The middle finger of each hand keeps the letters from falling out at the ends of the lines. The thumbs and forefingers hold the lines of type together.

Fig. 4-6. Correct position of a type form on a galley for tying it up—head at right and nicks at left.

Procedure

1. Place your composing stick on your galley as shown in Fig. 4-3.

2. Place your fingers as shown in Fig. 4-4. The middle finger of each hand keeps the type from spilling out at the ends of the lines. The thumbs and forefingers hold the lines of type together. Slide the lines forward out of the stick onto the galley.

3. Slide the lines carefully to the closed end (at right) of the galley as shown in Figs. 4-5 and 4-6. Now you are ready to tie up the type form.

Fig. 4-5. Placing the type lines carefully in one corner at the head of the galley before tying. The nicks should be toward the left.

4. Cut a piece of string long enough to go around the type form five or six times.

5. Hold a short end of the string in your left hand as shown in Fig. 4-7. Make the first turn around the type form (firmly but gently) and pass the string over the beginning of the turn. This will catch the short loose end that you held in your left hand. Now proceed to wrap the string around the form firmly four or five more times.

6. Hold the free end of the string firmly around the corner of the type

Fig. 4-7. Tying up type. In circle notice: (1) The first and second turns pass over beginning of the string. (2) The loop at the end is pushed down behind the wrappings. How would you untie the type?

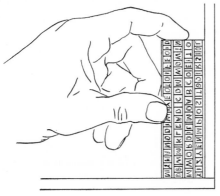

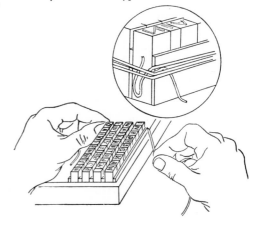

form with the forefinger of your left hand and push a loop of the free end down behind the wrappings with a brass rule (Fig. 4-7). Pull the loop snug up to the corner, but do not pull the loose end through. Your type form is now tied up. To untie the form, just pull the free end of the string.

With a little practice, you will be able to tie up your type forms quickly and securely.

7. Put your galley, with your type form, or job, in the galley rack.

You will have an opportunity to see how this job looks when you print it in Unit 10.

Discussion Topics

1. Why have a slug above and below a job when you tie it up?
2. Why use a brass rule to push the loop of the string down behind the wrappings? What would happen if you used a lead to do this?
3. Why should you not release the knee of the composing stick when you are lifting out a type form?

Galleys and Their Care

As mentioned earlier in this unit, a galley is a metal tray that has a rim on three sides and one end open (Fig. 4-6). The closed end is called the *head* of the galley. When you are working with a galley, you should have the head of the galley at your right and the open end at your left.

There are two don't's" about galleys:
1. Don't get your steel galley wet, but if you do, wipe it off immediately.
2. Don't drop your galley on the floor. It will be useless if it gets bent.

Whether or not type is set by hand or by machine, it is placed on a galley for proofing, correcting, and storing.

Unit 5. Lower-case Layout: Upper Left-hand Side

Unlike the capitals, the lower-case letters are not in alphabetical order. The more frequently used letters are in large boxes and are placed conveniently toward the center of the case. The less frequently used letters are in smaller boxes located toward the outside. This arrangement makes typesetting as easy as possible.

In the next few units you will learn this lower-case layout. Most students find it easier to learn it a little at a time,

rather than all at once. Learn first the group of letters in the upper left-hand part of the case. These letters are b, c, d, e, k, l, m, n, and h.

The first four letters, b, c, d, and e, are in alphabetical order, as are l, m, and n.

Procedure

1. Find the letters b, c, d, e, k, l, m, n, and h in the upper left-hand side of your type case. Mark each one on your case diagram.

2. Set your stick at 15 picas and place a 15-pica slug in it.

3. Set each of the following words several times in a line. Put a 3-to-em space after each word.

bed	den	bell	helm
need	hem	neck	blended

4. Distribute each line after you set it and before you set another line of words.

5. Before you put your case away, check yourself by taking a few letters at random from each of the boxes that you have been using. Have you put the letters back in the correct boxes?

Discussion Topics

1. How high is a piece of type from the bottom of the foot to the printing surface? One inch? Less than one inch? More than one inch?

2. What is the purpose of the shoulder below the letter on a piece of type? (See Fig. 2-1, page 4.)

Type Fonts and Sizes

A *font* is a complete assortment of type of one style and size. A font has more of the letters that are used most often, for example, e, t, h, o, a, and so on, than it has of the letters that are used less often, for example, k, p, w, and so on. Type is sold in fonts (Fig. 5-1).

Type is made in a large number of sizes from 6 to 72 points (Fig. 5-2). Big letters are more expensive than small letters. Why? Usually there are fewer big letters in a font. For example, a font of small type, like 6-point, may contain 28 or 30 capital A's; a big-size type, like 72-point, may have only four capital A's.

Fig. 5-1. A complete assortment of letters, figures, and so forth, of 12-point Baskerville.

ABCDEFGHIJKLMNOP
QRSTUVWXYZ
abcdefghijklmnopqrstuvwxyz
fiflffffiffl ( ) [] $1234567890
,."`:;!? ⅛¼⅜½⅝¾⅞
*1234567890**
ABCDEFGHIJKLMNOPQRSTUVWXYZ

ABCDEFGHIJKLMNOP
QRSTUVWXYZ
$1234567890 ,."`:;
⅛¼⅜½⅝¾⅞ *1234567890**
abcdefghijklmnopqrstuvwxyz
fi fl ff ffi ffl ( ) []

Fig. 5-2. Different sizes of the same letter from 6- to 14-point Baskerville M.

M M M M M M M M

Unit 6. Lower-case Layout: Lower Left-hand Side

The lower-case letters in the lower left-hand side are v, u, and t. In this unit you will be given words to set that use these letters and the letters that you used in the last unit from the upper left-hand side of your type case.

Procedure

1. Find the letters v, u, and t in the lower row of boxes. Add these letters to your case diagram. Look carefully at the u and compare it with the n in the row above. The crossbar of the u is below, that is, toward the nick end (Fig. 6-1).

2. Set your stick at 15 picas and put a 15-pica slug in it.

3. Set each of the following phrases and sentences. As soon as you have completed one line, distribute the type before you begin setting the next one.

Lend me ten men.	The tenth deck.
Cut the nettle.	But Ben chuckled.
The end vent.	The cement level.

4. After you have distributed the last line, check your work by examining a few letters from each box.

5. Cut 12 small cards about an inch square. On each card draw one of the lower-case letters that you are learning.

6. Place each card in its proper box.

7. Pick up the lettered cards and mix them up by shaking them in your hands. Now see if you can return each to the correct box without looking at your case diagram. If you make mistakes the first time, try again until you get them right.

8. Take the lettered cards out of the boxes before you put your type case away. Save the cards for future practice.

Discussion Topics

Here are a few questions to help you to test yourself. After you read each question, shut your eyes and picture in your mind how the case looks. How well can you remember the position of the various letters in your type case without your diagram and without looking at the case itself?

1. What letter is in the largest box?
2. What two letters are next to it on the left?
3. What letter is just below the largest box. (Continued on page 16.)

Fig. 6-2. Johann Gutenberg checking a freshly printed page while young Peter Schoeffer, his assistant, operates the press. The two inverted mushroom-shaped objects on the stool in the foreground are ink balls, or daubers. These were used to ink the type before each sheet of paper was printed. Notice the sheets hanging on the line in the background. What does this tell you about the printing ink used by Gutenberg?

Fig. 6-1. Comparison of n and u.

FIG. 6-3. A page from a book printed from carved wooden blocks. Notice the lettering has been carved to look like hand lettering. The first letters cut and cast in metal by Gutenberg were also made to look like the hand lettering on manuscripts. The people were familiar with this form of lettering at that time.

4. What letter is between v and t in the bottom row?
5. What letter is right above t?
6. What letter is in the box below b?
7. What are the two letters on each side of n?
8. What are the two letters on each side of c?

EARLY PRINTING

It is reported that the first books printed from metal types appeared in Germany five centuries ago, about 1450.

FIG. 6-4. A printing shop of the early sixteenth century. Notice the man at the right is setting type in a wooden stick. The man behind the press is holding two ink balls, or daubers. It was his job to ink the type before the next page, or sheet of paper, was printed.

A German named Johann (John) Gutenberg (Fig. 6-2) is said to have invented a method of printing from movable metal letters. In European countries before that time, the books were copied by hand or printed from carved wooden blocks (Fig. 6-3).

The invention of printing from movable type brought about great changes in Europe and throughout the world. Within a hundred years after Gutenberg's invention, more than twenty million books had been printed and sold. Before this time only a few people received an education because books were scarce and very expensive. When many inexpensive books were available, thousands of people learned to read. By reading, they learned more about other countries and other people and they wanted to see them. As a result, travel and trade increased and all industries prospered. This also led to new discoveries in all parts of the world.

It may be said that printing started the march of modern civilization.

Unit 7. Lower-case Layout: Upper Right-hand Side

The right-hand side of the lower-case layout is the center section of the type case. The lower-case letters in the upper right-hand side of the lower-case layout are i, s, f, g, o, y, p, and w. These letters are in the two rows of boxes below the figures 1 to 6, which you have already marked on your diagram.

Procedure

1. Find the letters i, s, f, g, o, y, p, and w in the upper right-hand side of the lower-case section of your type case. Mark each letter on your case diagram.

2. Draw each of these letters on inch-square cards. You now have cards for 20 of the 26 letters of the alphabet.

3. Put each of the 20 cards in its correct box in your case. Use your case diagram to do this.

4. Pick up all the cards, shuffle them, and try to replace them without looking at the diagram. Do this several times, until you do it easily. You and your neighbor can now test each other on how well you know the case.

5. Let your neighbor pick out a word from the list below, for example, the word "this." Without his telling you what the word is, he will point to the t box, and then to the h, i, and s boxes. Watch him as he spells out the word in this way, and when he is through, you say "this."

Repeat the same process for the 20 words that he picks from the list. Keep a score of how many you miss.

6. Take your turn and test your neighbor with 20 words. You may use some of the words that he used or pick out different ones. See who misses the fewer words.

this	step	union	success
when	blue	child	chimney
lost	sound	eight	monkey
five	would	insect	engine
mind	those	double	stingy
kept	hound	hustle	fickle
soft	lemon	employ	flight
show	field	linotype	people
them	stick	buckle	employ
must	uncle	nothing	bundle
line	knife	nickel	envelope
type	globe	myself	poison
slug	spend	pistol	swing

Discussion Topics

1. How many letters are there in the English alphabet?
2. How many vowels have you marked on your case diagram so far? Which one is missing?
3. People from other countries who learn English have a hard time with the syllable "ough." It has at least five different sounds as you may hear by pronouncing these words: through, enough, plough, thorough, ought. Can you think of another?

VARIOUS PROCESSES OF PRINTING

There are five basic methods of printing: relief, planography, intaglio, stencil, and photography.

Relief. Printing from a raised surface, such as the type in your case, is called *letterpress* printing and is one example of relief printing (Fig. 7-1). Daily newspapers and many books and magazines are printed by this process. This book you are reading was printed by letterpress.

Planography. Planographic printing is done from a plane or flat surface that has been treated chemically (Fig. 7-2).

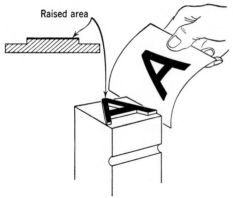

FIG. 7-1. Relief printing. Paper pressed against raised inked areas. The low areas do not print. Letterpress is a good example of relief printing.

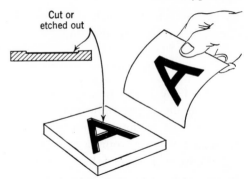

FIG. 7-3. Intaglio. During the printing process the plate is inked and wiped clean, leaving ink only in the cutout or etched areas. When the paper is pressed against the plate, only the cutout or etched areas print.

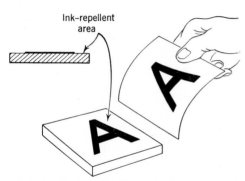

FIG. 7-2. Planography. The nonprinting areas are treated to repel ink. Therefore, only the image is inked up and prints when a piece of paper is pressed against the plate.

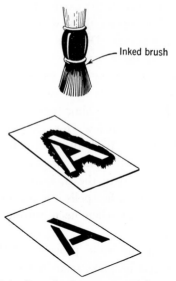

Photo-offset lithography (page 127) and the photogelatin process of printing are examples of planographic printing. The photogelatin process is often used to reproduce paintings, photographic posters, and displays.

Intaglio. The word *intaglio* is pronounced in-tal-yo. It means *carved.* Intaglio printing is done from plates into which the letters, designs, or pictures have been cut or etched (Fig. 7-3). Gravure, rotogravure, and engrav-

FIG. 7-4. Stencil. Letters or design to be printed are cut out, forming the stencil or printing mask. Printing is done by forcing ink through the cutout areas with an inked brush or roller. Ink may also be sprayed through the cutout areas onto the surface to be printed.

ing are examples of intaglio printing. Wedding announcements and fine stationery are often printed by the engraving process. Thermography, which you will have an opportunity to do later in the course, is an inexpensive process which looks very much like engraving.

Another kind of intaglio printing is called *rotogravure*. Plates for rotogravure are made by using both photography and chemical etching. Rotogravure printing may be seen in the Sunday picture sections of some of the larger newspapers and in the fashion pages of many mail-order catalogues. A kind of ink that dries instantly is used for rotogravure printing.

This process is also used to print cellophane wrappers and celluloid sheets.

Stencil. Stencil printing is done by cutting out the letters and daubing, rolling, or spraying the ink through the openings onto the desired surface (Fig. 7-4). Mimeograph and the silk-screen process are examples of stencil printing. Silk-screen printing is described in Section VI, "Silk-screen Printing," pages 198–224.

Photography. The photographic process is usually used for printing small quantities. If you are interested in photography, you have probably done this type of printing yourself. Unit 79, "Contact Printing," pages 247–

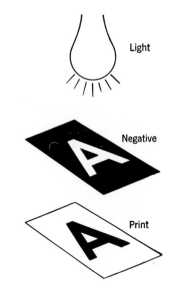

Fig. 7-5. Photographic printing. Light is used to print the image formed on the film in the camera on a light-sensitive paper.

257, describes this process in detail.

Most printing requires paper and ink. There are many kinds of each. Later you will learn more about the making of paper (pages 154–156) and about printing inks (pages 119–120). In the meantime, examine the various papers that you see in magazines and other places. See how many colors of ink and kinds of paper you can find.

Unit 8. Lower-case Layout: The Last Six Letters

You have learned the location of 20 letters. All that are left are a, r, and the little-used letters q, x, z, and j. The letters a and r are located in the two large boxes in the bottom row of the center section of your type case. The letters j, z, x, and q are located in four of the seven small boxes along the left-hand side of the left-hand section of your type case.

Procedure

1. Find the letters a, r, j, z, x, and q and add them to your case diagram. Your lower-case alphabet is now filled in completely.

2. Make small square cards for these last 6 letters as you did for the other 20 letters.

3. Practice placing these 6 cards in their proper places two or three times.

4. Shuffle all 26 cards together and place each one in its proper box. Repeat this operation until you can do it quickly and correctly. Check your accuracy each time with your case diagram.

5. Set your stick at 15 picas and put a 15-pica slug in it.

6. Set up the alphabet from a to z in your stick. Distribute the letters and repeat the process several times. How fast can you set up the alphabet? If you can do it in less than two minutes without looking at your case diagram, you are doing well.

For Practice

Below are some words and sentences that you may set for practice. Everyone needs practice in order to set type quickly and correctly. Here are four points that will help you:

First, when you are about to pick up a letter from a box, look ahead of your hand into the box and decide which letter you are going to take. Sight or spot a letter that is easy to pick up, one with the nick facing toward the left if possible.

Second, take out the letter that you sight or spot.

Third, turn the letter in your fingers as you carry it toward your stick. Have the letter face up and the nick out when it reaches the stick. Do not hurry.

Fourth, take time to place the letter gently but firmly in the line. Raise your left thumb from the preceding letter and put the new letter carefully in its place. Then lower your thumb again to hold the last letter in place.

Now you are ready to put into practice these four points.

1. Set your composing stick at 27 picas. How many inches is 27 picas?

2. Set up the following lines and justify them. These are some old chestnuts that have been in use a long time by people learning to set type. The second one contains all the letters of the alphabet.

Now is the time for all good men to
    come to the aid of the party.
The quick brown fox jumps over the
    lazy dog.

3. Show your stick to the instructor so that he may check your letters b, d, p, and q. You may find it helpful to examine Fig. 9-1, page 22, which shows all the "look alikes."

4. Distribute the lines you have set.

5. Set up a few of the following words, which contain all the vowels.

education	cauliflower
sequoia	unimportance
regulation	cautioned
exultation	ambidextrous

Discussion Topics

1. The most-used letter in English is e. Next is t, then in order, a, o, i, n, s, h, r, d, l, u, c, and m. With one exception these lower-case letters are all in big boxes. What is the exception?

2. The b box is about half the size of one of the big boxes. What other lower-case letters are in half-size boxes?

3. What lower-case letters are in boxes the same size as the letter k box? (There are four others.)

4. Two letters alongside each other on your lower-case diagram make a word. What is the word?

IMPORTANCE OF PRINTING

Everyone is literally surrounded with printing. Some phase of printing is used every hour of the day in some way. Newspapers, magazines, and books are everywhere. Printed advertising is used to sell nearly all the things we buy.

Modern life would slow down to a stop very quickly if all the printing presses were taken away. Business and industry depend on printing. They use printed forms on which to order their goods, to sell their goods, and to collect their bills.

There are hundreds of uses for printing. Here are a few:

Billboards	Tickets of all kinds
Greeting cards	Sports programs
Playing cards	Telephone directories
Halloween masks	Candy wrappers

Can you think of ten more uses for printing?

Unit 9. Punctuation Marks, Symbols, Ligatures and Letters That Look Alike

You are now ready to complete your case diagram by adding the remaining six punctuation marks, two symbols, and five ligatures.

A *symbol* is an accepted sign used instead of a word or words, for example, the symbol $ is used to represent the words "dollar" and "dollars."

A *ligature* in printing is two or more letters joined together on one piece of type, as, for example, fi, ffi, fl, ffl, and ff.

Two of the look alikes were probably responsible for the familiar expression "Mind your p's and q's." Two other pairs of look alikes with which you have now had some experience are b and d, and n and u.

PUNCTUATION MARKS

You will find eight punctuation marks in your case:

period (.)	hyphen (-)
comma (,)	apostrophe (')
colon (:)	exclamation point (!)
semicolon (;)	question mark (?)

You have already found the period and comma. The colon, semicolon, and hyphen are in the three little boxes around the period box. The question mark and exclamation point are in the small boxes under the letter j and alongside the letters b and l. The apostrophe is between the k box and the 4-to-em-space box in the top row of the left-hand section of your case.* Add these six punctuation marks to your case diagram.

The comma and the apostrophe look alike, but the apostrophe is at the top of the piece of type, away from the nick, and the comma is down almost to the bottom of the face of the piece of type, toward the nick side.

SYMBOLS

The dollar sign ($), or symbol, is just above the capital letter A. It is always placed in the stick in front of the figures like this: $64.

The symbol that stands for the word "and," the ampersand (&), is in the bottom row of the cap case at the right

FIG. 9-1. Look alikes. With the nicks up they are easy to tell apart.

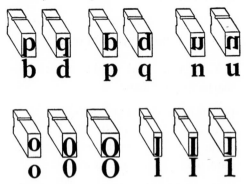

b   d   p   q   n   u

o   0   O   l   I   1

* Two commas turned upside down (") are used as the opening quotation mark. Two apostrophes (") are used as the closing quotation mark.

of the capital letter U. It is sometimes used in firm names, such as Smith & Brown and Black & Company.

Add these two symbols to your case diagram.

LIGATURES

Most ordinary type faces have ligatures. This is especially true when the top curl of the letter f overhangs the type body. To test this, set an f and an i in your stick. The top curl of the f may hit the dot of the i and leave a little space between the letters. This will break one or both of the letters if they are used together in a line of type.

In the box at the left of the figure 0, you will find the ligature fi. The top curl of the f takes the place of the dot of the i. This ligature should always be used when these two letters come together, as in the word "fine."

The ff ligature is in the small box just above the fi ligature.

The ffi and the fl ligatures are in the two small boxes at the left-hand end of the top row of the left-hand section.

The ffl ligature is in the last box of the bottom row of the right-hand, or cap, section of your case.

Add these five ligatures to your case diagram. Your case diagram should now be complete.

How many ligatures can you find on this page?

THE LOOK ALIKES

To keep from mixing up the letters b and d, p and q, and n and u, you must be sure to hold the letters with the nicks up (Fig. 9-1). You can tell them apart very easily in the following way:

n and u: The crossbar of the n is away from the nick; in the u it is toward the nick.
b and d: The up-and-down lines of both of these letters go away from the nick.
p and q: The up-and-down lines of these two letters go toward the nick.

To tell the difference between b and d, or between p and q, look at the round part of these letters. When the nick is up, the round part is always on the same side as it is in the printed letter. Study Fig. 9-1 carefully.

For Practice

1. Take three or four of each of the six letters that look alike and mix them up.
2. Set the letters up in your composing stick.
3. Put all the b's together, and so on.
4. Test yourself by matching each group with another letter taken from the case or by making a thumb-pressure proof on soft paper.
5. Practice by repeating steps 1 to 4 until you can identify each of these letters easily.
6. Return the letters to their proper boxes.

Discussion Topics

1. What is a symbol?
2. What is a ligature?
3. How can you tell the difference between a capital I, a figure 1, and a lower-case l? (See Fig. 9-1.)
4. How can you tell the difference between a lower-case o, a capital O, and zero? (See Fig. 9-1.)
5. The ampersand is really a ligature. It represents the Latin word *et,* which means "and." Can you see the e and the t in this ligature?

Fig. 9-2. Flow of work in a letterpress and lithographic printing plant.

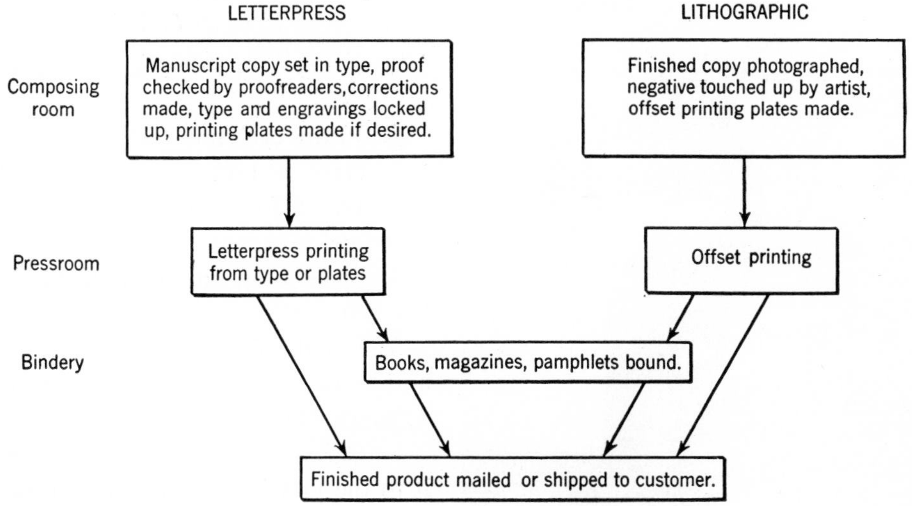

PRINTING PLANT ORGANIZATION

Most printing plants have three departments, a composing room, a pressroom, and a bindery. In the composing room the type is set and arranged for printing. In the pressroom the sheets of paper are printed. In the bindery the printed sheets are folded, fastened together, and bound as desired. (See Fig. 9-2 on page 23.)

Some plants have other departments besides the three named. For example, lithographers have departments for making printing plates by means of photography, and newspapers have departments for molding curved plates for their printing presses.

Each department has a superintendent, or head foreman, who plans the work of the department and gives orders to the subforeman, the trained craftsmen (usually called *journeymen*), the helpers, and the apprentices.

Unit 10. Reviewing Case Layout and Pulling Proof

Your California-job-case layout, or diagram, is now finished. In this unit you will review the whole case, remove type from your stick, tie it up, and make your first real printed proof.

FIG. 10-1. Proof press. How do you know that a proof has just been pulled?

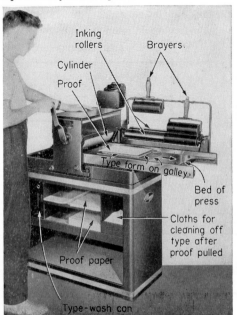

Procedure

1. Set your stick at 25 picas, place a 25-pica slug in it, and set the following as three lines:

    a. A B C D E F G H I J K L M N
    O P Q R S T U V W X Y Z
    b. a b c d e f g h i j k l m n
    o p q r s t u v w x y z
    c. fi fl ff ffi ffl & 1 2 3 4 5 6 7
    8 9 0 $. , ; : - ' ! ?

2. Justify each line carefully.
3. Place a lead in your stick after each line before you begin to set the next line.
4. Place a slug in your stick after the last line.
5. Lift the lines out onto your galley and tie them securely as you did in Unit 4, pages 10–12.
6. Carry the galley with the type on it to the proof press and place it on the bed of the press (Fig. 10-1).

7. Pull a proof in the following way:

a. Ink the type carefully. To do this, you use a soft roller called a *brayer.* Roll the brayer back and forth two or three times on the *ink plate,* using a wrist action. Hold the brayer by the handle as shown in Fig. 10-2.

b. Roll the brayer over the type two or three times. Do not let the metal frame of the brayer hit the type. Why?

c. Return the brayer to the ink plate.

d. Lay a piece of paper on the type. Do not let the paper move on the type after you lay it down.

e. Roll the proof-press cylinder over the paper once.

f. Lift the paper off the type carefully and look at it. If the proof is not clear and sharp and straight with the edges of the paper, re-ink the type and pull another proof on a fresh sheet of paper.

8. Wipe off the type with a soft cloth slightly dampened with a commercial type wash.

9. Take your galley with the type on it back to your stand.

10. Distribute the type if you have time. If you do not have time, put it away on your galley to be distributed later.

11. Pull a proof of the name and address that you set in Unit 4. Do the spaces between the names and initials appear equal? What size spaces did you use?

12. Wipe off the type form with a soft cloth slightly dampened with a commercial type wash. If you wish to use

Fig. 10-2. Inking a type form with a brayer. Move brayer, or proof roller, across from one corner to the opposite corner of the type form.

this type form to print stationery later on in the course (Unit 42), store it on your galley. If you do not wish to use this type form later, distribute the type.

NOTEBOOK

Now is a good time to begin keeping a notebook. A notebook with 8½- by 11-inch ruled pages is recommended. Paste in your completed case diagram and one of your best proofs of your first job. It is suggested that you add the best proof of each job you set during the course. Label each job neatly. Also, record the type face and size that was used. On the proof itself you might note the spaces used between words and the leading used between the lines of type.

Discussion Topics

1. How many different type characters are there on your proof of the three lines that you set at the beginning of this unit?

2. Do you find any other type characters in your type case? If you do, ask the instructor their names and where they are used.

3. Why is the brayer made of soft material?

4. Why clean the type before putting it away?

Type Cases

The California job case was in use in California in 1875. A Californian by the name of Dearing is said to have invented the case. The California job case (Fig. 10-3) is used for most type fonts that have capitals, lower-case letters, and figures.

Triple cases (Fig. 10-4) are used for lining type faces and for small capitals that are used with roman type. For a further description of this type of case see pages 46–47.

Blank cases (Fig. 10-5), which have no partitions, are used to hold smaller cases of various kinds. For example, brass-rule fonts are placed in *quarter*

Fig. 10-5. Blank case used to hold smaller cases.

Fig. 10-6. Quarter cases. Four of these cases fit into one blank case.

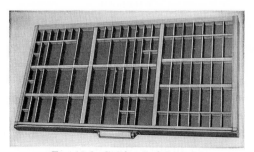

Fig. 10-3. California job case.

Fig. 10-4. The triple case used for lining gothic type faces and for small capitals.

Fig. 10-7. Adjustable lead-and-slug case.

cases. Four of these quarter cases fit into a full-sized blank case. Four fonts of brass rule can be stored in one blank case.

The printer uses many kinds of decorative units and such things as fractions, parentheses, brackets, dashes, and paragraph marks. He buys these in fonts and usually stores them in quarter cases.

The very large sizes of type are made of hardwood. The letters are too big to go into a California job case. They are stored in rows in a blank case, with movable strips between rows.

There are several kinds of cases for leads and slugs (Fig. 10-7). Extra quan-

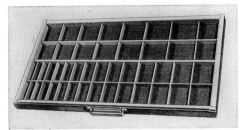

Fig. 10-8. Space-and-quad or lead-and-slug case.

tities of spaces and quads in all sizes are stored for convenient use in specially made cases (Fig. 10-8). A large lead-and-slug case and a large space case are often kept on top of a stand at some central point in the print shop.

Bill is assembling a type form.

Section II. HAND COMPOSITION

Unit 11. Centering Lines of Type
Printing Address Labels

We all like to see things balanced. That is why many type lines used in printing are placed in the middle of the space they occupy. The headings on this page are set in this way.

CENTERING LINES OF TYPE

Centering lines of type is not difficult. The following procedure tells you how to set your name and address in centered lines of type.

Procedure

1. Set your composing stick at 15 picas and place a 15-pica slug in it.
2. Set your name in all caps.
3. Center your name in your stick as follows:

    a. Place a 3-em quad on each side of the type you have set and add quads equally on both sides until the remaining space is less than an em.

FIG. 11-1. Removing the quad at the right end of a line before inserting the last space.

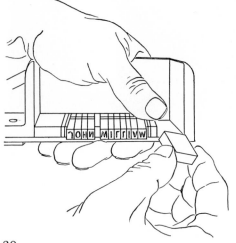

    b. Finish out the justification of the line by inserting spaces (next to the type) equally on both sides, that is, if you put a 3-to-em space at the right, also put a 3-to-em space at the left of your name.

    c. Lift out the quad at the right end of the line (Fig. 11-1) before you insert the last space. If you try to force the space into the line, the space will bend or break. It is easy to push the end quad back into place.

4. Place a 15-pica lead in the stick after the line and check the line for justification (Fig. 4-2, page 10).
5. Set your street address in caps and lower case in the next line and center it as you did your name. Put a 15-pica lead in your stick after the line and check the line for justification as before.
6. Set a third line with your town and state and center it as you did the first two lines. Place a 15-pica slug after this last line and check the line for justification.
7. Remove the three lines carefully from the stick to a galley.
8. Place a piece of metal furniture that is 15 picas wide and 5 or 6 picas deep below the type form. (*Furniture* is a printer's term for the largest wooden or metal spacing material.)
9. Tie the type form and furniture firmly as described in Unit 4, pages 10–12.

PRINTING ADDRESS LABELS

You may now use the lines you have just set and centered to print some address labels, which you can paste in your books or on envelopes.

Procedure

1. Ask the instructor for some small pieces of gummed paper.
2. Carry the galley with the type on it to the proof press.
3. Squeeze about one-fourth of an inch of ink from the tube onto the ink plate.
4. Roll a clean brayer back and forth to distribute the ink thoroughly and evenly over the plate and the brayer. Lift the brayer off the plate after each stroke.
5. Holding the brayer with the handle in a vertical position, roll it lightly back and forth over your type two or three times (Fig. 10-2).
6. Lay a piece of the gummed paper on the type. Try to place it so that the printing will be in the center of the paper. Do not move the paper after you lay it down.
7. Roll the press cylinder over the job once only.

> CURTIS S. WHITE
> 21 South Main Street
> Wisetown, Illinois

Fig. 11-2. A sample address label.

8. Carefully lift off the printed ad dress label. Print as many as time allows.
9. Wash the ink off the type with a soft cloth dampened with a commercial type wash.
10. Store the type on your galley for later distribution.

Discussion Topics

1. Why is it important, when filling a line with quads and spaces, to place spaces next to the type?
2. Do you know now why the piece of furniture was tied with the type lines?
3. What would happen if you used too much ink on the brayer? Too little ink?
4. What happens when the paper moves on the type before you print it?

ADDITIONAL INFORMATION ABOUT THE PRINTERS'
SYSTEM OF MEASUREMENT—THE PICA

Types are measured in points. The point size is the size of the body of the type and not the size of the printed let- ter. Figure 1-2, page 3, shows a 5-pica, or 60-point, letter N being measured with a printer's pica gauge.

Fig. 11-3. A printer's pica ruler, or gauge.

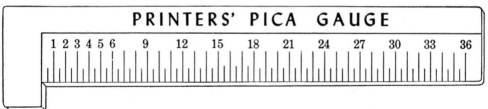

Leads and slugs, wood and metal furniture, and brass rules are all cut in pica lengths. The gauges on the printer's lead and rule cutter and on a composing-room power saw are all marked in picas. A printer's pica ruler, or gauge, is shown in Fig. 11-3.

There is one size of type that is called *pica type* because six lines of this type make about one inch. This size of type is more often called *12-point type*. The em quad of 12-point, or pica, type is 1 pica square. This pica em is the unit, or basis, of the whole system of printers' measurements.

One-sixth of an inch is a decimal that never ends. It is 0.1666666+. For convenience, the pica em is made exactly 0.166, which means than 72 picas are actually a little less than 1 foot.

Unit 12. Centering Lines of Type.   Setting
Inverted Pyramid and Diamond Shape

Lines of type on business cards and office forms are usually set in the center of the space they occupy. So are many newspaper headlines and headings in books.

Sometimes you see newspaper headlines set up in three or more lines, each one shorter than the one above it. This form of type composition is called an *inverted pyramid* because it is like a pyramid turned upside down.

```
BARNUM'S CIRCUS
  IS COMING TO
   OUR TOWN
```

Fig. 12-1. Three-line heading set as inverted pyramid.

Fig. 12-2. Copy for diamond-shaped type form.

```
           The
        early bird
     catches the worm.
     But it seems to me
  the dumb worm would not
     have been caught
       if he had only
          stayed in
            bed.
```

SETTING AN INVERTED PYRAMID

Each line of an inverted pyramid is centered.

Procedure

1. Set your stick at 12 picas.
2. Put a 12-pica slug in the stick.
3. Set the heading shown in Fig. 12-1 in three centered lines of capitals.
4. Place a 12-pica lead after each line and a slug after the last line.
5. Remove the job from the stick to a galley and tie up securely.
6. Pull a proof, make any necessary corrections, rejustify lines, and pull one or two good proofs for your notebook.
7. Clean off the type and distribute.

Setting a Diamond Shape

As in the case of the inverted pyramid, each line is centered when copy is set in a diamond shape. A diamond is a combination of a pyramid and an inverted pyramid.

Procedure

1. Set your composing stick at 12 picas.

2. Put a 12-pica slug in the stick.

3. Set the copy shown in Fig. 12-2 in the form of a diamond—line for line as shown. Put a lead after each line and a slug after the last line. Use caps and lower case.

4. Transfer the job to your galley and tie it securely.

5. Pull a proof and examine it carefully. Make any necessary corrections, rejustify lines, and then pull about three good proofs. Put the best one in your notebook.

Correcting Mistakes in Type Forms

To make corrections in a type form, you must lift out the lines that have the errors in them and put them back into your composing stick one line at a time.

Procedure

1. Place your galley on your case stand with the type in the correct position in the corner of the galley as shown in Fig. 4-7, page 11.

2. Untie the type form carefully.

3. Slide the lines that are below the one with the error a few inches toward the open end of the galley. Protect these lines with pieces of furniture as shown in Fig. 12-3.

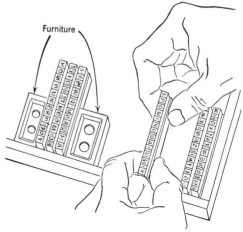

Fig. 12-3. Removing a line of type from a type form for correction.

4. Place a slug or brass rule on each side of the line that is to be corrected and lift it back into your composing stick. Take out only one line at a time. You may spill, or *pie,* your type if you try to put all the lines that are to be corrected back in the stick at one time.

5. Correct the errors, re-justify the line, and lift it back onto the galley.

6. Repeat the process for each line that has an error in it.

7. After all the lines with errors have been corrected, slide all the lines together again and re-tie.

8. Pull a final proof to check your corrections.

9. Clean off the type form.

10. Distribute the type and any other *dead* type (type that you no longer need) now on your galley before you go on to the next unit.

Discussion Topics

1. What is dead type?
2. What is pied type?

3. How can you find errors *before* you pull a proof?

4. Why is it necessary to lift the lines with errors back into your stick?

PARTS OF A PIECE OF TYPE

Figure 12-4 shows the names of the parts of a piece of type. Most important of these is the *face*, which is the surface that makes the print. The face is made up of raised lines. These lines are usually both wide and narrow and have rounded or flattened ends called *serifs*.

The *shoulder* of a type is the area below letters like a or b. It is needed for

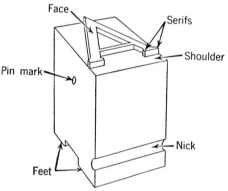

FIG. 12-4. Names of the parts of a piece of type.

the tails of letters like g, p, and j. The shoulder is always at the bottom, toward the nick.

As you have already found out, the *nick* is very important. It shows when the letter is right side up in the composing stick. The nicks of different kinds of type are different in size, position, or number. This helps the printer to separate the various kinds, or fonts, of type when they get mixed.

The *feet* of a piece of type, as mentioned in Unit 2, are the two projections at the base of the body. When only a part of the letter shows on the proof, it is said that the type is "off its feet."

The *pin mark* is not found on most modern types. This mark is made by the pin used to remove the type from the casting mold.

The height of type is a little less than an inch. It is 0.918, or nine hundred and eighteen thousandths, of an inch.

Unit 13. Indention.   Setting Poetry

Poetry is easy to set because the spaces between the words are all the same. You may have noticed that every line of poetry usually begins with a capital letter. The printer helps to show the rhymes by beginning some of the lines a little farther to the right than the others. This is called *indention*. Figure 13-1 shows different kinds of indention.

A poem is usually centered on the page. When you set a poem, the first thing to do is to find the longest line and to set it up. Then center this line. The rest of the poem is set to fit with this line.

In Fig. 13-2 is a four-line riddle to set. Perhaps you can answer it by telling who it is.

HANGING INDENTION

This form of indention is useful in many
kinds of job work. It is made by setting
the first line of the paragraph the full
width of the measure, and indenting
one or more ems at the beginning of
the following lines.

SQUARED INDENTION

This name is given to the squared and centered composition of
short indented lines (often capitals only) now in favor for undis-
played parts of a title page.

EVERY LINE IS SET WITH A
WIDE INDENTION ON EACH
SIDE, SO THAT THE WHOLE
WILL TAKE THE FORM OF
A SYMMETRICAL SQUARE.

Squared indention is used for short paragraphs in advertising
matter, bits of minor display, and miscellaneous composition.

DIAGONAL INDENTION

Diagonal indention is where

lines of type are so arranged

that they follow one another

diagonally in this manner.

HALF DIAMOND INDENTION

This gives prominence to display lines,
whether they are long or short,
and symmetrically distributes
the relief of white space
that is needed for
the display
of type.

FIG. 13-1. Four different kinds of indention.

Procedure

1. Set your composing stick at 15
picas and place a 15-pica slug in it.

2. Set the third line (the longest)
first and center and justify it. Put a lead
below this and each line following.

3. Set the first line with the same indention as you have for the third line.
This is called *aligning.*

4. Set the second and fourth lines
with one em quad more indention than
you have used for the first and third
lines.

5. Put a 15-pica slug after the last
line.

6. Remove the job from your stick
onto a galley.

7. Arrange the lines in their proper
order. When removing a line of type
from a type form, put a lead or slug on
each side of the line. When corrections
are finished, be sure that there are no
extra leads between lines.

8. Tie up the job carefully.

9. Pull a proof, make corrections if
necessary, re-justify, and pull one or
more good proofs for your notebook.

10. Distribute the type.

11. Set the limerick shown in Fig.
13-3. Which line should you set first?

12. Transfer the job to your galley,
tie it up, and pull one or more proofs.

13. Distribute the type.

14. Return the type case to its place.

FIG. 13-3. A limerick.

FIG. 13-2. A riddle.

Brothers and sisters
Have I none,
But this man's father
Is my father's son.

A printer who spilled a whole case
Was unable to bear the disgrace.
He thought that he orter
Jump into the water,
If he could find a dry enough place.

Discussion Topics

1. Blank verse is poetry that has no rhymes. Would any line of a poem in blank verse be indented?

2. If the lines of the poem are wider than the page, what is done?

3. What is *aligning,* or *alignment,* of lines?

PRINTING STYLE

A well-printed book has style, just as a well-dressed person has. Many little things make good printing style.

To be sure about the correct *spelling* of words, a dictionary is needed. The dictionary is also needed to tell how words are to be *divided* at the ends of lines.

Uniformity is very important. For example, paragraph indention should be the same all through a job. Words should be spelled the same way at the end of a book as they are at the be-

ginning of the book. The spaces between lines of text should be uniform.

Printers use *style books* which contain the answers to hundreds of questions that come up in typesetting. For example, you may set something that contains a sentence in quotation marks. You will want to know if the period at the end of the sentence precedes or follows the closing quotation mark. The style book may tell you that a period or comma precedes the closing quotation mark.

Unit 14. Setting Poetry

Setting the longer poem given in this unit (Fig. 14-1) will help you to become a little more skillful in picking up type and setting it in the stick. Read over the suggestions for setting type quickly and correctly given in Unit 8, page 20. Try to get an easy, smooth motion of your hand from the stick to the box and from the box to the stick. See if you can get along without using your case diagram.

Procedure

1. Set your composing stick at 20 picas and put a 20-pica slug in it.

2. Set eight lines in your stick with a lead after each line.

3. Lift the eight lines out onto your galley and tie them.

4. Put your galley back in the galley rack or out of the way, while you set the next eight lines in your stick.

5. Add the second eight lines to the first eight lines on your galley and tie them all together.

6. Repeat this procedure to the end of the poem. You now have the whole poem tied on your galley.

7. Pull a proof of the poem. *Do not* make corrections. Save the proof carefully for use in the next unit.

8. Store your type on the galley for later use.

A TRAGIC STORY

There lived a sage in days of yore
And he a handsome pigtail wore;
But wondered much, and sorrowed
more,
Because it hung behind him.

He mused upon this curious case,
And swore he'd change the pigtail's
place,
And have it hanging at his face,
Not dangling there behind him.

Says he, "The mystery I've found,—
I'll turn me round,"—
He turned him round,
But still it hung behind him.

Then round and round, and out and
in,
All day the puzzled sage did spin;
In vain—it mattered not a pin—
The pigtail hung behind him.

And right and left, and roundabout,
And up and down and in and out
He turned; but still the pigtail stout
Hung steadily behind him.

And though his efforts never slack,
And though he twist, and twirl, and
tack,
Alas! still faithful to his back,
The pigtail hangs behind him.

—Albert Von Chamisso

FIG. 14-1. A long poem.

Discussion Topics

1. Were any of the errors in your type caused by letters being in the wrong boxes?

2. Were any of the errors caused by mixing up the n's and u's, the b's and d's, or the p's and q's?
3. Do you have any misspelled words?
4. How can you prevent these and other kinds of errors in setting type?

SOME ODDITIES OF STYLE IN COMPOSITION

After the exclamation "Oh," an exclamation mark (!) is used. After just plain "O," we use a comma or no punctuation at all.

It is correct to use -st, -d or -rd, or -th after figures in dates preceding the month, but it is incorrect to do so if the day and year follow. For example:

3d of January   January 3, 1956

Use a capital for a title when it precedes the name, but use lower case if the title follows the name. For example:

Mayor Jones spoke.
Mr. Jones, the mayor, spoke.

Numbers less than 10 are usually spelled out unless they are used with units of measurement. For example:

We saw three men.
We saw 33 men.
Do 6 picas equal 1 inch?

When any number starts a sentence, it is always spelled out. For example:

Thirty-three men came.

Approximations, or round figures, are usually spelled out. For example:

About fifty men turned out for the team.

Unit 15. Proofreading and Proofreaders' Marks

Every proofreader uses the same proof-readers' marks, and every printer knows what they mean. If you used other kinds of marks, the man who makes the corrections might not understand them. These marks are important to know. Before you start to proofread the poem that you set in the last unit, study the most frequently used proofreaders' marks shown in Fig. 15-1 and their use as shown in Fig. 15-2.

As you proofread the poem that you have set, put a diagonal line (/) through the wrong letter or other error. Mark in the margin of the proof, using the correct proofreaders' mark, what correction is to be made. The proofreaders' mark in the margin should be opposite the line in which the error is to be corrected. The corrections for the right half of a line go in the right-hand margin, and those for the left half of the line go in the left-hand margin.

Procedure

1. Have another student read aloud from the copy of the poem that you set in Unit 14 while you follow on his proof. Then you read aloud from the copy while he follows on your proof.

Fig. 15-1. Some standard proofreaders' marks.

PROOFREADERS' MARKS

Mark	Meaning	Mark	Meaning
ℒ	Take out letter, letters, or words indicated.	⌒	Close up the space entirely; no space.
#	Insert space where indicated.	○	A circle drawn around an abbreviation, figure, etc., means "spell out."
ℒ	Turn the inverted letter indicated.	⟨sp⟩	Spell out—used in margin.
l.c.	Set in lower-case type.	¶	Start a new paragraph.
caps.	Put in capitals.	═	Straighten letters that are out of alignment.
s.c.	Put in small capitals.	‖	Straighten ends of lines.
wf	Change a wrong font letter, that is, one from another case.	⊙	Period.
X	Replace a broken letter.	⋏	Comma.
tr.	Transpose letters, words, or phrases indicated.	:/	Colon.
stet.	Let it stand as it is.	;/	Semicolon.
eq#	Equalize the spacing in the line.	᾿/	Apostrophe.
⋏	Insert at this point.	=/	Hyphen.
[or]	Move over to the point indicated (left or right).	—ᴍ—	One em dash.
⌶	Push down a space.	▢	Em quad space; or indent 1 em.

38

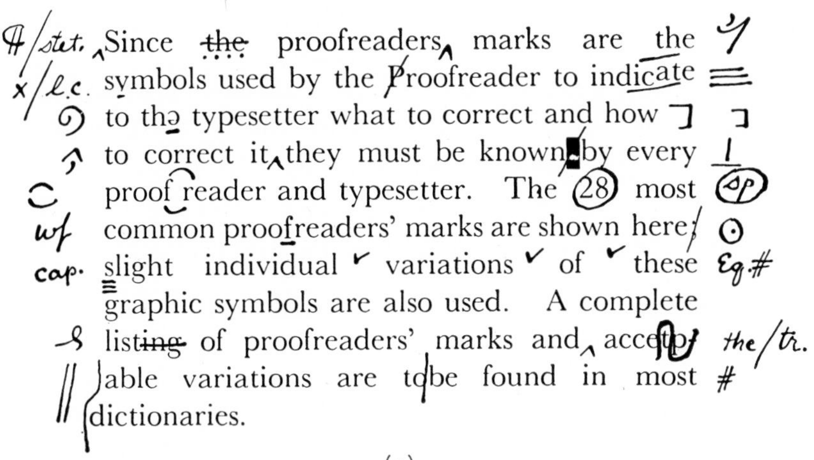

¶ /stet. ∧Since ~~the~~ proofreaders∧ marks   are   the ⁹⁄
✗/ℓ.c. symbols used by the ℙroofreader to indicate ≡
      ↻ to the typesetter what to correct and how ⌐   ⌐
      ∧ to correct it∧they must be known▪by every ⌐
  C   proof reader and typesetter. The ㉘ most ⓐⓟ
 w/   common proofreaders' marks are shown here/ ⊙
 cap. slight   individual ∨ variations ∨ of ∨ these εq.#
      ≡graphic symbols are also used.   A complete
  ℒ listi~~ng~~ of proofreaders' ∕marks and∧ accept▸ the/tr.
 ‖)able variations are to⸝be found in most #
 ‖ (dictionaries.

(a)

Since the proofreaders' marks are the symbols used by the proofreader to indicate to the
typesetter what to correct and how to correct it,
they must be known by every proofreader and
typesetter.   The twenty-eight most common
proofreaders' marks are shown here.   Slight
individual variations of these graphic symbols are also used.   A complete list of proofreaders' marks and the acceptable variations
are to be found in most dictionaries.

(b)

Fig. 15-2. (a) Proof marked for correction. (b) Proof corrected.

2. Mark each error in the proof with the correct proofreaders' mark. When there is more than one correction in a line, separate the corrections with a diagonal line (Fig. 15-2).

3. Show your marked proof to the instructor before you make the corrections in the type.

4. Make the corrections line by line as you did in Unit 12, page 33.

5. Pull another proof after you have made all the corrections. This proof is called a *revise*.

6. Compare the revise with the first marked proof and the copy from which it was set. Check each correction carefully. If there are any errors, mark them in the margins of the revise just as you did on the first proof.

7. Make the corrections in the type and pull a *second revise*.

8. Check the second revise as you did the first revise. Continue to make corrections and to pull new revise proofs until the poem is set correctly. Number each revise proof in the order pulled.

9. Clean the type with type wash.

10. Store the type on your galley for distribution in the next unit.

2. Why is it necessary to read the copy aloud?

1. Why are the marks to show corrections made in the margins of the proof?

3. It is said that the person who sets the type should never read his own proof. Why?

PROOFREADING AND COPY PREPARATION

There is a kind of editorial work called *copy editing* or *copy preparation.* Newspaper, book, and magazine publishers employ many copy editors. The work requires a good education. College graduates are preferred.

Before the type is set, these men and women correct mistakes in spelling and punctuation and make sure that such things as names and dates are correct in the manuscript copy.

Anyone who has set type and corrected mistakes in type lines, as you have now done, knows that it is much easier to correct mistakes in the copy with a pencil than it is to correct them after they are set in type.

Proofreading is done after the type is set. This job requires a good education plus a knowledge of printing and printing methods. Proofreaders in union plants sometimes serve the regular apprenticeship in the composing room before they are employed in the proofroom.

The person who reads from the copy while the proofreader looks at the proof is called a *copyholder.* A high-school graduate may be hired for this job without having to serve a trade apprenticeship.

Unit 16. Distribution of Type

Proper distribution of type is necessary to ensure a clean case with enough type for each job. A proper distribution of type will save you from little Willie's fate.

> Our little Willie
>   Mixed up his case;
> He put p's in the b-box—
>   Is he red in the face!

You may now distribute the type of the poem "A Tragic Story," which you set in Unit 14 and corrected in Unit 15.

Procedure

1. Place the dead type on a galley. Put the galley on your type stand with the open end to the left and with the type in the lower right-hand corner (Fig. 4-6, page 11).

2. Be sure that the type has been washed clean with a soft cloth dampened with type wash and wiped dry, before you untie it. If there is dried ink

on the letters, ask the instructor for a type brush. Use a little type wash and the brush to clean the type thoroughly.

3. Untie the type carefully.

4. Push the lines gently toward the open end of the galley so that you can get at the first line easily. Now you can reverse the steps of composition.

5. Place a slug on each side of the bottom line and pick the line up. Hold it with your left thumb and left middle finger.

6. Remove the top slug. The nicks on the type should be up (Fig. 16-1).

7. Take up the word at the right end of the line with your right thumb, right forefinger, and right middle finger as shown in Fig. 16-2.

8. Separate the first letter of the word with your right thumb and forefinger and drop it into its proper box. Follow with the second letter of the word, and so on. You just spell the word back into the case.

9. Take up another word and distribute it.

10. Continue until the line is all distributed.

You may pick up the spaces with the words and drop them as you do the letters. Or you may leave the spaces lying on the supporting slug until all the letters of a line are distributed. Then you can sort out the various sizes of spaces and put them in their proper boxes before going on to the next line.

11. Lay the leads that were between the type lines aside as you go. When you have finished distributing the type and spaces, put the leads and slugs back in their proper places.

12. Check your case after distributing

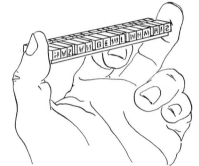

Fig. 16-1. Holding a line of type in the left hand ready for distribution.

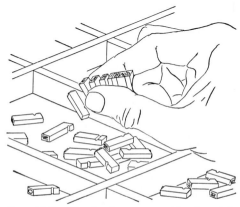

Fig. 16-2. Distributing type with the right hand.

type. To do this, take 10 letters out of one box, for example the n box, and see if they are all n's. Try several boxes to find out how well you have distributed the type.

Discussion Topics

1. If you drop a letter in the wrong box, what do you do?

2. What do you do if you find a letter in the wrong box?

3. If at any time you find that the type in your case is fouled (mixed up), will it save time and corrections to clean it (put it in order) before you start to set type again?

EACH PUBLISHER AND PRINTER HAS HIS OWN STYLE BOOK

Printing styles are not always the same. For example, in books many more words start with capitals than in newspapers. Of course proper names are always capitalized, but some newspapers treat "street" and "river" as common nouns. They say that there is only one Mississippi, but there are lots of rivers. In books and magazines such words are usually capitalized.

In Some Newspapers
Main street
Mississippi river
Big Rock Candy mountain
Municipal railroad

In Most Books and Magazines
Main Street
Mississippi River
Big Rock Candy Mountain
Municipal Railroad

Newspapers rarely use italic letters except in headings, editorials, and advertising, but italics are often used in book and job printing.

In newspaper headlines and in many other kinds of headings caps-and-lower-case style is used. All words start with capitals except articles (a, an, and the), connectives (and, or, if, and so on), and prepositions of less than four letters (to, in, and so on). For example:

Tom and Bill Will Go to College
It Is Time for the Matches to Begin
Film Theaters to Try One Show a Day
Broken Upon Arrival

What style has been followed for the unit titles in this book? For the section titles?

Unit 17. Type Styles, Sizes, and Display Faces

In newspapers, books, magazines, and other forms of printing, you see many kinds of types in many sizes. Some types are named after the persons who designed them, for example, Bodoni and Goudy (Fig. 17-1). This book is set in Baskerville type. Other type names are descriptive terms, as, for example, *sans serif,* which means without a serif (Figs. 17-1 and 17-3), and *script,* which looks like handwriting (Figs. 17-1 and 17-3).

In the following procedure you will have an opportunity to set some other and larger sizes of type than those you have been using. These larger sizes of type are called *display* types. Display types are used for large headings in books, magazines, newspapers, and advertisements. The types shown in Fig. 17-1 are examples of display types. The 14- to 48-point Bodoni shown in Fig. 17-2 is used for display purposes. The display unit headings in this book are set in 18-point Baskerville.

This is 24-point Bodoni Bold

This is 24-point Sans Serif Medium

This is 24-point Commercial Script

𝔗his is 24-point 𝔊oudy 𝔗ext

FIG. 17-1. These are all display types. Note the variety of type styles they represent.

FIG. 17-2. The roman type set here is Bodoni. Note the variety of sizes of this type face.

BODY TYPE

This is 6-point type.

This is 8-point type.

This is 9-point type.

This is 10-point type.

This is 11-point type.

This is 12-point type.

DISPLAY TYPE

This is 14-point type.

This is 18-point type.

This is 24-point type.

This is 30-point type.

This is 36-point type.

This is 48-point type.

SANS SERIF

Futura Medium

Franklin Gothic

Sans Serif Medium

ROMAN

Garamond

Bodoni Bold

Caslon Bold

SQUARE SERIF

Memphis Bold

Girder Light

P. T. Barnum

SCRIPT

Bank Script

Stationers Semiscript

Trafton Script

ITALIC

Garamond Italic

Bodoni Bold Italic

Caslon Bold Italic

TEXT

Cloister Black

Goudy Text

Shaw Text

FIG. 17-3. Six different type styles.

Procedure

1. Set your stick at 25 picas and put a 25-pica slug in it.

2. Ask the instructor for a case of display type. On the case you receive, you will find a label that gives the name of the type and its size.

3. Set a line of this type, giving its name and size. For example, if you have a case of 18-point Garamond Old Style, set up the following as a single line:

This type is 18-point Garamond Old Style.

4. Justify the line that you have set.

5. Put a 25-pica slug after the line and remove the line from your stick to your galley.

6. Return the case to its proper place.

7. Ask the instructor for a case of another display type.

8. Set a line of this type, giving its size and name as you did for the first kind of display type.

9. Continue with one or more of the other kinds of display type.

10. When you have set as many lines of display type as you can, make sure that there is a slug after each line and then tie all the lines together.

11. Pull some good proofs for your notebook.

12. Clean off the type carefully with type wash.

13. Distribute the lines, putting each type face back in its own case.

Discussion Topics

1. Why do we have so many styles of type?
2. Why not set everything in roman type?
3. What is the biggest type in your graphic arts laboratory?
4. What is the most noticeable difference between roman type and sans-serif type?
5. Why do type faces have names?

Type Designs and Type Sizes

Roman types come from a style of lettering used a long time ago in Rome, Italy, for inscriptions chiseled in stone monuments. The serifs on the capital roman letters used today have a chisel-like character. Figure 17-3 shows six different type styles: the sans serif, sometimes called gothic; the script; the roman; the italic; the square serif; and the text, which is sometimes called black letter, as the name *Cloister Black* indicates.

Each type face is made in many sizes. Figure 17-2 shows Bodoni set in sizes from 6 to 48 point. The smaller sizes of types that are used in setting books and articles in magazines and newspapers are called *body types.* The sizes of these body types range from 5 to 12 or 14 points. Sizes above 12 or 14 point are called *display types* (Fig. 17-2).

A type design may be made thinner or thicker, or wider or narrower, or it may be sloped. A number of variations of one design is called a *family* of types. Figure 17-4 shows several examples of different types that belong to the same family—the sans-serif, or gothic, family of type.

Fig. 17-4. Example of a type family. The type family shown here is the sans serif, or gothic. All lines are set in 14-point type. Note the smaller appearance of the Futura types.

Bernhard Gothic Heavy	Futura Medium
Bernhard Gothic Medium Condensed	*Futura Medium Oblique*
Franklin Gothic	Futura Medium Condensed
Franklin Gothic Italic	**Futura Extra Bold**
Franklin Gothic Condensed	***Futura Extra Bold Italic***
Franklin Gothic Condensed Italic	**Futura Extra Bold Condensed**
Alternate Gothic No. 3	Sans Serif Light
News Gothic	*Sans Serif Light Italic*
News Gothic Condensed	**Sans Serif Extra Bold**
News Gothic Extra Condensed	***Sans Serif Extra Bold Italic***

Unit 18. The Triple Case.   Setting a
Personal Card.   Letter Spacing

Business cards usually are set in small letters—all capitals. For this kind of work the printer uses what are called *lining* type sizes. Figure 18-1 shows lining sans-serif capitals, and Fig. 18-2, a business card using this style of type.

THE TRIPLE CASE

A California job case is not suitable for lining or gothic types because they have no lower-case letters. Most shops place these types in a *triple case* (Fig. 18-3).

Procedure

1. Get a triple case from the instructor.

2. Examine the letters in the three sections of the case. The left-hand section has the smallest-size type, the center section has type that is a little larger, and the right-hand section has still larger type.

3. Make a case diagram to show where the capitals and the punctuation marks are. The layout of the capitals in each section is just like the capital layout in your California job case. The figures and punctuation marks are in the three rows of small boxes above the capitals.

4. Set one letter from each section in your stick. You will see that they line up at the bottom as do the letters in Fig. 18-1. The body size is the same for all three sizes.

5. Look at the nicks. They are different on each size of type. Why?

```
6-POINT BANK GOTHIC, A LINING TYPE   H ■
6-POINT BANK GOTHIC, A LINING   H ■
6-POINT BANK GOTHIC, A LIN   H ■
6-POINT BANK GOTHIC, I   H ■

TWO SMALL SIZES IN ONE LINE
THIS LINE IS TWO LARGER SIZES
TWO LARGEST SIZES OF 6 PT.

12-POINT BANK GOT I ■
12-POINT BANK C I ■
12-POINT GOTI I ■
12-POINT BA I ■

M M M M M M M M
```

FIG. 18-1. Lining gothic capitals in 6 and 12 point.

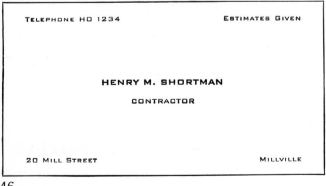

TELEPHONE HO 1234   ESTIMATES GIVEN

HENRY M. SHORTMAN

CONTRACTOR

20 MILL STREET   MILLVILLE

FIG. 18-2. A business card using lining gothic type.

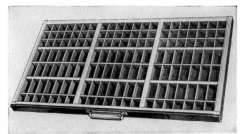

FIG. 18-3. The triple case used for lining gothic type faces and for small capitals.

SETTING A PERSONAL CARD

If the triple case you have been using does not have 6-point lining type, ask the instructor for a triple case of 6-point lining type. Figure 18-4 shows three different combinations of lining types used in setting personal cards.

Procedure

1. Set your composing stick at 18 picas and put an 18-pica slug in it.

2. Set your name in the two largest sizes of type. Use the biggest size for the first letter of each name and for your initial, if you have one. Use the middle size for the other letters. Center your name and put a slug after the line.

3. Set your street address in the two smallest sizes. Use the middle-sized caps for the initial letters and figures. Set the rest of the letters in the smallest size. Set the address in one line and center the line. Put a slug after the line.

4. Set the city and state in one line. Put a comma between the city and state. Center this line and put a slug after it. Remove the lines from the stick to your galley.

5. Ask the instructor for a No. 88 card. Fold it in the center lengthwise.

DAVID W. CHURCH

22 NORTH STREET

GREENCASTLE, CALIFORNIA

MARY ANN WHITE

16 WEST FOURTH STREET

SUNLIGHT, COLORADO

KENNETH H. MACINTYRE

108 MAIN STREET

CLEARVIEW, PENNSYLVANIA

FIG. 18-4. Personal cards.

Put the same number of slugs between the three lines and space out evenly. The address line should be just a little above the folded line on the card and the city-and-state line 1 pica above the lower edge of the card.

6. Tie up the job.

7. Pull a proof on proof paper and make corrections if necessary. *Do not* pull a proof on the card. If you do, the type may be broken. Why?

8. Store the job on your galley. You will have an opportunity to prepare it for printing in Unit 27 and to print it in Unit 48.

Small Capitals for Roman Types

Large and small capitals are often seen in books. The main center headings in this book are set in large and small capital letters. Just like lining types, the small capitals are cast on the same body as the capitals, and they align at the bottom.

Ask the instructor for a case of small capitals that matches the type in your job case. Set the following as one line in your composing stick. Set your stick at 20 picas and put a 20-pica slug in it. Use regular roman capitals out of your own type case for the initial letters. Use the small caps from the case of small capitals for the other letters:

These Two Lines Are Set in Caps and Small Caps

Notice the alignment of the large and small capital letters.

Return each letter to its proper case and box.

Letter Spacing

When words are set in all capital letters or all small capital letters, they may look crowded together. To avoid this crowded appearance, thin strips of metal called *thin spaces* may be added between the letters. This spacing out between the letters of a word is called *letter spacing*.

The thin spaces you may find most useful are ½, 1, and 2 points thick. The ½-point spaces are made of copper. The 1-point spaces are made of brass. The 2-point spaces are cut from 2-point strip leads. The following words are set in capital letters first without letter spacing and then with 2-point letter spacing.

NO LETTER SPACING WITH LETTER SPACING

Notice the effect of the 2-point letter spacing between the letters P and A in the word SPACING. Although the spacing is the same as that between the letters S and P, it looks greater. Therefore, to give an even appearance, the space between the P and the A is reduced to 1 point and appears as follows:

EVEN SPACING

Even letter spacing improves the appearance and readability of words set in all capital or all small capital letters.

Discussion Topics

1. How tall, in points, is the face of the smallest letter you used? (Use 2-point leads for comparison.)
2. Why set business cards in all capitals?
3. Why are there no boxes for spaces in a triple case? Where did you look for the spaces and quads you used?
4. How can you tell the difference between a ½-point and a 1-point thin space by just looking at them quickly?

Job, or Commercial, Printing

It is estimated that about one-third of the production workers in the printing industry are employed in job, or commercial, printing plants. These plants produce a greater variety of printed matter than any other type of printing shop. Letterheads, business forms, posters, displays, calendars, and folders are only a few of the many thousands of items produced by job plants.

There are many kinds of jobs in commercial printing plants. They employ salesmen, office workers, and accountants as well as managers, superintendents, and their assistants. In the mechanical departments of such plants there are foremen, compositors, typesetting-machine operators, proofreaders, lockup men, pressmen and assistants, papercutters, and bookbinders.

If you are interested in finding out more about the employment opportunities in the printing industry, turn to "Occupations in the Graphic Arts Industry," pages 268–270, and visit a job, or commercial, printing plant.

Unit 19. Setting Straight Matter.   Paragraph Composition.   Group Project: Part I

Plain paragraph composition is called *setting straight matter*. In this unit and in the next seven units, several students may work together on the same project (such a project is called a *group project*) or one student may undertake a small project of his own. Whether you decide to work together on a group project or alone on an individual project, the planning, the selection of material, the preparation of the selected material for setting in type, and so on, are the same.

In a group project each member of the group must have a definite job. He must know *what* he is to do and *when* each part of his work is to be done. This is called the *organization* of the project. A group or individual project must be planned carefully and a plan of operation worked out before the project itself is begun.

THE PROJECT

By working together, a group of students can produce a printed booklet of which they will all be proud. It takes a longer time for one person, working alone, to do this.

THE COPY

The first thing for you or your group to decide is what material you wish to set in type. This is called the *copy*. This copy should be interesting and not too long. Copy of about one thousand words is long enough for a group of five students to set; one-fifth of this amount, or about two hundred words, is long enough for a student working alone.

The English teacher may be able to help you select suitable copy for your project. Some classes have selected their own town as the subject for their project. In this case each student interviewed an interesting person and wrote up the story of that person or wrote a story about the town that was of interest to all. With the instructor's assistance, the students selected the stories that could best be used by the group for their project.

It is much better to set in type and to

print something written by someone you know than to take material out of a book.

THE PLAN

After you have selected your copy, the next thing is to make a plan, or outline, of procedure. In a group project the first thing to do is to give an assignment, or job, to each member of the group. If you are working alone, you will do all the jobs that are outlined below yourself.

Foreman and editor. There are two special jobs: foreman and editor. The foreman keeps a written plan for all the work and must know at all times what everyone is doing. He directs the others according to this plan. The editor takes care of the copy and hands it out each day to the others.

Job assignments. On a sheet of paper the foreman lists the names of the group members. Opposite each name he writes the jobs that that person is to do day by day. These are the jobs:

1. Edit copy (correct it).
2. Copy each paragraph on a separate sheet.
3. Prepare the cases.
4. Decide on the width of lines (Table 19-1).
5. Get a supply of leads and slugs.
6. Set type.
7. Assemble paragraphs on galleys.
8. Pull proofs.
9. Read proofs.
10. Make corrections.
11. Assemble paragraphs into pages.

Original copy. The original copy should not be cut up. It is kept by the editor. He uses it to check the order of the paragraphs as they are set. It is also used by the proofreaders.

From the original copy each paragraph is copied onto a separate sheet of paper and these sheets are numbered in order. These are called *takes.* When the editor hands out a take to a compositor (the one setting the type), he must note on his list who has received that take.

Galleys. One member of the group should be in charge of the galleys. At the end of each class, he receives from each compositor the lines set during the class period. He ties the lines up, even if the takes are not finished. When a take is completed, he assembles it with the other completed takes according to number and ties them together for proofing.

PLAN FOR THIS UNIT

The group. (1) Select the copy to be used. (2) Elect foreman and editor.

Foreman. (1) Prepares plan and makes assignments. (2) Works with all the others.

Editor. Corrects the copy, checking spelling, punctuation, and grammar. Divides the copy into paragraphs if necessary.

Assistant A. (1) Decides on the width of lines to be used. Table 19-1 gives the approximate number of pages that a 200- and a 1,000-word project will make if set in either 10-point or 12-point type, leaded 2 points, with different width lines (from 16 to 26 picas). For example, if you are setting a group project of about a thousand words in 12-point type, leaded 2 points, and if you wish to have a finished booklet of four pages, you might select the 25-pica measure for your type line. Since with this measure the last of the four pages

TABLE 19-1. LINE WIDTH FOR PROJECT*

Line width, picas	Number of pages			
	Group project, 1,000 words		Individual project, 200 words	
	10 point†	*12 point†*	*10 point†*	*12 point†*
16	5.9	8.5	1.17	1.7
17	5.1	7.4	1.02	1.5
18	4.6	6.7	0.9	1.3
19	4.1	5.9	0.8	1.2
20	3.7	5.5	0.75	1.1
21	3.3	4.8	0.67	1.0
22	3.1	4.5	0.62	0.9
23	2.8	4.0	0.56	0.8
24	2.6	3.8	0.52	0.7
25	2.4	3.4	0.47	0.69
26	2.2	3.2	0.44	0.65

* Table 24-1, page 64, is correlated with this table. It gives the proper type-page length and the desired trim sizes that go with the line widths (type-page widths) given in the above table. These two tables have been worked out on the basis of the Regular Oblong Proportion.

† Two-point leading between lines.

will not be completely filled, there will be plenty of room for the project title on the first page. (2) After the type page width has been decided, gets a supply of leads and slugs.

Assistant B. (1) Makes copies of paragraphs on separate sheets as fast as the editor gets them ready. (2) Numbers the sheets in order.

Compositors. Prepare cases by checking type boxes and filling space and quad boxes if the supply is low.

Discussion Topics

1. Why is it necessary to make a plan for your booklet? Why have your group make its own plan?
2. Why edit the copy before the type is set?
3. Why set original copy?

NEWSPAPER PRINTING

The type for most newspapers is set on Intertype or Linotype machines. On most papers even the big headlines are machine-set.

Country weekly papers and daily papers in small towns usually are printed on flat sheets, one side at a time, and then folded. Papers with five thousand or more subscribers are generally printed on rotary presses. Rotary presses print both sides of the sheet and deliver the newspapers folded and ready for the carriers.

Flat-bed presses may be used to print

FIG. 19-1. Flat-bed press used to print a small-town weekly paper. This press will print up to eight newspaper pages directly from type.

FIG. 19-2. A part of the large rotary press used to print the *New York Herald Tribune.*

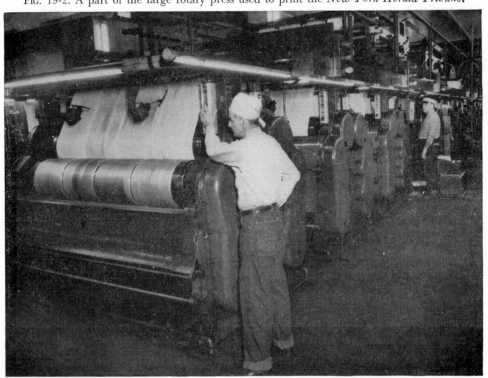

directly from type forms (Fig. 19-1). Rotary presses (Fig. 19-2) print from curved plates that are cast from molds of the type pages. These molds are made by pressing a sheet of cardboard-like material down over the type. This process is called *stereotyping*. (For a more detailed description of stereotyping, see pages 134–135.)

Newspapers employ a large number of people for a wide range of jobs. The jobs include editors, reporters, advertising managers, and salesmen; circulation managers and carriers; foremen, compositors, machine operators, stereotypers, and pressmen.

Employment in the newspaper field, especially in the mechanical departments, is steady and well paid. Newspapers employ nearly a third of the people in the printing industry in this country today.

Unit 20. Justification and Even Spacing of Lines Group Project: Part II

In this unit you will begin to set the copy selected for your project in the last unit. Setting copy in paragraph form is more difficult than setting poetry. The type lines of paragraphs are all the same length. In order to make the printed lines all the same length, the spaces between the words must be made larger or smaller. In any one line, however, the spaces between words should *appear* to be the same.

In Unit 4, page 10, you learned the test for justification. After a line is justified, it should slide freely in the stick; but when it is pushed forward between the jaws of the stick, the line should not fall back again (see Fig. 4-2, page 10).

Plan for This Unit

Foreman. (1) Sees that each composing stick that is being used for the project is set to the right pica measure. (2) Checks the first line of each paragraph being set to be sure that each is indented the same amount. (3) Watches justification.

Editor. (1) Hands out takes. (2) Finishes preparation of copy if it is not already completed.

Assistants A and B. Continue to make copies of paragraphs on separate sheets as the editor gets them ready.

Compositors. Set type.

Galley man. Assembles and ties up finished and unfinished takes at end of period.

Setting Paragraphs

Before beginning to set your first paragraph, read over the suggestions in Unit 8, page 20. These suggestions were about the picking up of type letters from the case and putting them in the stick.

Procedure

1. Take the copy for your paragraph and place it on your California job case

at the back between the capitals and lower-case sections. It will cover some figures, but you can always move it aside when necessary to get a figure that is covered.

2. Check with the foreman of the project to be sure that your stick is set to the correct pica measure for the project.

3. Put a slug of the right length in your stick.

4. Start your first line with an em quad for paragraph indention. Use 3-to-em spaces between words. Set as much of the first line as you can. When you get near the end, you will find one of three things:

a. You will have space left, but the next word will not go in the line. In this case, you *increase* the spaces between the words, that is, make all the spaces wider. To do this, replace as many 3-to-em spaces now *between* the words in the line as necessary (Fig. 20-1). (Never place space at the end of a line except at the end of a paragraph.) To remove a space from a line, use a narrower space to push it forward until you can lift it out with your fingers. First, replace each 3-to-em space with a 2-to-em space. Then, if the line is still not justified, try combinations of spaces

until the line is correctly justified. Try each of the following in the order given:

2-to-em space
3-to-em space plus 4-to-em space
3-to-em space plus 3-to-em space
3-to-em space plus 2-to-em space

b. One or two letters of the last word will not go in the line. In this case you *decrease* the spaces between words, that is, make them all narrower, in order to get these letters into the line. To do this, replace as many 3-to-em spaces now *between* the words in the line as is necessary (Fig. 20-1). Try each of the following in the order given:

4-to-em spaces
5-to-em spaces

If the line is still too tight, replace the 5-to-em spaces with hair spaces. These may be made of copper or by cutting a piece from a 3- by 5-inch card. First replace the 5-to-em spaces after commas in the line. Then replace the 5-to-em spaces between such words as "many went." There appears to be more space between words when letters such as y and w come together.

Fig. 20-1. Increasing or decreasing the spaces between words. This is done by using the four sizes of spaces singly or combined in various ways.

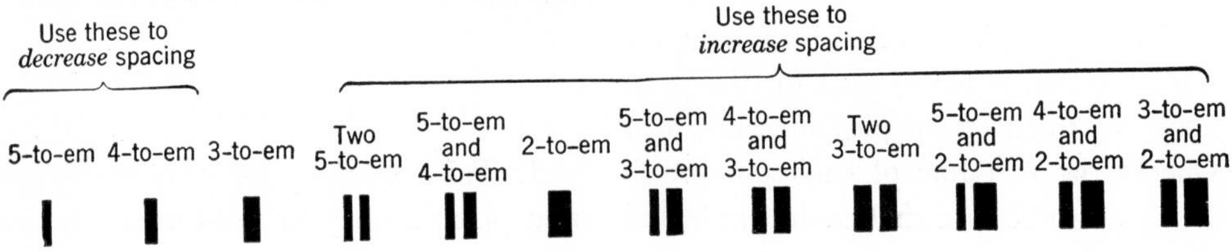

c. All the last word will not go in the line, but one or two syllables of this word will go in. In this case you *divide* the word according to syllables, set a hyphen at the end of the line, and set the rest of the word in the next line. Use a dictionary to check the correct point at which to divide any particular word in question. Some words should not be divided.

With the four sizes of spaces you have in your case and combinations of these four sizes, you can justify most lines and have them look evenly spaced. You cannot always have the spaces exactly the same, but they should be so nearly alike that they *look* the same in the printed line.

After you justify your first line, show it to the instructor.

5. Put a lead or leads between the lines according to the plan for the project. Set as many lines as time permits.

6. About five or ten minutes before the end of the class period, take your stick to the galley man and wait while he lifts the lines onto a galley.

7. Mark on your take the place that you stopped.

8. Replace your stick in the rack and your case in its proper stand.

9. If you are working on a group project, return the copy of your take to the editor.

Discussion Topics

1. Are two 5-to-em spaces wider than one 3-to-em space?
2. Do two 4-to-em spaces equal one 2-to-em space?
3. What fraction of an em are two 3-to-em spaces taken together?
4. A 2-to-em space plus a 4-to-em space equals what fraction of an em?
5. Is two-thirds more or less than three-fourths?

SETTING HEADINGS AND SUBHEADINGS

Solid masses of type seem to discourage the ordinary reader. Headings and subheadings that break up the text assist the reader by telling him in a brief way what he is reading.

Newspaper subheads are flush left or

FIG. 20-2. Samples of subheadings used in books and magazines.

FIG. 20-3. Spacing text heading in a three-line space.

Caps and Lower-case Roman
Caps and Lower-case Italic
ROMAN CAPS AND SMALL CAPS
Boldface Caps and Lower Case

In order to permit each line to print on the back of the one on the other side of the same page,
(line space)
Center Headings
(line space)
such as this one may be set in a two- or three-line space. In this illustration, the center heading is set in a three-line space.

centered and may be set in a small, heavy-face roman type. Books and magazines use many kinds of subheads set in many styles (see Fig. 20-2).

In books a subhead on a page may occupy the space of three lines of type as shown in Fig. 20-3. A two-line space is used for the single-column cap-and-small-cap headings in this book. This two lines of space is divided with 10 points above and 3 points below the heading, which equals one line space, and the heading itself occupies the second line space.

If your project has main headings set in all capital letters, such headings should be letter-spaced (see page 48).

Unit 21. Spacing.   Group Project: Part III

It is said that the best way to learn is by doing. This is true of typesetting. Every line is a sort of puzzle, or problem. Questions come up that you never thought of before.

Most of these problems are spacing problems. At first, it takes a little time to get even spacing and good justification. Perhaps you will need to try several combinations of spaces in a line before you get one that works.

Read every word and look carefully at every letter in a line *before* you start to justify the line.

Fig. 21-1. A monotype form showing the individual pieces of type. Note the nicks.

Fig. 21-2. A linotype slug.

Spacing

1. Always put a 3-to-em space between the period at the end of a sentence and the capital that starts the next sentence.

Example: Type is an alloy. It is gray in color.

2. Put a space after a comma. It may be a little thinner than the rest of the spaces in the line.

Example: Lead, tin, and antimony are used in type alloys.

3. Do not put a space between quotation marks and the quoted word or words.   (*Continued on page 59.*)

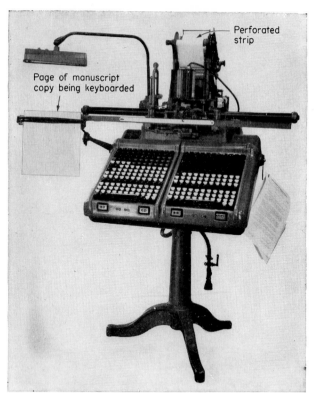

FIG. 21-3. A Monotype keyboard machine. The keyboarding of the copy on this machine produces a ribbon-like perforated strip of paper.

FIG. 21-4. Monotype type-casting machine. The ribbon-like perforated strip of paper from the Monotype keyboard machine is placed in the type caster. The type caster casts the keyboarded copy letter for letter and automatically produces justified lines of type (Fig. 21-1).

(a)

(b)

Fig. 21-5. (a) The Intertype line-casting machine. (b) The Linotype line-casting machine. In both cases the keyboarding and casting are done on the same machine. These machines cast solid, justified lines of type (see Fig. 21-2).

Example: Alloys are "solutions" of metals in other metals.

4. Use two commas placed upside down at the beginning of a quotation. Use two apostrophes at the end of a quotation.

Example: "Serifs" are the small terminals on some kinds of type.

5. If you require a dash, ask the instructor for an em dash. Do not use two hyphens.

Example: Type—of all sizes—is cast in molds.

Plan for This Unit

Foreman. (1) Helps galley man to assemble completed takes. (2) Sets type.

Editor. (1) Passes out takes. (2) Instructs proofreaders.

Compositors. Continue typesetting.

Galley man. (1) Ties up completed takes in numbered order and pulls two sets of proofs. (2) Delivers one set of proofs to the editor and the other set to the instructor.

Proofreader and copyholder. Read proof, mark errors, and return proofs and original copy to editor. (See Unit 15, pages 38–40, for method of proofreading.)

Discussion Topics

1. Do you put a space on each side of an em dash?
2. Is a 5-to-em space enough between words in a line?
3. Is an em quad too much space between words?
4. Is it easier to set type in wide lines than in narrow ones? Why?

Machine Composition

Very few printing plants set type by hand today. Most of the type composition for books, newspapers, magazines, and commercial jobs is done by machines. These machines cast type in justified lines.

The Monotype machine makes lines of separate letters (Fig. 21-1). The Linotype and Intertype machines cast the individual letters in a solid bar the width of the line (Fig. 21-2).

These machines have keyboards similar to that of a typewriter (Figs. 21-3, 21-6). The persons who work on the keyboards are called *operators*. They read the copy and at the same time press the keys that spell out the words. Operators of typesetting machines usually serve apprenticeships as other

compositors do. They learn to set type by hand before they learn to operate the keyboards.

Fig. 21-6. Close-up of a Linotype keyboard.

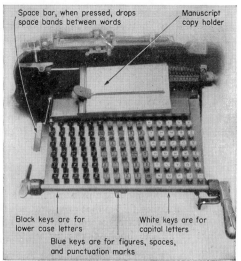

Space bar, when pressed, drops space bands between words

Manuscript copy holder

Black keys are for lower case letters

White keys are for capital letters

Blue keys are for figures, spaces, and punctuation marks

Unit 22. Initial Letters. Group Project: Part IV

Before printing was invented, entire books were lettered by hand. This hand lettering was usually done by monks. To ornament the pages, they lettered a large first letter, or initial, for each division of the book they were working on. They often surrounded this large initial letter with flowers and other decorations painted in gold, red, blue, green, yellow, and other colors.

Many of our present-day books have big initial letters at the beginning of chapters. This letter may be as high as two or more lines of the body type.

An initial letter should be nicely fitted to its place. Figures 22-1 and 22-2 show examples of well-fitted initial letters.

Fig. 22-1. Two-line initial letters. Note how the "nd" of the and and the "ike" of the like are cut into the initials A and L. This improves the spacing, appearance, and legibility of the example.

Here is a good example of a two-line initial, with a letter that is straight up-and-down on the right side, toward the paragraph of small type that follows.

And here is another two-line initial, with a slanting side. In this case the small-cap letters that follow the "A" are moved as close as possible to its top.

This is the way to set two-lines with an initial "T." Notice that both of the lines are indented the same amount. This is not like the indention with the letters "H," "A," and "L."

Like other craftsmen, the printer has certain ways of doing things that are hundreds of years old. Initial letters were used by the old monks in all the books that they wrote by hand.

From the past 500 years of printing we have received many kinds of decorative initials and florets. The planning of a printed piece is made easier by the wide selection available from typefounders' catalogues. The initial here is one of the many kinds and sizes that can be used to start paragraphs.

Fig. 22-2. A five-line decorative initial.

If you wish to start the first paragraph of your project with an initial, ask the instructor to help you to select the proper size of initial. You will also need to decide whether you are going to follow this initial with small capital letters or large capital letters (Figs. 22-1 and 22-2).

Procedure

1. Set your composing stick at the desired measure.

2. Place a slug in your stick.

3. Place the initial in your stick, flush left.

4. Set the rest of the first word in caps or small caps, however you have decided to do it.

5. Finish out the first line and justify it.

6. Measure the length of the type to the right of the initial in this first line and get a lead of this length to put after the first line before setting the second line.

7. Set the second line, justify it, and so on.

8. Study the examples shown in Figs. 22-1 and 22-2. Sometimes it is desirable to put a space between the initial and the first word of the second line. Capitals with straight up-and-down sides, like M, I, H, or B, take a space. Capitals

$$\mathcal{A} \; \mathcal{B} \; \mathcal{C} \; \mathcal{E} \; \mathcal{L} \; \mathcal{M} \; \mathcal{N} \; \mathcal{P} \; \mathcal{R} \; \mathcal{T} \; \mathcal{Y}$$

Fɪɢ. 22-3. Swash letters are often used for initials.

like A and L also take a space. Capital T takes no space. Why?

In Fig. 22-1 the first letters in the first line following the initial L have been cut into the side of the initial to bring them closer to the letter.

Plan for This Unit

Foreman. Supervises the making of corrections in paragraphs that have been set and proofread. (See Unit 12, page 33, and Unit 15, pages 38–40.)

Editor. (1) Passes out takes to those who need them. (2) Sets type.

Compositors. (1) Continue typesetting. (2) Make corrections and re-proof corrected matter.

Galley man. (1) Assembles and ties up completed takes and pulls two sets of proofs. (2) Delivers one set of proofs to the editor and one set to the instructor.

Proofreader and copyholder. Read new proof, mark errors, check revises, and return proofs and original copy to editor.

Discussion Topics

1. If you wished to print an initial letter in color, how would you determine how much to indent the lines that were to follow it?

2. Would a sans-serif initial look all right when the rest of the type is set in roman type?

3. Why is it necessary to put lines back in the stick when making corrections?

Some Pointers on Proper Word Divisions

Printers divide words according to syllables. Some words like "classroom" are easy to divide. It is not as easy to see the syllables in other words, such as "serv-ice" or "knowl-edge." There is only one sure way to find out how to divide a word and that is to look it up in a dictionary.

Some words cannot be divided. Do not divide any of the following:

Words of one syllable like "through" or "though"

One-letter syllables like the e in "enough"

Four-letter words like "into"

Plurals of single-syllable words like "classes" and "peaches"

Divide compound words on the hyphen; for example, "make-believe" and "self-control."

Avoid two-letter divisions, particularly when they occur at the end of a paragraph.

Unit 23. Overrunning Lines for Better Spacing
Group Project: Part V

In Fig. 23-1, (a) and (b) are the same paragraph. Why does paragraph (b) look so much better than paragraph (a)? Turn the page upside down and look at these two paragraphs again. In (a) you will see what look like rivers of white. The spacing of (b) is more uniform, and, therefore, there are no rivers in it.

Now you should check in a similar way the proof of the paragraphs that you have set. If you find any rivers of white in your proof, you will have a better-looking job if you go back over a few of the lines and run words or parts of words forward or backward to improve the spacing.

Fig. 23-1. (a) This paragraph has been set with too much space between the words. This results in rivers of white space. (b) The same paragraph as that shown in (a) set with less but more uniform spacing between words. Which paragraph is the easiest to read?

A compositor must set in type the words just as they appear in his copy, and he may divide words only on the syllables as shown in the dictionary. In order that the composition may be pleasing to the eye, white spaces between words should seem to be all alike.

(a)

A compositor must set in type the words just as they appear in his copy, and he may divide words only on the syllables as shown in the dictionary. In order that the composition may be pleasing to the eye, white spaces between words should seem to be all alike.

(b)

Procedure

1. Hold upside down a proof of the material that you have set. Do you see any rivers? Ask the instructor to suggest which paragraph you should re-set or re-space.

2. Place the type for two or three lines of one paragraph out in one long line along the head of your galley.

3. Take up each line in order and re-justify it in your composing stick. In this way you can run words or syllables of words forward to the next line or back to the preceding line. By doing this, you will get better spacing and may avoid too many consecutive or awkward divisions of words.

PLAN FOR THIS UNIT

Foreman. Follows up on proofreading. Has galley men pull three sets of galley proof of the new and the corrected (revised) paragraphs. Gives one set to the editor, one set to the proofreader, and one set to the instructor. Has proofreader read proofs of new and revised paragraphs. Assembles paragraphs that have been approved and that are ready to make up into pages.

Editor. (1) Gives out new takes. (2) Sets type.

Compositors. (1) Sets type. (2) Makes corrections. (3) Re-runs lines of paragraphs forward or backward to improve spacing.

Proofreader and copyholder. (1) Reads revised (second) proof to see that corrections have been made. (2) Reads proofs of new paragraphs.

Discussion Topics

1. Why do we have to turn a page upside down to see the rivers of white?
2. Newspaper columns are full of rivers of white. They are rarely found in books. Why?
3. Good, even spacing is an example of good workmanship. Good workmen like to do their best. Do you?

DEMAND FOR FINE PRINTING

Good printing is in demand today. Excellent printing results from good craftsmanship. It is art combined with skill. A beautiful piece of printing starts with good composition, which you are learning now. Because of this demand for good printing in recent years, new and distinctive type faces have been designed and made. These new type faces are used to set magazine advertisements, booklets, commercial forms, and artistic books.

Although many things that once were handmade by skilled workmen are now made by machines, the use of handwork in type composition is increasing today instead of decreasing.

Typesetting machines are being improved all the time, and these machines need operators who can set type that is well spaced and perfect in style.

There are opportunities in the printing field for young men who have learned good typesetting.

Unit 24. Page Make-up. Group Project: Part VI

After the type for your project or booklet is all set and while the final corrections are being made, it is a good time to plan the pages. For this plan you must decide how long each type page is going to be and prepare a paste-up dummy. A paste-up dummy shows the type that is to appear on each page (including the running head and folio, or page number) and the margins, which will determine the final or trim size of your project.

PLAN FOR THIS UNIT

Foreman. (1) Pulls several extra proofs of the first galley of type and gives to the editor. (2) Has galleymen pull three sets of galley proof of the other corrected paragraphs and of the sample and final running heads and folios. Gives one set to the editor, one to the proofreader, and one to the instructor.

Editor. (1) Decides on page length to be used for the project. (2) Prepares a preliminary and final page dummy.

Compositors. (1) Makes final correction. (2) Sets sample running heads and folios. (3) Sets revised running heads and folio lines if samples are not satisfactory.

Proofreader and copyholder. Reads proof of corrected paragraphs and running heads and folio lines.

PAGE LENGTH

In general each page should have the same number of lines of type. But if a page ends just before the last short line of a paragraph, three things may be done: (1) This short line may be included. Then the page that faces this long page must also have an extra line in order to balance. (2) The last sentence or two of the paragraph may be rewritten and shortened to cut out the short line. Or (3) if the line is almost full, a word or two may be added to fill out the line. If filled out, the line may be used to start the next page.

Procedure

1. Pull several extra proofs of the first galley of type.

2. Mark the number of each paragraph with a colored pencil in the mid-dle of each paragraph. This will help you to keep the paragraphs in order while you are preparing your page dummy.

3. Trim the proofs all around as close to the print as possible with scissors.

4. Measure the total length of the type you have set and decide how long the page of your project is to be. Table 24-1 will help you to determine the most desirable type-page length and final size, called *trim size,* for your project. This table is based on the proportion of 2 to 3, which is known as *Regular Oblong Proportion.* If you selected your line width on the basis of Table 19-1, page 51, the page lengths given in Table 24-1 should give you the approximate number of type pages indicated for your line width in Table 19-1.

If your type-page area is correct, the

TABLE 24-1. TYPE-PAGE LENGTH AND TRIM SIZE*

Type area		Page area (trim size)			
		Page width		Page length	
Line width, picas	Page length, picas	Picas	Inches	Picas	Inches
16	24	23	$3\frac{5}{6}$	34	$5\frac{5}{6}$
17	26	24	4	37	$6\frac{1}{6}$
18	27	25	$4\frac{1}{6}$	39	$6\frac{1}{2}$
19	29	27	$4\frac{1}{2}$	41	$6\frac{5}{6}$
20	30	28	$4\frac{2}{3}$	43	$7\frac{1}{6}$
21	32	30	5	45	$7\frac{1}{2}$
22	33	31	$5\frac{1}{6}$	47	$7\frac{5}{6}$
23	35	33	$5\frac{1}{2}$	49	$8\frac{1}{6}$
24	36	34	$5\frac{2}{3}$	51	$8\frac{1}{2}$
25	38	35	$5\frac{5}{6}$	53	$8\frac{5}{6}$
26	39	37	$6\frac{1}{6}$	55	$9\frac{1}{6}$

* Table 19-1, page 51, is correlated with this table. It gives the number of pages a 1,000- and a 200-word project will make for various widths of type lines. The above table shows how long to make a page of any type-line width from 16 to 26 picas. The appropriate trim size to go with the type-page sizes indicated are also given. These two tables have been worked out on the basis of the Regular Oblong Proportion.

trim size given in Table 24-1 will leave margins around your type page equal to the area of your type page. Trim size is usually given in inches, but it is given in both inches and picas here for your convenience.

5. Cut four or five blank pieces of paper twice the size of your page and fold them in the middle. For example, for a booklet 6 by 9 inches in size, fold a sheet 9 by 12 inches in the middle.

A *page* is one side of a printed leaf. A *leaf* is two pages. The folded sheet you have just made is four pages.

6. Measure off enough lines from your trimmed proofs to make two type areas the size you have selected. Be careful to cut between the type lines.

7. Open out one of the folded blank sheets on a table. Lay on it the two trimmed type proofs, and move these around on the blank pages until they look right. You will find that you get the best result when the type areas are placed out of the center toward the top and toward the fold (Fig. 24-1).

8. When you have placed the two pages where they look best to you and to the others, if you are one of a group, paste them down.

9. Mark on this sheet the distance in picas between the type pages. Also, mark the widths of the top, side, and bottom margins. This is your preliminary page dummy. You will use it in preparing your final page dummy.

Fig. 24-1. Page make-up. Note position of type areas in this double-page layout.

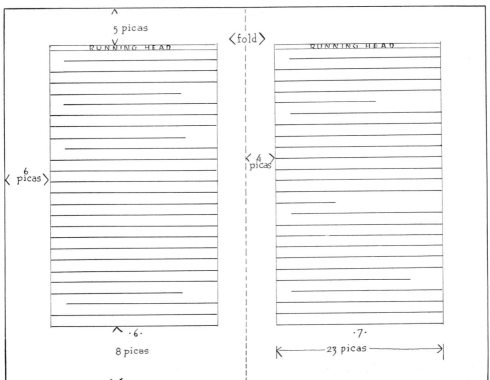

RUNNING HEADS

A *running head* is a line at the top of the page with the name of the booklet or book or the title of the chapter or section. For example, see the running head on this page, *Hand Composition*.

If you decide to use a running head on your project, you will have two lines less type matter on the type pages than shown on your preliminary paste-up dummy.

FOLIO

Printers call a page number a *folio*. Sometimes the folio is placed in the same line as the running head. It will be printed at the left on left-hand pages and at the right on right-hand pages. Or the folio may be centered in the white area at the bottom of the page; such a folio is called a *drop folio* (see page 30).

Procedure

1. Set a sample running head and a pair of folios (even and odd numbers) in type.

2. Lay proofs of the running heads and folios on your paste-up dummy and see how you like them. If you decide to use either or both, paste them in position.

3. Count the number of lines in the final type page. Every full page of your project should have this number of lines.

FINAL PASTE-UP DUMMY

Before you prepare a final dummy that shows each page of your project, you must decide how much space you wish to leave at the top of the first page for the title of your project.

Procedure

1. Take a fresh proof of your whole project, number each paragraph as before with a colored pencil, and trim the proof as close to the print as possible.

2. Measure off on the trimmed proof the correct number of lines to fill out the first page. If the title of the project is to go on the first page, be sure to leave enough space for it on this page. After you have marked off the desired number of lines for the first page, check the very next line to see if it is short (last line of a paragraph). If this line is short, either include it on the first page or take it over with the line that precedes it to the top of the next page. Never start a page with a short line. Such a line is called a *widow*.

Do not cut your proof.

3. Measure off the correct number of lines for the next two pages. Use your preliminary dummy for this purpose. Remember that, if used, the running heads will replace two lines of text. These two pages will face each other when printed and, therefore, should be the same length. Check for widows and make the necessary adjustments.

4. Repeat the same procedure until you have marked off all the copy into correct page lengths.

5. Draw the exact location of each type page on one of your blank folded sheets. Use your preliminary dummy to determine the location on each page of the type area.

6. Cut your proof at the points marked and paste up the pages.

7. Set the necessary running heads and folios in type and pull a proof of these lines.

8. Paste the running head and folio proof lines on your final dummy. This final dummy will be used in Unit 28 when you prepare your project for printing.

Discussion Topics

1. If a page is set in 10-point type with 2-point leads between lines and contains 44 lines of type, how deep (or long) is the page in picas?

2. If a 30-line page set in 12-point type is 40 picas deep, how much leading is there between lines?

3. When there are no leads between lines, type is said to be *set solid*. How many lines of 10-point type, set solid, are there in a page 35 picas deep?

SETTING TYPE PHOTOGRAPHICALLY

Since the Second World War, the demand for fine printing discussed earlier, page 63, and the steadily rising cost of such printing has encouraged the development of methods to set type photographically. A few of these methods are represented here by the Photon, Fotosetter, Linofilm, and Monophoto. One method has been developed which is a combination of hand-set type and photography. This method is called the *Hadego*.

FIG. 24-2. Photon, or Higonnet-Moyroud, photographic type composing machine.

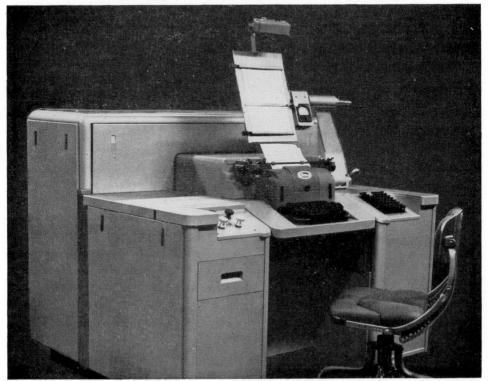

The *Photon* (Fig. 24-2) is also known as the *Higonnet-Moyroud* after the two Parisian telephone engineers, René A. Higonnet and Louis M. Moyroud, who invented the machine. In 1946 the two inventors obtained the assistance of an American, William W. Garth, Jr., who organized the Graphic Arts Research Foundation for the purpose of the development and the production of the Photon. The Photon uses a standard typewriter keyboard at full electric-type- writer speed. It produces a photographic positive or negative having automatically justified lines of type.

The Photon is now in commercial use. The *Quincy Patriot-Ledger* began setting advertising copy with the Photon machine in September, 1954. Later the *Ledger* began using the Photon machines to compose type for the social pages and other parts of the newspaper.

The *Fotosetter* (Fig. 24-3) has been developed by the Intertype Corporation.

FIG. 24-3. Fotosetter. Compare with FIG. 21-5*a*.

The camera unit that replaces the hot-metal slug-casting unit

In appearance and operation the Foto-setter machine is similar to the Intertype line casting machine (Fig. 21-5*a*, page 58). It can be operated by a skilled line casting machine operator with very little additional training. The only change from the Intertype slug casting machine is the replacement of the metal pot by a camera. The Foto-setter is an automatic, photographic line composing machine. It produces justified composition in galley form directly on film or photographic paper in one operation.

The Fotosetter is well established in commercial use today. It is particularly well suited to advertising but is also used in setting type for books. The type of some of the books that you use may have been set on a Fotosetter machine.

The *Linofilm* is a photographic method of setting type developed by the Mergenthaler Linotype Company. The Linofilm system is made up of four parts: a keyboard unit, a photographic unit, a corrector, and a composer. The keyboard unit in one operation produces both typewritten copy that can be easily checked and perforated tape. The perforated tape is fed into the photographic unit. This unit sets type on sensitized film or paper automatically.

The keyboard unit consists of a standard typewriter, a small panel for selector and control keys, a justifying unit, and a perforator. Justification of the line is done mechanically and punched into the tape automatically. The operator punches into the tape the specifications for capitals and lower-case letters of roman, italic, and boldface and also the specifications for small caps. The oper-

ator can enlarge or reduce type size from 4 to 108 points. He can also set lines or blocks of type up to 96 picas wide by any depth.

Errors found in the typed copy are corrected on the perforated tape before photographing. The film or type produced by the photographic unit may be corrected by an automatic splicing device called the *corrector*.

The Linofilm Composer handles layout and arrangement on a machine basis.

The *Monophoto* (Fig. 24-4) has been developed by the Monotype Corporation. The same standard keyboard used on the Monotype machine (page 57) is used on the Monophoto machine. This means that skilled monotype operators are also required for the operation of the Monophoto machines. The only change is in the machine that casts the type. Here the metal pot, pumps, and mold have been replaced by a photographic unit, and the individual matrices, or molds, for each letter, figure, and so on, within the matrix case have been replaced by a master negative plate containing transparent characters on an opaque background.

The type of photographic composition described in each case above can be reproduced on offset-lithographic (see page 127), gravure (see page 138), and letterpress plates by using standard platemaking methods. These methods may be used for newspapers, magazines, book publishing, advertising, printing labels, and so on. One characteristic common to all is the ease with which types of various kinds and sizes may be produced.

New photo-matrix case

Camera unit

(a)

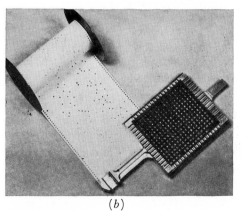

(b)

Fig. 24-4. (a) Monophoto. (b) A photo-matrix plate and a perforated strip or ribbon produced by the Monotype keyboard machine.

70

Fig. 24-5. Hadego photocompositor.

The *Hadego* (Fig. 24-5) was developed in Holland and imported by the American Type Founders. They have done a certain amount of development work to adapt it to American production conditions. In this process special plastic type is set by hand in a composing stick in much the same way as you have been learning to do in this course. The stick of type is then placed in the machine, which enlarges it to the size desired and photographs it. This process is used primarily for the production of advertising material.

Unit 25. Page Make-up (Continued)
Group Project: Part VII

The type for every page in any book or booklet must be made up to a uniform size. Even if there are only a few lines on a page, the page must be filled out with blank material—metal furniture, or leads and slugs—to the same length as the other pages.

You will see the reason for this when you lock up your project in preparation for printing it.

PLAN FOR THIS UNIT

Foreman. (1) With the compositors, makes up a trial page using the second page of the project as shown in the dummy. (2) Has proof pulled of project title and of trial page. (3) Completes make-up of other pages of the project and has proofs pulled of each page for proofreader and instructor.

Editor. Completes final dummy.

Compositors. Set title of the project for first page.

Proofreader and copyholder. (1) Complete reading of final proof. (2) Read proof of trial page and final pages.

THE TRIAL PAGE

Since your trial page should be a full page of type, use the second page shown in your dummy.

Procedure

1. Place the lines shown in the dummy for the second page on your galley. Transfer only six or eight lines at a time to your galley. Why?

FIG. 25-1. A page of type with measuring strips in place on each side of a page. A piece of furniture has been placed at the bottom of the form. The piece of furniture is being pulled toward the head of the galley and up. This lifts the type of the type form from the galley. If the page is properly justified, the measuring, or side, strips lift with the rest of the type.

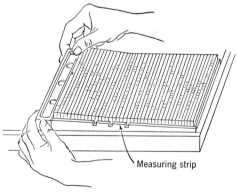

Measuring strip

2. Count and check twice the lines that you have transferred to your galley to make sure that you have the right number and the right lines.

3. Add the type line of the running head and the folio.

4. Place a slug above the running head and another between the running head and the first line of the page type. If a drop folio is used, put a slug above and below it.

5. Measure the over-all length, or depth, of your made-up page with an accurate pica gauge. As you make your measurement, push hard against the bottom of the page with a piece of furniture to squeeze the lines together. Your page probably will not measure an exact number of picas. Why?

6. Add enough leads or slugs *below* the last line of the type page to bring the page to an exact pica measure. Each page must be made up to this exact length with the same number of leads and slugs below the last line of the type page or below the folio, if a drop folio is used.

7. Ask the instructor for two pieces of strip material the length of your page. These are called *measuring strips.*

8. Place one of these measuring strips in your galley as shown in Fig. 25-1. Assemble the type for the trial page on it. When you are ready to test the page for length, put the other measuring strip on the other side of the page and a piece of furniture that is wider than the type page at the bottom of the page.

9. With both hands draw up the wide piece of furniture and lift it slightly from the galley. If the type page and the two measuring strips lift at the same

time, as shown in Fig. 25-1, the page is correctly justified.

10. Remove the measuring strips and tie up the page firmly.

11. Pull a proof and give it to the proofreader to proofread.

Assemble and check the type for each page in the same way.

First Page of the Project

Now you are ready to make up the first page of your project as you have laid it out on your dummy.

Procedure

1. Set up the title of your project in one or two centered lines. Use a type size that is larger than that used for the body, or text, type. Select a type face that harmonizes with the body type. The heading may be in caps or in caps and lower case, whichever you like best.

2. Divide the space that you have left at the top of the first page into thirds. Use your dummy for this.

3. Paste a proof of your project title just above the second mark from the top of the page. This will leave one-third of the space below the title and two-thirds minus the width of the title above the title line.

4. Get enough pieces of metal furniture to make a strip as wide as the type page and to fill the space left above the title on the dummy.

5. Below the furniture place the project title that you have set.

6. Measure the space below the title on the dummy and place metal furniture of this width below the project title.

7. Fill out the rest of the page with the text lines indicated for this page on

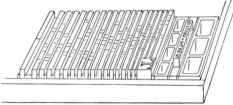

Fig. 25-2. First page of a booklet. A wide piece of furniture has been set at the top of the page above the title. A slightly smaller piece of furniture has been set between the title and the first line of text. Where is the folio on this page?

the dummy. Allow room at the bottom of the page for the folio and the slugs and leads that go with it, as shown in Fig. 25-2. A drop folio is usually used on the first page of a book or booklet even if the folios of the other pages are set with the running heads.

8. Adjust the length of the page by adding leads or slugs between the heading and the first line of the text.

9. Do *not* put any more leads between the lines of the text.

10. Test the page for length as you did in steps 8 and 9 under "The Trial Page," above.

11. Remove the measuring strips and tie the page up firmly.

12. Pull a proof and give it to the proofreader to be proofread again.

Other Pages

You are now ready to complete the paging of your project as shown on the dummy.

Procedure

1. Place the running head, with a slug above and below it, at the head of the galley and against the measuring strip.

2. Fill out the page with the correct number of lines shown on the dummy.

3. Add the folio with its leads and slugs if a drop folio is used.

4. Test each page for length. If a page is too short, look it over carefully to see if a lead has been left out somewhere. If it is too long, the type matter will lift up when you test it but the measuring strips will not. When this happens, look for an extra lead that may have been slipped in somewhere by mistake.

5. Tie up the page firmly.

6. Pull a proof of it and, if you are working with a group, give it to the proofreader to be proofread again.

7. Continue with the rest of the pages in the same way.

THE LAST PAGE

Usually the last page of a job does not have enough lines of text to fill out the whole page. If this is true of your project, add enough metal furniture, leads, and slugs between the last line of the text matter and the drop folio (if one is being used) to fill the page to the regular length.

Discussion Topics

1. In books and booklets extra leads are *never* placed between paragraphs. Why?
2. Why is it better to use metal rather than wood furniture in pages?
3. Why should you re-read the page proof?

THE LAYOUT AND ITS IMPORTANCE

Before a piece of copy of any kind can be set, someone must prepare a pencil-drawn plan showing the page size, type-page area, the size of type that is to be used, and the arrangement of the type matter. Such a plan is called a *layout*.

Some printing houses and some publishers hire designers who are specially trained to do this type of work. The designer's layouts are usually approved by the one in charge of the job before any type has been set. This avoids the costly re-setting of a job if it is not satisfactory.

In general a good layout should have (1) one line of type bigger than any of the others, (2) the biggest line placed above the center of the page, or printed piece, and (3) a contrast of light type (gray areas) with heavy type (black areas). The title-page layout in Fig. 26-1, page 76, illustrates these three principles. In the next unit you will prepare a title-page layout for your project.

Unit 26. Title-page Composition
Group Project: Part VIII

A title page dresses up any pamphlet or book. On it are shown the complete title of the printed piece and the author's full name. It may also tell when and where the piece was printed. The title page of a school project, such as the one you are now working on, may also show what class did the preparation and printing. Sometimes a school seal or printer's ornament, known as a *colophon*, is used on the title page. The title page that you prepare in this unit will be printed on the front of your project.

PLAN FOR THIS UNIT

Foreman. Has proof men pull at least three proofs of each title page set in type. Gives a copy of each to the editor, proofreader, and instructor.

Editor. Prepares copy for the title page of the project. With the assistance of the whole group, selects the best title page from the proofs submitted.

Compositors. Each one sets in type one of the three or more best title pages from the layouts submitted by the members in the group. Make any necessary corrections indicated by the proofreader.

Proofreader and copyholder. (1) Proofread the proof of each title page set in type. (2) Proofread any revise proof that is prepared.

TITLE-PAGE LAYOUT

If you are working on a group project, the editor, as indicated in the "Plan for This Unit," should prepare the copy for the title page, and each member of the group should make a copy of this for himself and prepare a layout for the title page. Re-read the suggestions given in the last paragraph of "The Layout and Its Importance," page 74.

You will notice in Fig. 26-1 that no folio is used on the title page.

Procedure

1. Cut a piece of paper to the trim size of your project.

2. Draw a very light penciled line to show the space occupied by the printing, that is, the type-page area. The page dummy will be useful for this purpose.

3. Draw parallel lines to show the position and size of each line on the title page. Note the size and kind of type you wish to use for each line.

4. Carefully letter the words of the copy between these lines. Figure 26-1 will give you the general idea.

5. If you are working on a group project, all the title-page layouts that have been prepared by the group members should be spread out together on a table and a vote taken as to which ones are to be set in type.

SETTING THE TITLE PAGE

If you are working on a group project, each one in the group may be given the responsibility for one of the different elements of the title page. For example, one might set the title, another the author's name, and so on. If there is more than one outstanding layout prepared,

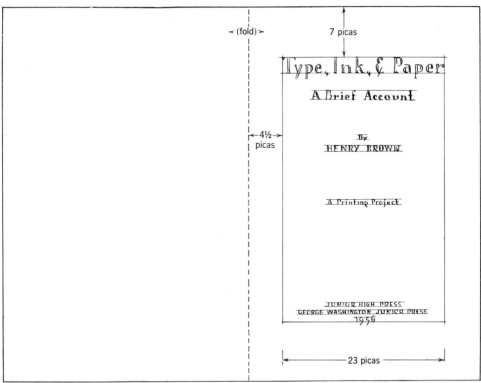

< (fold) >   7 picas

Type, Ink, & Paper

A Brief Account

By
HENRY BROWN

A Printing Project

JUNIOR HIGH PRESS
GEORGE WASHINGTON JUNIOR PRESS
1956

|← 4½ →|
picas

|←————————— 23 picas —————————→|

FIG. 26-1. Layout for a title page. The light lines at top and bottom and on the sides show the type area. These lines are not to be printed.

each of the best title pages may be set in type by different members of the group.

Procedure

1. Set the lines of type according to the directions on the layout. When the lines are set, put metal furniture, leads, and slugs between the type units to space them out as shown on the layout.

2. Make the title page the same length as the other type pages in the booklet. Test for length in the same way as you did the other pages (Fig. 25-1, page 72).

3. Pull a proof and proofread it carefully or give it to the proofreader to check.

4. Show the proof of the title page to the instructor for his approval. At this time the best title page set in type should be selected by the group for use in the project.

5. Paste the proof of the selected title page on the first page of one of the four-page blanks that you cut in Unit 24, page 65, and add these pages to your final page dummy.

6. Clean off the type of all the title pages set.

7. Store the type of the selected title page with the other pages of the project. You will prepare these pages for printing in Unit 28.

8. Distribute the type of the rejected title pages.

1. The date on title pages is occasionally set in roman numerals. Can you read this date: MCMXLIX?
2. Why is a penciled layout necessary when you set a title page or other piece of printing?
3. Did you use large type for the name of the booklet on the title page? Why?
4. How does your title page compare with some of the title pages in your textbooks?

ORGANIZATION OF BOOKS

Traditionally the parts of a book, such as the title page or table of contents, are usually printed in the same order. The most usual features of books, in order, are as follows:

1. Back half-title page
2. Frontispiece
3. Title page
4. Copyright notice
5. Preface or Foreword
6. Table of Contents
7. Introduction
8. Part half-title page (if any)
9. Text of book
10. Appendix
11. Bibliography
12. Index

The pages that precede the first page of the text are called the *front matter* of the book. These pages are usually numbered in lower-case roman numerals. The folios are not put on the first four pages, namely, the half-title page, frontispiece, title page, or copyright page.

The main parts of a book, such as the foreword, table of contents, introduction, first page of the text, bibliography, appendix, and index, usually start on right-hand pages. The frontispiece, an illustration, usually faces the title page.

The order for a simple eight-page booklet may be something like this:

Title page (page 1, folio omitted)
Blank page (page 2)
First page of booklet (page 3)
    followed by
Pages 4, 5, 6, 7, and 8

Unit 27. Locking Up Forms for the Job Press

To print type on a regular press, the type must be held together tightly in an iron or steel frame which is called a *chase*. Blocks of wooden furniture are placed around the type. Iron wedges, called *quoins* (pronounced like "coins"), are placed between the pieces of the wooden furniture that are next to the type and the pieces next to two adjoining sides of the chase. The quoins are tightened with a key (Fig. 27-1). The quoins are usually placed at the top and

Fig. 27-1. A key being used to tighten the quoins.

right of the type form. The chase trademark should be placed at the right of the type form. The quoins clamp everything tightly together so that nothing can fall out during the printing process (Fig. 27-3). This process is called *lockup.* A job locked up in a chase is called a *press form,* or a *form* for short.

To make sure that all the type is as even as possible, the type form is assembled in the chase on top of a smooth, level, metal-topped table called an *imposing table,* or *stone.* At one time these imposing tables were actually made with smooth stone tops and hence the name stone. The men who prepared the type forms on these stone tables were called *stonemen,* a term that is still applied to those doing this type of work.

Before the quoins are tightened completely, a special block of wood called a *planer* is placed on top of the type and is tapped gently with a mallet. This pushes down any pieces of type that may have worked up during the handling of the form. Every letter must be on its feet and must rest on the stone.

This process is called *planing down.* A form must be planed down every time it is locked up or relocked.

The small presses commonly used in the printing shop are called *platens.* This type of press uses a flat metal plate, or platens, to press the paper against the type.

The personal card you set in Unit 18 may now be locked up in preparation for printing in Unit 48, page 129.

Procedure

1. Slide the job from its galley onto the imposing table. Do not untie it.

2. Get a platen-press chase from the rack.

3. Place the chase on the composing table, or stone, with the job in the center and the head of the job toward you. In Figs. 27-2 and 27-3 you will notice that there is solid wooden furniture between the head, or top line, of the job and the chase and between the left-hand side of the job and the chase.

4. Measure the space between the head of your job and the chase and to

Fig. 27-2. First step in locking up type forms in a chase. In most cases the type would be centered in the chase.

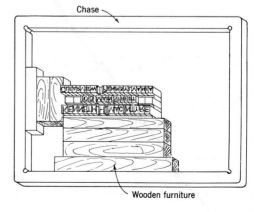

the left of your job and the chase. Get pieces of furniture from the furniture case to fill these two spaces. These pieces may be a little longer and a little wider than the job itself. When the furniture around a form is longer than the sides of the form, it is placed in pin-wheel fashion as shown in Fig. 27-3.

This is the *chaser* method of lockup. It is also possible to make up the job to the exact size of the furniture. This is called the *fill-out* or the *furniture-within* method. The chaser method is most common.

5. Put the furniture in place at the head and to the left of the job in the chase.

6. Place two pieces of furniture on the other two sides of the job.

7. Untie the job carefully, moving the furniture up to the type as you unwind the string.

8. Check the type to see that no letters have slipped or fallen out of place.

9. Put a pair of quoins at the foot and another pair at the right of the job. The half of the quoin nearest to the type should taper toward the solid furniture as shown in Fig. 27-3.

10. On each side of the quoins put short, thin, wooden strips called *reglets*. The reglets keep the quoins from scarring the furniture.

11. Fill out the space between the quoins and the chase with furniture.

12. Tighten up the quoins with your fingers. Check the form again to see that everything is in place.

13. Now take the *quoin key* and tighten up the quoins until they are snug *but not tight* (Fig. 27-1).

14. Lay the wooden planer carefully

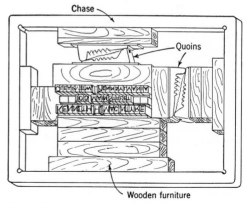

Fig. 27-3. Type form locked up ready for press.

on the type and tap it gently with the mallet. Make sure that all the type is even and that each letter is on its feet. Never plane down a form that is locked tightly. Why?

15. Tighten up the quoins until they hold the type firmly. Do not use force on the key and lock the form too tightly. You might spring the chase at the corner.

16. Lift a corner of the chase a little and slip a 2-pica piece of furniture under it. Press down firmly on each type line to see if you can find any loose lines or letters.

If your justification has been good, the job will *lift*, that is, every letter will be tight. If a line is loose, the form must be lowered to the stone, unlocked, and the justification of the line corrected. The job must be planed down again and re-locked. You can see why good justification is important.

17. When the form is satisfactory, lift it off the stone and place it in the form or chase rack. Be careful not to hit the face of the type against the rack when you slide it in.

Discussion Topics

1. What happens if there is loose type in the form?

2. Why would it be impossible to lock up a poorly justified form no matter how hard you twisted the quoin key?

LOCKUP MATERIAL

Chases are made in many sizes to fit the many sizes of presses from the little hand presses up to the big presses seven feet wide.

Imposing tables, or stones, are made of marble or of steel. A steel "stone" is usually called an *imposing surface*.

Wooden furniture cases hold an assortment of widths and lengths. The usual widths are 2, 3, 4, 5, 6, 8, and 10 picas. The usual lengths are 10, 15, 20, 25, 30, 40, 50, and 60 picas.

Reglets are made of wood. They are usually 6 and 12 points thick and 10 to 51 picas long. These inexpensive reglets protect the more expensive wooden furniture from damage by the quoins during lockup.

All wooden material should be kept dry, clean, and free from scars or dents.

Unit 28. Imposition for Folders and Booklets
Locking Up Two- and Four-page Forms

When pages of books are locked up, they must be arranged so that, when the sheets are printed and folded, the pages will be in the right reading order. This is called *imposition*. For example, if the project you have set has four pages, the first page and the fourth page will be locked up together, and the second page and the third page will be locked up together. Your final page dummy prepared in Unit 24 shows which pair of pages will go together.

LOCKING UP A TWO-PAGE FORM

If you have (1) corrected all the type set for your project, (2) had your final proofs approved by the instructor, and (3) made a final check to be sure that all your type pages including the title page are the same length, then you are ready to lock up your project, or job.

Procedure

1. Take two full pages of type. In a three- or four-page job, these pages would be pages 2 and 3. Slide the pages onto the stone, with the heads of the pages toward you. The even-numbered page should be on your right and the odd-numbered one on your left. Place a chase carefully on the stone around the pages.

2. From your final dummy find out how many picas space is to be put between the pages. Use furniture exactly the same length as the pages to fill the space between the pages. If the pages are not made up to 35, 40, 45, or 50

picas, add furniture at the bottom of each page to increase its length to one of these standard sizes.

3. Center the two pages in the chase.

4. At the head of the pages, between the pages and the chase, put a strip of furniture that will extend beyond the type on both sides as shown in Fig. 28-1.

5. Put furniture of exactly the same length as the type pages on each side of the pages. Use enough furniture to fill out the width of the long strip at the head of the pages (Fig. 28-1).

6. Put another long strip of furniture across the foot of the pages and side strips. This piece of furniture should be the same length as the one at the head of the pages, and 5 or 6 picas wide, if there is room in the chase.

7. Untie the left-hand page, moving up the furniture as you do so. Untie the right-hand page in the same way. Check both pages for misplaced or lost letters along their edges.

8. Put two quoins, with reglets on each side of them, on the right side and two at the foot of the pages (Fig. 28-1). The half of the quoin nearest the type should taper toward the solid furniture. Fill out the space between the quoins and the chase with furniture.

9. Tighten up the quoins with your fingers. Check the form to see that all letters are on their feet.

10. Use the quoin key to bring a light pressure all around the type form. Plane down the form carefully and thoroughly.

11. Tighten up the quoins with the quoin key until they hold the type firmly.

12. Raise the chase a little, put a

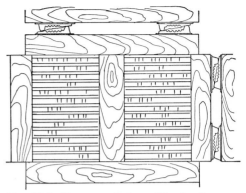

Fig. 28-1. Two-page lockup. The furniture on the sides of the pages is the same length as the pages. The furniture at the top and bottom extends beyond the pages on both sides.

piece of 2-pica furniture under one corner, and push down firmly on the type in all parts of the form. You may need to rejustify a line or to add a lead to each page below the drop folio, or last type line if a drop folio is not being used. Pages often squeeze up when the pressure of the quoins is applied during lockup.

13. When the form is satisfactory, put it in the form or chase rack carefully.

14. Repeat the same procedure for pages 1 and 4. You will print these forms in Unit 46.

LOCKING UP A FOUR-PAGE FORM

The principle for the four-page form is similar to that used for the two-page form just described.

Procedure

1. Make a folded paper dummy, or imposition sheet, by folding a sheet of paper in half and then in quarters. This makes eight pages. Number each page and unfold the sheet. Note the pairs of

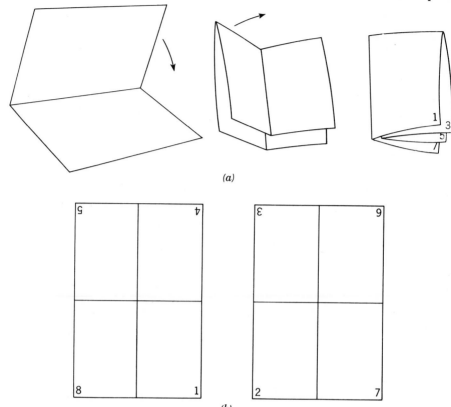

(a)

(b)

F<small>IG</small>. 28-2. (*a*) Folded paper dummy with pages numbered in sequence. (*b*) Together both sides of the unfolded numbered page dummy become your imposition sheet for an eight-page booklet.

pages that must be laid on the stone head to head (Fig. 28-2*b*). The space between the opposite heads of pages is twice the top margin plus two picas allowed for trimming.

2. Lay the four page forms in position on the stone.

3. Place a chase carefully on the stone around the pages with the trademark toward your right (Fig. 28-3). The four pages should be centered in the chase.

4. Put page-length furniture between and on both sides of the pages.

5. Put strips across the head and foot of each pair of pages as shown in Fig. 28-3. Untie the pages carefully as before.

6. Use two quoins on the right side (short side) of the pages and three across the top of the whole assembly of four pages (Fig. 28-3).

F<small>IG</small>. 28-3. Position of pages, furniture, quoins, and chase trademark in a four-page form.

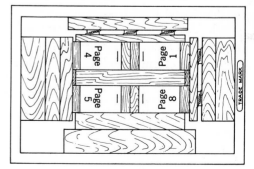

7. Tighten the quoins lightly and plane down the form.

8. Tighten up the quoins until they hold the type firmly.

9. Raise the chase a little and put a piece of 2-pica furniture under one corner. Push down firmly on the type in all parts of the form. If the form is satisfactory, put it in the form or chase rack carefully.

10. Repeat the same procedure for the remaining pages.

Discussion Topics

1. When an eight-page booklet is locked up two pages at a time, the folios in any of the four forms add up to nine. What do the four folios add up to if the booklet is locked up four pages at a time?
2. In testing the lockup, why do we lift a corner of the chase only 2 picas?
3. Why is it necessary to allow for trimming when printing book forms of four pages or more?

IMPOSITION FOR BOOKS

In book work it costs only a little more for press and bindery work on a big sheet than on a small one. Book publishers usually use the large presses that can print 16, 32, or 64 pages at a time.

For a book with pages 6 by 9 inches, for example, a sheet 38 by 50 inches may be used. On each side of this sheet 32 type pages can be printed. The finished sheet, with 32 pages printed on each side, makes a 64-page section of the book. This is called a *64-page signature*. The imposition of a form for printing such a sheet is a very skillful job. A 64-page sheet may be planned so that it can be cut in half after printing and folded in 32-page signatures.

A machine folds the printed sheet five times (four times if cut) and delivers it folded to 6¼ by 9½ inches. The trimming cuts off the folded edges and makes all the edges smooth and the margins of the printed pages uniform.

Unit 29. Using Rule Borders

Printer's rules are type-high strips made of brass or of type metal. They are used to print lines of various kinds. For example, a border line around an advertisement may be printed with rules.

In this unit you will set a card with a rule border. For this purpose, a rule with its printing surface along one side of the strip, called a *side-face* rule, is used. One side of such a rule is straight up and down; the other side is beveled at the top (Fig. 29-1). The rules to be used in this job are 1-point rules on 2-point bodies. In most rule cases you will find rules cut accurately to all lengths up to 30 picas or more.

For the job in this unit you will need the following:

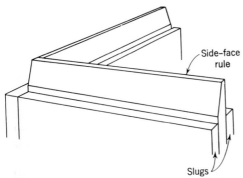

Fig. 29-1. A corner formed with side-face rules.

2 20-pica slugs
2 24-pica slugs
6 18-pica slugs
4 24-pica leads
4 18-pica leads
2 24-pica side-face rules
2 18-pica side-face rules

Procedure

1. Get out the slugs, leads, and rules listed above.

2. Examine one of the rules carefully. Notice the bevel and the printing surface. Care should be taken not to scratch or nick the printing surface. Why?

3. Put a 20-pica slug along the lower edge of your galley.

4. At the head of your galley, resting on this slug, put a 24-pica slug and two 24-pica leads.

5. Place a 24-pica rule next to the two 24-pica leads, with the straight side toward the inside of the panel you are making (see Fig. 29-2).

6. Lay an 18-pica rule on the lower slug at right angles to the 24-pica rule. This rule must have its straight side toward the outside of the panel. The printing edges of the two rules should now meet at the corner.

7. Put three 18-pica slugs and two 18-pica leads on the 18-pica rule.

8. Set your stick to 20 picas and set one of the sayings shown in Fig. 29-3 or some other short saying of your own choosing. Use the size of type indicated.

9. Lift the type from your stick into the center of the panel.

10. Fill out above and below the type with metal furniture, leads, and slugs to 18 picas. Have the type lines slightly above center.

11. Finish panel by placing a 24-pica rule, two 24-pica leads, and a 24-pica slug at the bottom, and two 18-pica leads, three 18-pica slugs, an 18-pica rule, and a 20-pica slug at the open side. Remember that the top and bottom rules have their straight sides toward the inside and the side rules have their straight side toward the outside of the panel.

12. Tie up the job and pull a proof.

13. Clean the job, distribute the type, and return the slugs, rules, leads, and furniture to their proper places.

Fig. 29-2. A 24- by 18-pica rule-border panel.

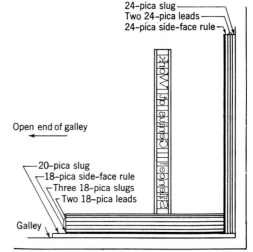

An empty sack cannot stand alone. (14 point)
—BENJAMIN FRANKLIN (10-point caps)

Silence! Genius at Work (18 point)
Never lend money. Borrow it?
Just try! (18 point; 2 centered lines)

Fig. 29-3.

Discussion Topics

1. What does your panel measure in inches?
2. What size card would you suggest on which to print the rule panel you set?
3. Rule that is accurately cut to pica measures is sold in fonts by the type founders. It is called *laborsaving* rule. Why?
4. What care is taken in handling rule?

SOMETHING YOU SHOULD KNOW ABOUT THE KINDS OF RULE MATERIAL

Some examples of the many kinds of rules that are made for printing use are shown in Fig. 29-4.

The plain brass rules may be bought in fonts cut to pica measure, or they may be bought in 24-inch strips. Either brass or type metal is used for these strips.

A common font of brass rules contains sizes from 1, 1½, 2, 2½, and so on, up to 9½ picas and sizes 10, 11, 12, and so on, up to 36 picas in length. Such rules are type high and range in thickness from 1 to 12 points. The rules are called *side-face* or *center-face* according to the position of the printing surface on the rule. The face is not always the same width as the body. For example, a 1-point side-face rule may be on a 2-point, 3-point, or 6-point body. The printing surface of the *full-face* rule is the entire width of the rule. Thus it is possible to have printing surfaces of rules from a thin hairline to 12 points in width.

Side-face rules can be joined at a corner by the method used in this unit (Fig. 29-1). Other rules must be mitered, that is, their ends cut at a 45-degree angle. A mitering machine is used for this purpose. The rules set around Fig. 29-3 were mitered in this way.

Fig. 29-4. Examples of various types of printer's rules.

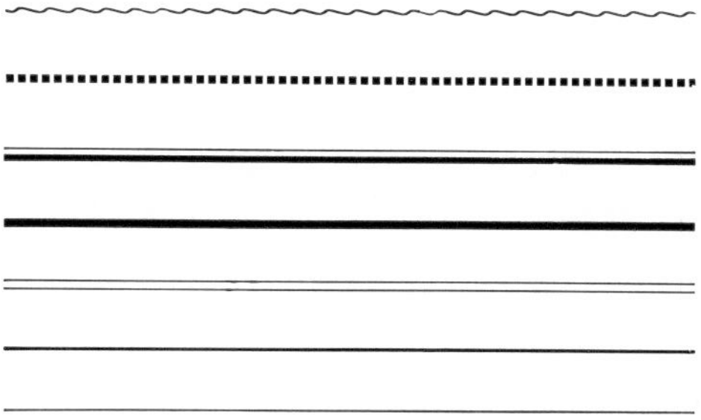

Unit 30. Setting Rule Forms

In school you have filled out many forms, perhaps with your name, home address, and so on. Most forms have light lines in the blank spaces where you write. For such lines the printers may use brass rules.

In this unit you will set a rule form. For this purpose, a rule with about a ¼-point printing surface, or face, in the center of a 2-point body is used. Such a rule is called a *2-point center-face hairline,* or *quarter-point,* rule (Fig. 30-1).

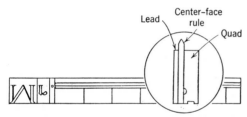

Fig. 30-1. A center-face rule is aligned with the bottom of the type letters in the line. Insert shows cross section of the type line.

The absence excuse blank shown in Fig. 30-2 may be used as the copy for the ruled form that you set in this unit.

Procedure

1. Decide on the size of paper on which you wish to print this form. A good size is 3⅜ by 5½ inches. This cuts without waste from a standard sheet 17 by 22 inches.

2. Make a penciled layout on a piece of paper of the size you choose. On the layout show how the lines will look, how long they will be, and how far apart.

3. Get a case of 10-point type and put it on your case stand.

4. Get a case of 2-point center-face hairline rules.

5. Set your stick to the full measure of the job.

6. Get some leads and slugs the width of the job.

Fig. 30-2. Absence excuse blank.

Date_____

Teacher_____

Student_____has permission

to be absent from your class in_____

on_____during the_____period.

Signed_____
Principal

7. Set enough quads in the stick to indent the date line as shown on your layout. Then set the word "Date."

8. Measure the length of the rule after the word "Date" on your layout and set a line of 6-point quads as long as the rule. Each 6-point 2-em quad is 1 pica wide. (Do *not* use a slug for this purpose. The slug will be shorter than the rule. Leads and slugs are always cut ½-point short so that they will not hold the pressure off the type lines.)

9. Justify the line by adding 10-point quads and spaces before the word "Date."

10. Put the rule in place on the 6-point quad line and put a lead below it as shown in Fig. 30-1 (insert).

11. Set the next line in the same way but put the 10-point quads and the justifying spaces *after* the rule. Continue with the rest of the lines.

12. Lift the type lines onto your galley.

13. Put slugs and leads between the lines to space them out as they are on your layout. To measure this spacing, fold the layout and lay it folded on the type.

14. Tie up the job and pull a proof.

15. Make any necessary corrections and pull as many proofs as you need.

16. Clean the job and distribute the type, leads, slugs, and rules.

Discussion Topics

1. How many pieces 3⅜ by 5½ inches can be cut without waste from a sheet 17 by 22 inches?
2. Why are rules needed in the absence excuse blank, which you have set, or other forms like this?
3. What does *align rules with the bottom of the type letters* mean?

Decorative Borders and Ornaments

Types in the form of little flowers or geometric designs are set up in lines and used for borders. Figure 30-3 shows a few examples of these.

By combining different decorative borders, very interesting borders can be made. Figure 30-4 shows an initial with such a border.

In Fig. 30-5 are a few examples of decorative page ornaments and emblems.

Fig. 30-4. Initial letter set inside a combination of type border.

Fig. 30-5. Type-cast ornaments and small decorative cuts.

Fig. 30-3. Examples of decorative borders.

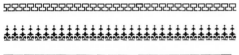

Unit 31. Setting Down-and-cross-rule Forms

Some blank forms are made up of many little boxes. Printers make this kind of form by printing the horizontal rules first and then printing the up-and-down rules. When ruled forms are printed in this way, there are no breaks where the lines cross each other.

In this unit you will set the ruled forms shown in Figs. 31-1 and 31-2. When you print these two ruled forms later on in the course, you will have the printed ruled form shown in Fig. 31-3.

Procedure

1. Get the following rules from the rule case:

No. of rules	Kind of rule	Length, picas
1	2-point light parallel	28
2	2-point body with 1-point side face	28
6	2-point body with 1-point side face	15
4	2-point body with ½-point side face	28

2. Get a supply of 28-pica leads and slugs.

3. Place a case of 10-point type on your case stand.

4. Set your composing stick at 28 picas.

5. Set all the type lines shown in Fig. 31-1. Indent the words "Monday," "Tuesday," and so on, one 10-point em from the right in your composing stick.

6. Place a 28-pica slug at the head of your galley. Place one of the 2-point side-face rules with 1-point face next to the slug.

7. Lift the type from your stick onto your galley above the rule.

8. Insert the four 2-point side-face rules with ½-point face between the days of the week and space out the type lines and rules with slugs and leads to match the spacing shown in Fig. 31-1.

9. Tie up this part of the job and push it toward the open end of your galley out of the way.

10. Set the heading "Periods" in 10-point small caps and letter space 2

FIG. 31-1. Horizontal form.

Monday

_____

Tuesday

_____

Wednesday

_____

Thursday

_____

Friday

PERIODS

	1	2	3	4	5	6

FIG. 31-2. Vertical form.

PERIODS

	1	2	3	4	5	6
Monday						
Tuesday						
Wednesday						
Thursday						
Friday						

FIG. 31-3. Complete printed form.

points (see page 48 for Letter Spacing). Center this heading as shown in Fig. 31-2.

11. Put a 28-pica slug at the head of your galley.

12. Place the type line with the heading "Periods" below this slug.

13. Place the 28-pica parallel rule below the type line containing the heading "Periods."

14. Get a supply of 3-pica leads.

15. Set your stick at 3 picas.

16. Set and center each of the figures (1 to 6) in the 3-pica measure.

17. Put the type line with the figure "6" flush left on the parallel rule in your galley (step 13 above), with a 3-pica lead above and below it. Fill out the column to 15 picas.

18. Put a 15-pica rule next to this column and put the "5" column in place. Continue until all the columns 1 to 6 are set left to right.

19. Put one of the 15-pica rules after column 1.

20. Put metal furniture, 8 by 15 picas, next to column 1.

21. Place the 28-pica 2-point side-face rule with 1-point face across the bottom of the columns and put a slug below it. The printing face of the rule should be toward the up-and-down rules.

22. Tie up this part of the job.

23. Pull proofs of both parts of the job on thin paper.

24. Lay one proof over the other and see how the finished job will look (Fig. 31-3).

25. Store both parts of this job on your galley. You will have an opportunity to print them in Unit 49, page 132.

Discussion Topics

1. The top and bottom cross rules are always placed in the up-and-down form. Why?

2. Which side of the side-face bottom rule did you turn toward the up-and-down rules? Why?

3. Why should the word "Periods" be letter-spaced?

Unit 32. Good Shop Housekeeping
Cleaning Up a Case of Type

Where people work in businesses or in industrial plants, all have to keep their workplaces in order. It is a good thing to learn how to do this, and the school graphic arts shop or laboratory is a good place to start.

In almost any school graphic arts laboratory there will be about three or four hundred thousand separate pieces of type, leads, rules, and miscellaneous items. Each one has its right place. When cases are fouled, or mixed up, no one has any fun setting type, and everyone is unhappy over the errors that result and that must be corrected.

Cases do get fouled and must be cleaned up frequently. There is just one way to do this. The letters in each box must be set up in a composing stick, and the ones that do not belong in the box must be taken out of the line and put in the boxes in which they do belong.

Procedure

1. Set a stick at 20 picas.

2. Start at the upper left-hand corner of the case and set up all the letters in that box. In this case the letters form the ffi ligature.

3. Turn all the nicks up as you set the letters in your stick. If there are more letters in the box than will go in

one line, put a 20-pica lead in the stick and set a second line.

4. Check the nicks. If the nick or nicks on any letter do not match those on the other letters, take out the letter and lay it aside—it belongs to another font of type.

5. Check the face of the letters. Take out any letters that belong in other boxes in the case and put them in their right places.

6. Look carefully for broken letters. If you find any, lay them aside and give them all to the instructor after checking each compartment or box.

7. Return the good letters to their box and label the box with a little piece of paper marked "OK." This will show you which boxes you have cleaned.

8. Go on to the next box of letters, and so on.

9. Check figures and punctuation marks in the same way.

10. When you have finished the letters, figures, and punctuation marks, do the spaces and quads. A good way to check spaces is to lay them flat on your galley and feel the different thicknesses with your finger. Be specially careful with the 4-to-em and 5-to-em spaces.

11. Take out of the case any odd sorts, such as em dashes, fractions, or asterisks, and ask the instructor where to put them.

Discussion Topics

1. What is a wrong font? How do wrong fonts get into your case?
2. How do letters get broken?
3. Why should broken letters be given to your instructor?

Unit 33. Good Shop Housekeeping.   Sorting Pied Type, Leads and Slugs, and Rules

The pied type that is picked up around the shop must be sorted and put in the right cases.

Sorting Pied Type

Any spare time you have in the shop may be well spent sorting pied type. It is good practice in identifying different type sizes, fonts, and space material.

Procedure

1. Place the pile of type on the stone or table.

2. Spread out the separate pieces so that you can see each one.

3. Sort out all the spaces and quads into a pile by themselves.

4. Sort the type letters by size, that is, put all the 6-point letters together in a separate pile, and so on.

5. Set up each size of type in a stick and sort the letters according to nicks. Ask the instructor which case each of the different kinds of type belongs in and then distribute the letters there. As you start to distribute the letters in each case, re-check the nicks with let-

ters already in each case to be sure that you are right.

6. Sort the spaces by point size, that is, put the 6-point spaces together, the 8-point spaces together, and so on.

7. Put the spaces into the central space case, if there is one, or put them into the individual type cases.

Quads are easy to sort and put away.

To Size Up Leads and Slugs

When you have a lot of leads and slugs of all lengths, they should be sized up and sorted.

Procedure

1. Line up all the leads and slugs against the head of your galley as shown in Fig. 33-1.

2. Take out the longest slugs and move them to the left of the rest.

3. Take the longest leads next and put them at the left of the longest slugs. Continue to move the slugs and leads to

Fig. 33-1. Sizing up or sorting leads and slugs before returning them to the lead-and-slug case.

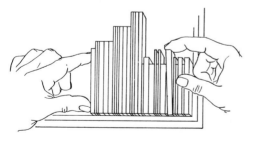

the left according to length. When you are through, you will have a series of steps with each step separated into slugs and leads.

4. Put the leads and slugs away in the lead-and-slug rack.

Brass and Metal Rules

Brass and metal rules should be sorted according to face and thickness. Then all the rules of one kind can be sized up as the leads and slugs were and put away in the right cases.

General Cleanup

When you sweep the floor, always pick up the type, spaces, and so on. Put these materials where they will be out of the way until they can be sorted. All broken type should be kept in one box, linotype slugs and shavings in another, brass in another, and other similar materials together. *Never mix scrap metals.*

Always throw wastepaper into the box provided for it. Never throw anything on the floor.

Discussion Topics

1. What is a clean proof?
2. It takes only half as long to put away a lot of assorted leads and slugs if you size them up first. Why?
3. Most of the pied type comes from the floor. Can you suggest a way to have less of it?

Unit 34. Setting Personal Stationery

You may wish to print a box of stationery as a present for someone else or for yourself. In this unit you will set the type for such a job. Later on in the course you will have an opportunity to print it. Figure 34-1 shows a few examples of personal stationery. These may help you to decide what line arrangement and type you would like to use for your job.

At a stationery store or stationery counter you will find many kinds and sizes of boxed stationery. Ask the clerk to help you to select a box of sheets or cards with matching envelopes that will be suitable for your purpose.

Procedure

1. Write out the copy that you wish to print on the sheets or cards and on the envelopes.

2. On one of the sheets or cards that you have selected, make a careful penciled layout. This should show where the printing is to be placed, the kind and sizes of type to be used, and what goes on each line.

Most people like stationery printed in small, plain type, usually all in capitals, and with each line centered. The printing is placed about four picas from the top edge of the sheet or card. It may be in the center of the sheet, or in either of the upper corners.

3. Make a penciled layout on one of the envelopes. The envelope may be printed on the front side in the upper left-hand corner or on the back in the center of the flap.

4. Show your layouts to the instructor for his approval.

Fig. 34-1. Suggestions for personal stationery.

93

5. Set your stick at 20 picas.

6. Place the case of type you are going to use on your type stand.

7. Get some 20-pica leads and slugs.

8. Set the type, line for line, as shown on your layout. If you are using a lining type (Unit 18, page 46), check the nicks in every line very carefully. (The various sizes of this kind of type sometimes get mixed up.)

9. Tie a piece of 20-pica metal furniture with the type when you tie up your job. This will help to keep the lines of type on their feet.

10. Pull a proof of your job. Proof-read it and correct the type if necessary. Pull a good proof of the job and show it to the instructor.

11. Clean off the type and store it in your galley. You will have an opportunity to print the project in Unit 47.

Discussion Topics

1. Why is this kind of job usually set 20 picas wide?
2. What is the reason for always making a layout before you start to set any job?
3. Why is the envelope printed?

Unit 35. Setting Tickets

Many schools and local clubs have special events for which tickets must be prepared. Many of these tickets may be set and printed in the school print shop or the graphic-arts laboratory.

Tickets are usually fairly small in order to be conveniently carried in a purse or pocket. A good size for a ticket is 2 inches by 3½ inches. If there is more copy than usual or if a linoleum block or a small emblem is to be used, the ticket may be larger, for example, 2½ by 4 inches. This size is also good for a ticket with a rule border.

Examine a few printed tickets before you start your job.

Procedure

1. Carefully read the copy given you for a ticket to make sure that the copy is complete. A ticket should always tell these things:

What the event is.
Who is sponsoring it.
Where it is to be held.
When it is to be held—
     date and hour.
How much is to be paid
     for the ticket.

2. Get several blank tickets of the right size and make two or three layouts. In designing the ticket, remember the first principle of a good design is to have one part—in this case, one line of type—bigger than the rest. This line probably will be the one that tells what the event is to be. It may say "Picnic Supper" or "Baseball." Or if the event is a play, the big line may be the name of the play. Plan to have the big, or display, line above the center of the ticket.

Although the easiest design to prepare is one in which each line is centered,

---

Graduation Exercises

Woodland Junior High School
May 24, 1957

50¢   High School Auditorium
8:20 p. m. sharp
Admit One, Reserved Section

Fig. 35-1. Ticket set in off-center style.

you may wish to try an off-center design for this project. If so, place the display line flush to the left and a few of the lower type lines flush to the right to balance the big line as shown in Fig. 35-1. The rest of the copy may be centered or moved to the right or left. Use your own judgment.

Make your trial layouts freehand with the letters sketched in. Erase or re-draw until you get an arrangement that you like. Then make a more careful layout with each line of type drawn to size.

3. Show your final layout to the instructor for his approval before you begin to set the ticket.

4. Set the type line for line as shown on your final layout.

5. Tie up the type.

6. Pull a proof and check it carefully against your final layout and with the original copy given to you for the ticket.

7. Make any necessary corrections and pull another proof.

8. If the ticket you have set is not to be printed, clean and distribute the type. If the ticket is to be printed, clean off the type and store it on your galley.

Discussion Topics

1. We set the name of an event in large type on a ticket. What other line should be emphasized?

2. Does a border of some kind make a ticket look better?

3. Does a ruled line under a line of type make the line stand out?

NUMBERING JOBS ON THE PRESS

Bank checks, tickets of all kinds, and many other printed jobs are numbered with consecutive printed numbers. These are produced by what is called *typographic numbering machines*. These machines are type high. They have five or more wheels. On the edge of each wheel is a series of numbers, usually 1, 2, 3, and so on. A plunger with "No." on it turns the wheels each time the press prints a number (Fig. 35-2).

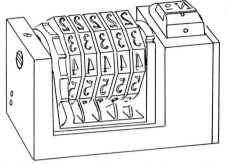

FIG. 35-2. Typographic numbering machine used to print tickets, bank checks, and so on, with consecutive numbers.

These machines can be made to print numbers in any order. For example, most machines print 1, 2, 3, 4, and so on, up to 99,999. Other machines start with 99,999 and number backward to 1. Other machines number 1, 3, 5, 7, and so on.

The figures on typographic numbering machines cannot be larger than about 14-point type. Bigger numbers than this must be printed on special presses.

Unit 36. Setting School Program

A program helps the members of an audience to understand what they are seeing and hearing. Programs are very necessary at plays, musical events, and graduation ceremonies. At large athletic events, you often hear someone who is selling programs call out: "You can't tell the players without a program."

In preparing a program, you need to arrange the copy in keeping with the setup that people have learned to expect. In Fig. 36-1 is part of a graduation program in which good style has been used. The names of the different events and of musical numbers are set in roman caps and lower case. The

FIG. 36-1. Part of a school program showing the use of roman and italic letters and small capitals.

GRADUATION EXERCISES
WASHINGTON DISTRICT HIGH SCHOOL
HIGH SCHOOL AUDITORIUM
JUNE 28, 1957 ➤ 8 P.M.
Overture, "Pomp and Circumstance" . . . . . . *Elgar*
HIGH SCHOOL ORCHESTRA
MR. URIAH R. HOLT, *Conductor*
Invocation . . . . REVEREND GEORGE H. SMITH
Pastor, First Methodist Church
Address, "The New World We Live In" . . .
. . . SUPERINTENDENT ORRIN H. LLOYD

names of composers are set in italic type. It is usual to set titles, like *Conductor,* in italic. Italic type is also used in such items as "John Jones, *Tenor,*" or "Mary Lloyd, *Violin.*" But when a title like "Superintendent," precedes the name, it is set in caps and small caps. Names of individuals and groups taking part in the program are set in caps and small caps.

The line of dots on a program carries the eye across the page. These dots are called *leaders.* In Fig. 36-1 the leaders are ordinary periods separated by em quads. If the space between the columns of type is narrow, the leaders may be omitted.

In programs for plays the list of the actors and their parts is set as shown in Fig. 36-2. Lists of players in athletic events are lined up right and left with their positions in the center (Fig. 36-3). It is easier to do this if no leaders are used.

CAST

Lord Luddington	Thomas Harvey
Lady Jane	Sarah Browne
The Butler	Henry Thomas

CAST

LORD LUDDINGTON	**THOMAS HARVEY**
LADY JANE	**SARAH BROWNE**
THE BUTLER	**HENRY THOMAS**

Fig. 36-2. Two different ways of setting a list of actors and their parts on a play program.

Fig. 36-3. This is one way of listing players in athletic events. The list below is from a football program. Sometimes the players from each school are listed on separate, facing pages. In such cases the positions are given to the left of each list of names and the players' numbers to the right of the names.

<table>
<tr><th colspan="3">HIGHLAND PARK
HIGH SCHOOL</th><th colspan="2">GREENVILLE
HIGH SCHOOL</th></tr>
<tr><th>No.</th><th>Name</th><th>Position</th><th>Name</th><th>No.</th></tr>
<tr><td>86</td><td>N. Smithers</td><td>L.E.</td><td>M. Barber</td><td>63</td></tr>
<tr><td>77</td><td>S. White</td><td>L.T.</td><td>R. Wells</td><td>61</td></tr>
<tr><td>71</td><td>T. Murphy</td><td>L.G.</td><td>T. Hall</td><td>59</td></tr>
<tr><td>59</td><td>H. Green</td><td>C.</td><td>U. Briton</td><td>25</td></tr>
<tr><td>64</td><td>D. Short</td><td>R.G.</td><td>W. Percy</td><td>73</td></tr>
<tr><td>74</td><td>M. Jackson</td><td>R.T.</td><td>C. Rose</td><td>26</td></tr>
<tr><td>82</td><td>E. Riley</td><td>R.E.</td><td>J. Fisher</td><td>31</td></tr>
<tr><td>11</td><td>G. Toole</td><td>Q.B.</td><td>H. Gordon</td><td>45</td></tr>
<tr><td>22</td><td>J. Symons</td><td>L.H.B.</td><td>N. Blake</td><td>48</td></tr>
<tr><td>20</td><td>D. Jones</td><td>R.H.B.</td><td>K. McIntyre</td><td>56</td></tr>
<tr><td>37</td><td>F. Stevens</td><td>F.B.</td><td>F. Johnson</td><td>71</td></tr>
</table>

Before you begin to prepare the copy of a program for any event, examine as many printed programs of the same type as you can find. These examples will help you to find out what information is needed on such a program and to determine the most appropriate size sheet to use, the kind and size of type, and the arrangement of the copy most suitable for the type of program you have selected to set as your project.

Procedure

1. Decide on the size of the sheet to be used for the program. Usual sizes are 5½ by 8½ inches and 6 by 9 inches. If the program is very long, it may be printed on both sides of the sheet or on a longer sheet.

2. Make a layout on a piece of paper of the size selected for the program. Show where each line is to go and how it is to be set.

3. Mark in pencil on the manuscript copy of the program the type sizes and the style of type (italic, caps and small caps, and so on) to be used.

4. Show the layout and the marked manuscript copy to the instructor for his approval before you start to set the type.

5. After the type has been set and any necessary corrections have been made, carefully pull four or five proofs.

6. Send a good proof to the person in charge of the event for his or her approval.

Discussion Topics

1. How can you tell a small-cap s from a lower-case s?
2. What other kinds of leaders besides those shown in this unit can you find in print?
3. Does a plain rule border or decorative border make a program look better?

Unit 37. Preparation for Perforating on the Press.   Personal Pads

To make it possible to tear sheets of paper straight, they are perforated. Stamps, receipts, and tickets with stubs are perforated.

Perforating may be done on special machines as a separate operation or it may be done on a printing press at the same time the sheets are printed. When you see ink around the little slots in the paper, it is a printed perforation and has been done on a printing press.

In this unit you may set the type for some pads for yourself or for your fa-

ther, mother, or a teacher. The printing may be just a name, or it may include an address. Some pads say "From the desk of," followed by the name of the person for whom they are prepared, as shown in Fig. 37-1.

Procedure

1. Make a layout on a sheet the size of the pad you wish to make. A convenient size for such a pad is 4 by 5½ inches when trimmed.

2. Show the position for the perforations ¾ inch from the top of the pad and above the printing.

3. Letter in the wording where it is to go and indicate the size of type to be used.

4. Show your layout to the instructor for his approval before you start to set the type.

5. Ask the instructor for a perforating rule 25 picas long.

6. Set your composing stick to 25 picas and set the type lines shown on your layout.

7. Make up the job by putting a slug at the head of your galley and the perforating rule next. Then put enough slugs or metal furniture on the galley to give the spacing shown on your layout between the perforating rule and the type.

8. Tie up the job, pull a proof, and make any necessary corrections. Pull a proof of the corrected type.

9. Show your final proof to the instructor for his approval.

10. Store the job on your galley. You will have an opportunity to print and perforate it in Unit 50, page 137.

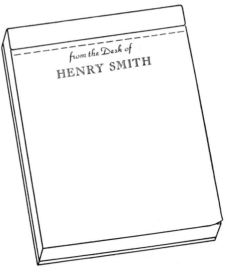

FIG. 37-1. Scratch pad with perforated printed sheets. The sheets are fastened together with wire stitches. The stitches and end of the pad are covered with a gummed cloth, or binding tape.

Discussion Topics

1. Do printed perforations tear as easily as the round-hole kind of perforations used for postage stamps?

2. The perforating rule that you used for this job was made of what kind of metal?

3. A person's name on a job like this is frequently set in caps. Why?

SPECIALTY PRINTING

Every closed package of merchandise needs a label to tell what is inside. The printing of labels and containers is a very large part of the printing industry.

Labels are printed in large sheets and usually are in three or four colors. Gold bronze (powdered bronze) is used on many of them. After printing, the sheets of labels are covered with a thin coat of varnish to make them bright and to protect them from moisture. The completed sheets of labels are then cut.

Some labels are printed on the tin sheets from which cans are made. This printing is done on special presses. After the printing of such labels, the tin sheets are baked in order to dry the printing ink. Then the tin stock is cut and the cans are formed.

Virkotype is used for printing paper and metal labels as well as greeting cards, wedding invitations, stationery, and so on. Virkotype is a commercial form of thermography, which you will have an opportunity to use in Unit 48.

Glass is often printed by a process called *silk screening*. This is a kind of stencil work with which you will become better acquainted in Section VI, pages 198–224. After the glass objects have been printed in this way, they are put in an oven to dry the ink.

Jobs in the label industry are specialized. Most of the training of the workmen is done in the plants.

Unit 38. Die-cutting a Printed Job Greeting Cards

Printing presses are used to cut irregular shapes from paper or cardboard sheets. To do this, a die made from sharp steel cutting rules is placed on the press. The sharp rules cut through the paper, forming the pattern desired. The inking rollers are taken out of the printing press when die cutting is done. Why?

Pasteboard boxes are die-cut and folded. Odd-shaped labels and the blanks for envelopes are die-cut.

In this unit you will prepare the type and die for a die-cut greeting card (Fig. 38-1). The size of the card is 4 by 11 inches, which folds to 4 by 5½

FIG. 38-1. Christmas card with greeting showing through the die-cut opening.

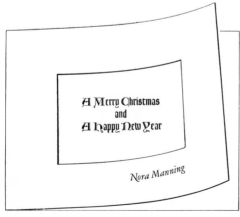

inches. In the card a window 2½ inches wide and 2 inches high is cut with a die. Through this window are seen the words of greeting, for example:

A Merry Christmas
and
A Happy New Year

Season's Greetings

Happy Birthday

Happy Easter

If any one of the last three greeting suggestions is used, you may wish to add a fancy border above and below the greeting. Below the window on the outside is the name of the sender (Fig. 38-1).

It will be very effective if you use cardboard that is colored on one side and white on the other for your card. A plain piece of white or colored cardboard will do, however.

Procedure

1. Cut a piece of cardboard 4 by 11 inches and fold it in the middle. With a knife, cut out a 2½- by 2-inch window a little above the center of the top flap. This is your layout for the card.

2. Cut two pieces of side-face steel

cutting rule 15 picas long and two pieces 12 picas long for the cutting die. These pieces of cutting rule will have to be cut from a strip. *Do not use the lead cutter* for this purpose. To cut these pieces of steel cutting rule:

   a. Make a mark with a pencil on the long strip of rule exactly 15 picas from the end.

   b. Set the strip in a vise with this mark just showing above the vise jaw.

   c. With a three-cornered file make a groove right on the pencil mark.

   d. Bend the rule without taking it out of the vise. It will break exactly where you marked it. If the ends are a little bent, flatten them with a small hammer against an anvil.

3. Make the die. Either cut a block of wood 14 picas and 8 points long by 12 picas wide, or use metal furniture, slugs, and leads to make up this size.

4. Put the rules around the block with the straight edges of the 15-pica rules toward the inside and the straight sides of the 12-pica rules toward the outside of the cutting die.

5. Put slugs around the job and tie it up. *Do not try to pull a proof.* The die will cut the tympan (see Fig. 41-3, page 111) of the proof press.

6. Set your stick at 15 picas and set the type for the greeting in one to three centered lines of 18-point caps and lower case. Use Goudy Text or Old English if one of these types is on hand. If not, use 24-point italic or cursive type.

7. Set the name in 10-point or 12-point roman capitals or in 14-point italic caps and lower case as shown in Fig. 38-1.

8. Tie the two type units (the greeting and the name) separately and pull a proof of each.

9. Cut around the type areas on the proof with scissors and paste the two little pieces of proof in place on the layout that you prepared in step 1 above.

10. Show the pasted proof of the type and cutout to the instructor.

11. Store the two type units and the die on your galley. You will have an opportunity to print and die-cut your card in Unit 53.

Discussion Topics

1. According to the postman, Christmas cards should be mailed two weeks before Christmas. Why?

2. The window in the card should be a little above the center. Why?

3. What other greeting cards could be prepared in this way?

COMMERCIAL ARTISTS AND DESIGNERS

When a manufacturer wants a picture of his product or a new label for a packaged article, he sends for a *commercial artist*. There are thousands of men and women employed in this field. Some of them are employed full time by printing or advertising firms. Others have their own studios and do work for many firms.

Commercial artists and designers usually specialize in one kind of art work. Some draw fashion illustrations for stores or for garment manufacturers. Others do nothing but lettering. Photography is much used in advertising for illustrations of foods and for fashions. Commercial artists also paint pictures in full color for business uses. All this kind of work is within the graphic-arts field.

To be a successful commercial artist or designer requires talent and training. A knowledge of the different type faces and the printing process is often helpful to a commercial artist or designer.

Unit 39. Setting a Two-color Job.   Rules Card

In color printing, each color is usually locked up in a separate form and printed separately. In color printing, black is counted as a color.

The type for a job to be printed in more than one color is first set complete in one form, just as if it were going to be printed in one color. Then the job is

4

48 point (red)

THINGS TO DO

24 point

Before the Bell Rings

18 point

1.

18 point (red)

Pick up the pie from the floor and distribute it.

10 point

2.

18 point (red)

Put away all the leads and slugs that have not been used.

10 point

3.

18 point (red)

Hang up your composing stick in its place on the stick rack.

10 point

4.

18 point (red)

Return your case of type to its proper place and put your galley away.

10 point

broken down, or separated, and re-made with separate forms for each color. This is called *skeletonizing*.

Figure 39-1 shows a rules card, the specifications for each line, and the two parts which are to be printed in different colors separated. The five centered figures are to be printed in red and the rest of the copy in black.

Procedure

1. Make a layout on a 3- by 5-inch card with the lines of type running the 3-inch way. Use a red pencil, if you have one, for the five centered figures. Letter the rest with black pencil.

2. Use the type sizes indicated at the right in Fig. 39-1 (opposite page).

3. Set the lines 14 picas wide.

Fig. 39-1. Two-color rules card. On page 102 is the job as set. Below, the black and red forms have been separated, or broken down. This last operation is sometimes called *skeletonizing*.

4

THINGS TO DO

Before the Bell Rings

1.

Pick up the pie from the floor and distribute it.

2.

Put away all the leads and slugs that have not been used.

3.

Hang up your composing stick in its place on the stick rack.

4.

Return your case of type to its proper place and put your galley away.

BLACK FORM

RED FORM

4. Space out between the lines until the job is 25 picas deep, *face measure,* that is, from the top of the 48-point figure 4 to the bottom of the letters of the last line of 10-point type.

5. Tie up the job, pull a proof, and :f necessary, correct the type and pull a revised proof.

6. Show the final proof to the instructor for his approval.

7. Break the job for color in the following way:

a. Lift out each of the lines of centered figures and replace each line with a line of quads.

b. Place the figure lines below the others on the galley and space out between them just as they were before. You may use the folded proof of the job to check this spacing. If you like to add, you may count up the number of picas and points between the figure lines in the black

form to determine the proper spacing between the figures.

8. Tie up both parts of the job separately and pull proofs of each part on thin paper. Lay one proof over the other and hold them up to a bright light. Do the lines that are to be printed in red fit in their right places on the black form? If not, untie the job, adjust the spacing, and pull new proofs. Check the spacing again in the same way.

9. Store the type for both parts of this job on your galley. You will have an opportunity to print the two-color card in Unit 52.

Discussion Topics

1. Why is color used in advertising?
2. Would a job printed all in red be as easy to read as one printed in black?
3. Would a light blue be better than red to attract attention?

POSTER PRINTING

Everyone has seen giant posters. The pictures on them are printed from engraved blocks or plates, but the wording is often printed from big wooden letters. Wood type is made in all sizes from 1 inch high up to 2 feet or more.

There are firms in some cities that specialize in this kind of printing.

Billboards are often painted; but when the same billboard is to be shown in a large number of places, it is

printed, or lithographed, from plates.

No press is big enough to print these big signs in one piece. Therefore, they are printed in 28- by 42-inch sections. Then the sections are pasted together on the wall or billboard.

Billboard printers employ artists, salesmen, and advertising writers as well as printers, pressmen, and engravers. They also employ many sign painters.

Unit 40. Bookplate, Napkin Corner, Place Card

Many interesting and useful projects may be printed with type, paper, and ink. The procedures for three projects —bookplate, napkin corner, and place card—are given in this unit.

BOOKPLATE

An attractive bookplate printed with your name on it pasted on the inside of the front cover of each of your books will show that you have started your own library. It will also identify the book as yours in case it is borrowed. An example of such a bookplate is shown in Fig. 40-1.

Copy for a bookplate usually reads "From the Library of," followed by the name of the owner. Sometimes you will see the Latin words *Ex Libris,* which mean "From the Library of," on a bookplate.

Procedure

1. Make a penciled layout for your bookplate. It should be 2½ inches wide by 3⅞ inches high. The type area is 9 picas wide. A 12- by 20-pica side-face rule border is to be set around it, with a 12-point decorative border inside it, as shown in Fig. 40-1. If you can find a small type ornament that is suitable, use it at the top of your design. The type should be 18 or 24 point, set in caps and lower case in three, four, or five centered lines. Old English, italic, or cursive type is recommended. For a modern effect, you might use an 18-point sans-serif type.

2. Show your layout to the instructor for his approval before you start to set the type.

FIG. 40-1. Bookplate with type ornament, type border, and rule.

3. Make up the border with two 12- and two 20-pica 1-point side-face rules. Inside this ruled box put a 12-point decorative border. Separate the decorative border from the rule with 2-point leads.

4. Set your composing stick at 9 picas. Set and center each line of type.

5. Remove the type lines from your stick and carefully place them inside the border.

6. Center the lines of type inside the border and add the necessary space material on each side of the lines.

7. Add space material above and below the type to fill out the space inside the border.

8. Tie up the job. If the lines of type are loose, add space material to justify the lines evenly.

9. Cut the paper for the bookplate 3 by 4½ inches. Although any paper may

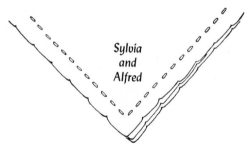

Fig. 40-2. Personalized paper napkin.

be used, gummed paper is recommended. The paper is cut larger than the finished bookplate to leave room for the *grippers* on the proof press (see Fig. 41-3, page 111). The grippers hold the paper in place during the printing. The bookplate is then trimmed after it is printed.

10. Pull a proof, make any necessary corrections, and clean up the job.

11. Store your job on your galley and put the cut paper in a safe place. You will have an opportunity to print this project in Unit 45.

Napkin Corner

Small, light-colored napkins with someone's name or initial, as, for example, "The Smiths," "Mary and John," or "E.M.T.," printed in one corner make a nice gift. Figure 40-2 shows a napkin corner printed with a cursive type.

A package of 50 napkins will be enough for this project.

Procedure

1. Make a layout on one of the napkins and show it to the instructor for his approval before you start to set the type. Use a cursive type if there are some available. A cursive type looks like hand

lettering. A sans-serif type is good for initials.

2. Set your stick at 15 picas. Set the type and center each line.

3. Tie up the job.

4. Unfold one of the napkins and pull a proof on it.

5. Make any necessary corrections and pull another proof.

6. Clean up the type and store it on your galley. You will have an opportunity to print this job in Unit 42.

Place Card

A place card with a flower design may be used at any time. Such a place card is shown in Fig. 40-3. If a little decorative cut, such as a Halloween pumpkin, a Thanksgiving Turkey, a Christmas wreath, or a Santa Claus, is available, you may wish to print place cards in two colors for someone who is going to have a party or a dinner on one of these days.

Procedure

1. Make a layout in pencil on a 3- by 5-inch card. Show your layout to the in-

Fig. 40-3. Place card with space for name.

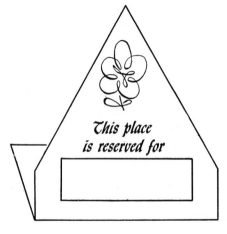

structor for his approval before you start to set the type.

2. Set your composing stick at 12 picas. Set the type and center each line. Center the decorative ornament if you are using one.

3. Use a 1-point side-face rule for the little panel 4 by 12 picas.

4. Set the job as one form. If you wish to print the ornament in another color, break the job into two forms as you did in Unit 39. Tie up the job.

5. Pull a proof of the job, make any necessary corrections, and clean off the type.

6. Store the job on your galley. You will have an opportunity to print it in Unit 45 (if it is a one-color job) or in Unit 52 (if it is a two-color job).

When you print this job, print it on 3- by 5-inch pieces of cardboard or stiff paper. Cut off the two upper corners of each card and fold under the lower portion as shown in Fig. 40-3 to make it stand up.

Discussion Topics

1. What other way could you print and fold the 3- by 5-inch place card that you set in this unit?

2. Take an 8-point 3-em quad and put it in the stick with the long side up and down. What size 24-point space is it now?

3. Do the same with a 3-em 6-point quad. What size 18-point space is it when it is turned vertically?

PRINTING OF WALLPAPER AND FABRICS

In a wallpaper store hundreds of different designs are to be found, and each roll of wallpaper is printed on a press. The designs for wallpaper are engraved, one color at a time, on hardwood cylinders. Some wallpapers may show 8 or 10 colors and gold.

Fabrics like calico, percale, and all kinds of prints are printed on special presses. Dyes are used on fabrics in place of printing inks.

Some decorative fabrics are block-printed. A wood or linoleum block is cut for each color. The fabric is stretched out on a long padded table. A block is inked with a special kind of printing ink that will not wash out. Then it is laid on the fabric and the ink is transferred by pounding the block with a rubber mallet.

Sugar sacks, flour sacks, burlap bags, and flags are other examples of printed fabrics.

FIG. 40-4. Rollers used for printing cotton fabric.

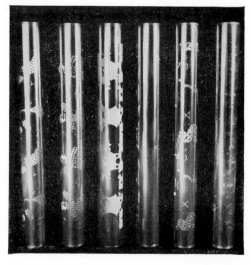

Johnny enjoys seeing the results of his type setting and composition as he hand-feeds an open platen press.

Section III. ELEMENTARY PRESS WORK

Unit 41. The Platen Press and Its Care

Throughout this section you will be working on a platen press. The flat iron plate that exerts or receives pressure on the press is called a *platen;* hence the name. Two platen presses that open and shut like a clam shell are shown in Figs. 41-1 and 41-2. These two presses are used for small jobs. Such presses may also be used without the inking rollers for die cutting and creasing. The platen press shown in Fig. 41-2 is power-driven. Note the safety guard on the fly-wheel.

In order to use the press in your shop safely and efficiently, you must learn the safety rules given below, the names of the various parts of the press, and how to take care of it. You will understand the reasons for the safety rules as soon as you begin to use the press. These rules are followed by experienced pressmen who do know how to work safely. You must learn how to work safely *before* you start to use the press.

FIG. 41-1. A small hand-operated pilot press.

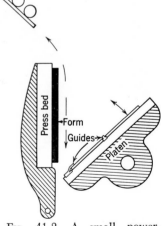

FIG. 41-2. A small power-driven platen press. The above drawing shows how it works. (*Graphic Arts Production Yearbook,* copyright 1948 by Colton Press, Inc.)

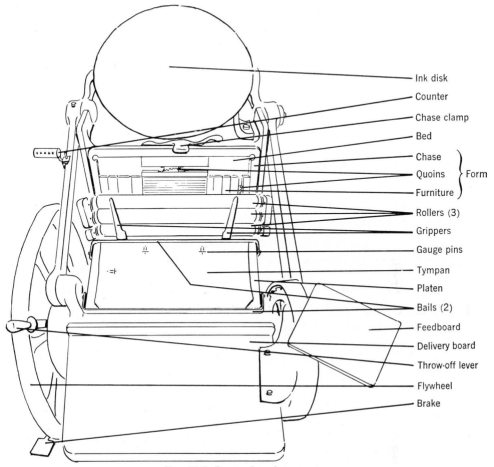

Ink disk
Counter
Chase clamp
Bed
Chase
Quoins } Form
Furniture
Rollers (3)
Grippers
Gauge pins
Tympan
Platen
Bails (2)
Feedboard
Delivery board
Throw-off lever
Flywheel
Brake

Fig. 41-3. Parts of a platen press.

SAFETY RULES

1. Only one person at a time should operate the press. Everyone else must stand back, away from the press.

2. The power must be turned off when the press is being oiled.

3. The press must be turned by hand when it is being washed.

4. The press must be stopped whenever ink is to be applied to the ink disk.

5. The floor must be kept clear and clean around the press. Any oil that drops on the floor must be wiped up immediately. This is to prevent anyone from slipping or tripping and falling into the press when it is moving.

6. Always stop the press to remove a sheet of paper that has fallen down into the press.

7. When working around a press, always wear clothing that will not catch in the working parts of the press.

PARTS OF A PLATEN PRESS

With the aid of Fig. 41-3 identify each of the following parts of the press in your shop:

Ink disk	Tympan
Counter	Platen
Chase clamp	Bails
Bed	Feedboard
Form	Delivery board
Rollers	Throw-off lever
Grippers	Flywheel
Gauge pins	Brake

How to Change Tympans

The platen is covered with a double sheet of heavy paper called the *tympan*. It is clamped to the platen by two U-shaped steel bars called *bails*—one at the top and one at the bottom.

Procedure

1. Lift the top bail and remove the sheets of paper or cardboard from underneath the tympan. Lay these carefully to one side. These sheets are called *packing*. You need less packing for one or two lines of type than you do for a form that has a great deal of type in it.

2. Remove the old tympan from the platen by lifting the lower and upper tympan bails. When lifting the bails, you may have to pry them up with a tympan bail wrench or metal bar.

3. Use the old unfolded tympan to measure the size of the new one as you tear it from the roll of tympan paper. Do not waste tympan paper.

4. Fold the new tympan in the center; then fold it ¾ inch from the folded edge.

5. Place the tympan on the platen. Raise the lower bail and fit the folded edge to the sharp edge of the platen, smoothing out the paper as you do so. Hold the tympan firmly while you push the lower bail down as far as it will go.

6. The doubled tympan should lie smoothly along the lower edge of the platen. If it seems wrinkled, lift the lower bail and try again.

7. Lift up the free end of the doubled tympan and tuck it under the upper bail. Smooth it down and pull it up tight. Then push the upper bail down until it stops. The whole tympan is now held firmly. It should be smooth and tight.

8. Lift the top bail and replace the packing. It is good practice to remove one or two sheets of the old packing when you put it back. If you need more sheets, you can put them under the tympan later.

9. Ask the instructor to check your new tympan.

Oiling the Press

A long-spout oilcan full of medium-grade lubricating oil and a clean rag are used for oiling the press. The rags used for oiling the press should be kept in a metal bin.

Put a small amount of oil in each of the oilholes on the press. Wipe off any oil that does not go into an oilhole or that runs out of a bearing.

Ask the instructor to show you how to oil the platen cam roll and the flat surfaces of the platen locks.

When you are finished, put the oil can and the rag that you have used back in their proper places.

Discussion Topics

1. What are the rules for operating a press safely?
2. Why must the tympan be smooth and tight?
3. What does the packing do?
4. Why do we oil machinery?

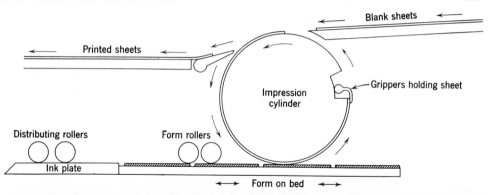

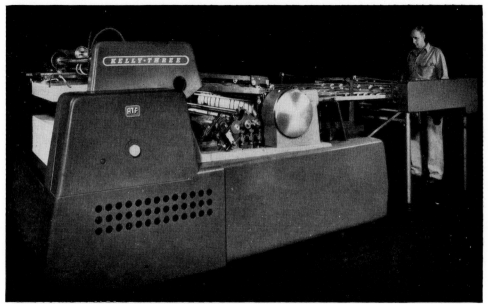

Fig. 41-4. Large commercial flat-bed press. Note the mechanical feeder at the right-hand side of the photograph. The drawing shows how the press works. (*Graphic Arts Production Yearbook,* copyright 1948 by Colton Press, Inc.)

5. Why do we wipe off the excess oil?
6. How often should a school press be oiled? (Hint: It is better to oil a machine too often than to risk not oiling it at all.)

PLATEN PRESSES AND FLAT-BED PRESSES

Formerly all platen presses were fed by hand. Today many of these presses are fed by mechanical feeders. A feeder of this sort picks up a sheet from a pile, places it in position on the platen, and removes it from the platen to another pile after it is printed. It does all this in about one second, that is, at the rate of 3,000 to 3,600 sheets an hour.

Larger sheets are printed on flat-bed cylinder presses (Fig. 41-4). The type form is placed on an iron bed that travels back and forth horizontally under a revolving cylinder. The paper is fed into the press, usually by a mechanical feeder, and is printed as it passes be-tween the type form and the cylinder. It is then automatically placed in a neat pile at the end of the press.

Study the drawing in Fig. 41-4.

Unit 42. Getting Ready for the Press

In this unit and the one that follows you will have the opportunity to print one of the smaller projects that you have set in the earlier part of this course. You may wish to print stationery with the name and address that you set in Unit 4 or the napkin corner that you set in Unit 40. It is recommended that you do a project that does not have rules in it for your first job on the platen press.

After you have selected the job you wish to print and have the paper on which to print it ready, lock up the job in a chase. (See Unit 27, pages 77–79, for a review of this operation.) You may now get the press ready to operate.

Procedure

1. Examine the rollers. They are soft but firm. They are smooth, but they feel tacky. Rollers are made of glue, glycerin, and molasses or sirup with other substances added to keep them soft and able to spread ink smoothly on type or other printing surfaces.

2. Ask the instructor for some black ink suitable for the paper you will be using. Squeeze about one-quarter of an inch of the ink from the ink tube. Use an ink knife to remove all the ink from the mouth of the tube. Replace the cap on the tube.

3. With the ink knife, spread the ink on the left-hand side of the ink plate or ink disk on the press. Wipe off on the plate as much of the ink from the knife as you can. Then use a rag and some solvent to wash the knife clean.

4. If your press is motor-driven, ask the instructor to show you how to operate the *motor switch* and the *speed controls*. At the same time, the instructor will show you how the *throw-off lever* operates.

5. Run the press at a moderate speed until the ink is evenly distributed over the ink disk. Always ink up the press before you put the chase in place.

6. Stop the press.

7. Move the flywheel by hand until the rollers are at the bottom of their stroke.

8. Get the locked-up form that you are going to print and test the form to be sure that all the type is held firmly in the chase.

9. Wipe off the press bed and the back of the form.

10. If the press is small and the form is light, you can stand in front of the press to put the form in place. But if the form is at all heavy, lift it in from the right-hand side of the press.

11. Set the chase on the two steps, or slugs, at the bottom of the press bed. The quoins should be at the top and

right as you put the chase into the press. Be careful not to let the face of the form hit any part of the press as you put the chase into the press. Lock the chase into the press (Fig. 42-1).

12. Raise the chase spring clamp (Fig. 41-3) at the top of the bed with your right hand. As you do so, move the chase back under the clamp with your left hand. Lower the spring clamp. It will hold the chase firmly in place.

13. Check the *grippers* (Fig. 41-3). The first thing to do after you put a form on a platen press is to examine the grippers. These are the two steel bars that hold the sheets firmly against the platen. They must not strike any part of the form. With a wrench loosen the nuts on the bolts that hold the grippers in place. Move both grippers back out of the way of the form. Tighten the nuts.

14. Make the first impression on the tympan as follows:

a. Pull back on the throw-off lever to printing position; turn the press flywheel forward by hand.

b. As the platen comes up close to the form, look down between the platen and the type form to see that the grippers are not going to strike any part of the form.

c. When you are sure that everything is satisfactory, draw back the throw-off lever and pull an impression on the tympan.

15. Wash off the tympan with a clean rag and type wash. The print will still show on the tympan but the ink will not smear.

16. Mark the guide edges. For this purpose use a piece of thin paper that is

Fig. 42-1. Locking the chase into the press.

the same size as the sheet on which you are going to print your job. If the job is to be printed in the center of the sheet (as it would be in the case of the bookplate), proceed as follows:

a. Lay the thin sheet of paper so that the top edge of it is along the top of the printed impression on the tympan.

b. Make a pencil mark on the edge of the sheet in line with the bottom of the last line of type. The space below this mark on the sheet equals the total width of the top and bottom margins.

c. Fold the bottom edge of the sheet up to the mark. The sheet is now the length of the type form plus one margin.

d. Place the folded edge along the bottom of the last line of the printed impression and with the left-hand edge of the sheet along the left-hand edge of the impression on the tympan.

e. Make two pencil marks on the tympan at the top edge of the sheet— to the right and to the left.

f. With the sheet in the same position, make a pencil mark on the sheet in line with the right-hand side of the

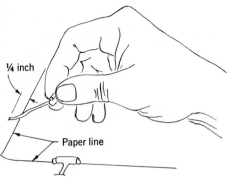

¼ inch

Paper line

Fig. 42-2. Inserting gauge pins in the tympan.

printed impression, which you can see through the sheet.

g. Fold the right-hand edge of the sheet to this pencil mark.

h. Place the folded right-hand edge of the sheet in line with the right-hand edge of the printed impression on the tympan.

i. Make a pencil mark on the tympan along the left-hand edge about two inches from the top of the sheet.

These three pencil marks on the tympan indicate the position of the sheet to be printed.

17. Insert the *gauge pins.* Figure 42-2 shows just how and where to push the point of a gauge pin through the tympan. Bring the point out again and set the pin in place. The point should enter the tympan ¼ inch from the pencil mark. The gauge pins can be moved if necessary.

18. Feed a sheet to the three gauge pins and turn the press by hand to pull a trial proof.

19. Check this proof carefully to see if the printing is in the right place and straight with the edge of the sheet. If the printing is not straight with the edge of the sheet, adjust the position of the pins as follows:

a. Place a sheet against the pins.

b. Move the sheet until it is in the proper position.

c. Move the pin or pins up to the edge of the sheet.

d. Pull another trial proof by turning the press by hand.

20. When you have the printing in the right place, take a sheet to the instructor for his approval of the positioning.

21. If he approves the sheet, lightly tap the points of the pins into the tympan with the gripper wrench.

The form is now ready for makeready.

Discussion Topics

1. In removing ink from a tube, you must always press the bottom of the tube, not the top. Why?

2. The rollers should always be at their lowest point when a form is being placed in a press. Why?

3. Why do you always place fresh ink on the left-hand side of the ink disk?

PRESS ROLLERS

Composition rollers used on platen presses are usually made of glue, glycerin, and molasses. New rollers should be well seasoned, preferably in a dark place, before use. When rollers have been used for awhile, they get hard and must then be returned to the roller makers to be made over.

Rollers may melt on a hot day from the friction of the press. In many locations printers buy separate sets of winter rollers and summer rollers. The summer rollers are made to stand more heat than the winter ones.

Rollers must be washed clean with solvent each time they are used. In commercial shops this is done at the end of the working day.

Water ruins rollers. They must be kept dry and should be stored so that the roller surface will not touch anything.

Unit 43. Adjusting the Impression and Feeding the Press

After you have the instructor's approval of the position for a press job, the next step is to see that the pressure of the printing is the same on all parts of the sheet.

Adjusting the Impression

If the type in the form is in good condition and the press is properly adjusted, the job should print evenly. Checking and adjusting the press is necessary to ensure a good job of printing.

Procedure

1. Pull a proof on a clean sheet of paper cut for the job. This paper is called *stock*.

2. Examine the proof to see if all the printing is sharp and clear. If it is not clear anywhere on the sheet, add one sheet of book paper under the tympan and pull another proof. Add sheets, one at a time, until the form, or some part of it, prints clearly. For example, if one side or one corner is not sharp and clear, ask the instructor to adjust the press. He will do this by moving the *impression*

screws under the platen. *Never move these screws yourself* unless the instructor tells you to do so.

In letterpress printing, the type is pressed into the paper a little and shows slightly raised letters on the back side of the sheet. This is called *impression*. The impression should be even all over the sheet. It should be just heavy enough to print the letters clearly. If the impression is too light, you will have to use too much ink and the sheets will be easily smeared. If you have too heavy an impression, the type will be damaged and the back of the sheet will be rough.

3. Check the impression by turning the sheet over and holding it so that the light is reflected from it. You can see the raised letters. If the impression seems too heavy, take out a sheet of the book paper under the tympan. If the impression is too light, add a sheet of the book paper under the tympan.

4. When you have a fairly even impression, not too heavy and not too light, take a proof to the instructor for his final approval.

HAND-FEEDING A PRESS

In spite of the wide use of automatic feeders on presses in modern plants, much work is still hand-fed as described below.

Procedure

1. Place a small pile of the paper stock that is to be printed on the feed-board at the right of the press. Fan the sheets out so that the top sheets project a little toward the press. This will make it easier for you to pick up one sheet at a time.

2. Fasten a piece of sandpaper to the middle finger of your left hand as shown in Fig. 43-1. This well help you to remove each sheet from the platen after it has been printed.

3. Ask the instructor to show you how to set the press counter and to demonstrate the motion of feeding.

4. Be sure that all persons are standing well away from the press before you start it.

5. Draw back the throw-off lever into printing position. When the press is

Fig. 43-1. When feeding a platen press, lay sheet down against the two lower gauge pins with your right hand. Then push the sheet to the left until it reaches the side gauge pin. Sandpaper on the middle finger of your left hand (circle) will help you to remove each sheet from the platen after it has been printed.

running, this lever remains in printing position. It is used only when the one feeding the press fails to place a sheet correctly. It is operated with the left hand. The throw-off lever must always be either fully off or fully on at the time the press passes the printing point.

6. Start the press at its very lowest speed. Do not hurry. The important thing is to feed the press smoothly.

7. Standing directly in front of the press, take up the top sheet with the thumb and first two fingers of the right hand. When the platen reaches its open position, lay the sheet down against the two lower gauge pins and, with a continuation of the motion, push the sheet to the left until it reaches the side gauge pin (Fig. 43-1). Never try to do anything to a sheet after the press starts to close. If the sheet is not in the correct position at this time, use the throw-off lever to prevent the sheet from being printed.

8. After a sheet is printed, use your left hand to remove it from the platen and to place it on the receiving board. Immediately following this operation, insert the next sheet in the press with your right hand. In removing a sheet from the press, grasp it where there is no printing; otherwise the fingers will smear the wet ink. The sandpaper on the middle finger of the left hand will help to prevent smearing of the printed sheets.

9. Continue with the rhythmic placing and withdrawing of sheets. Use your left hand to push the printed sheets into a neat pile against the front board and the side pin in the receiving board.

10. Watch the sheets carefully as they come from the press. Note the inking.

Add ink to the ink plate as often as it is necessary in order to maintain uniform color. Each time fresh ink is added, run the press with the throw-off lever in "off" position until the ink is evenly distributed. Watch also for filled letters, for badly fed sheets, and for type letters and spaces that may have worked up during the printing.

11. Test the accuracy of your feeding by occasionally feeding a printed sheet in again. The two impressions should coincide exactly.

12. Run the press at a speed that allows you to feed a sheet each time the press closes. If you have to use the throw-off lever every few sheets, you are going too fast.

13. After a run is completed on the press, the job and press must be washed, or cleaned, as described in the next unit.

14. Remove the job from the chase and return it to your galley for distribution. Return the furniture and the chase to their proper places.

Discussion Topics

1. It is not safe to let someone else work the throw-off lever when you are feeding the press. Why?

2. Will you have to stop the press and add ink more often on a big form than on one that has only a few lines on it?

3. What would you do if a sheet stuck to the type and were drawn into the rollers?

4. Why put only a small amount of paper on the feedboard at a time?

PRINTING INKS

Ink was first developed in China about 2500 to 3000 B.C. The early inks are thought to have been made by mixing lampblack, or soot, with oil and gum. During the early fifteenth century in Europe, the van Eyck brothers invented a drying varnish that made the present form of printing ink possible. Today between 500,000 and 600,000 pounds of ink is used in the United States daily to print newspapers alone.

Different kinds of paper, printing surfaces, and printing presses require different types of ink. There are water-color and oil-base inks. The water or oil in which the coloring matter, or pigment, is carried is called the *vehicle*. A common vehicle is linseed-oil varnish. In order to control the time it takes for ink to dry, *driers* may be added to the ink.

When using a can of ink, remove as much as you need from the surface with an ink knife. Do not dig into the ink or leave the ink knife in the can. Replace the lid immediately. Dust and dirt will make the ink gritty. If the can is left open too long, a scum will form on the surface of the ink. A tube of ink should be re-capped as soon as the ink needed has been squeezed out.

Printing inks are available in many colors. If you need a lighter tint than you have, the darker color may be mixed with white. A thick piece of glass with a white piece of paper under it makes a good mixing surface for ink. Always start with white or the lightest color. Use a printing knife for the mixing of colors and mix the colors thoroughly. Mix just as much as you need—do not be wasteful. To check the mixed color, spread a thin layer of the mixed ink on a piece of the printing paper to be used. Be sure that the ink plate and press rollers are free of dust before you put ink on the press. When you have completed your printing operation, clean the press as described in Unit 44.

Unit 44. Washing a Platen Press

Washing a press is easy if it is done right. Furthermore, if you use the right method, you will not get your hands covered with ink and type wash.

Procedure

1. Be sure that the power switch on the press is turned off before you start to wash the press.

2. Get a valve-top can of type wash and a clean press rag. The rag should be about two feet square. Be sure that there are no buttons or metal objects (hooks, fasteners, snaps, pins, and so on) on the rag that would scratch the type.

3. Take the form out of the press carefully.

Fig. 44-1. Use a round pad about five inches in diameter thoroughly dampened with type wash to clean off the ink disk, rollers, and type.

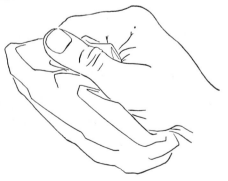

4. Dampen the rag with type wash and wipe the surface of the form.

5. Put the form in the rack.

6. If the job is finished, remove the gauge pins from the tympan and put them in the press drawer. This is a safety measure.

7. Now make a round pad about five inches in diameter by doubling up the rag in your hand (Fig. 44-1).

8. Wet this pad by holding the valve top of the type-wash can down and letting the liquid run out onto the cloth until the surface is wet. Stop before the type wash starts to drip from the cloth.

9. Stand at the right side of the press and mop the ink disk with the pad until the ink is softened up. Do not try to remove the mixture of ink and type wash yet.

10. Move around to the front of the press and turn the flywheel by hand until the rollers come up to the edge of the ink disk. Mop the rollers with the pad as they roll up over the disk to the top. Soften up all the ink on the rollers.

11. Now re-fold your pad with the inky part inside and with the drier and cleaner part outside. If you do this carefully, you will not get your hands smeared.

12. With the rollers still at the top of

the disk, wipe the part of the disk below them. Then wipe the rollers, turning the flywheel as you do so. As each roller leaves the ink plate at the bottom, wipe it clean by revolving the roller without turning the wheel.

13. Finally wipe the ink disk clean. The whole operation will take you only a few minutes.

14. Turn the wheel until the rollers are in their lowest position and wipe off the bed of the press. If the type wash and ink have dripped onto the tympan, wipe the tympan off, too.

15. Return the type-wash can to its proper place and put the rag in the metal bin for soiled rags.

16. Ask the instructor to inspect the press.

Discussion Topics

1. Why does the instructor always inspect the ends of the rollers?
2. The electric-power switch should be turned off when you wash the press. Why?
3. What will be the result if the ink is allowed to dry on the rollers and ink disk?

MAKING CUTS TYPE HIGH

Illustrations taken from drawings or photographs are made by photoengravers in the form of thin metal plates. These metal plates are then mounted on wooden blocks. Printers call these *cuts*. You may have used just such a cut in your bookplate or place card. (For a more detailed description of line and halftone engravings, see pages 138 and 140.)

The height of the plate plus the block should be the same as the height of the type. Very often wooden blocks shrink and become smaller. When this happens, the pressman must raise the wooden blocks by pasting paper on the back of them. This is called an *underlay*.

To find out how much paper to use and just where to put it on the back of the blocks, the pressman uses a *type-high gauge* (Fig. 44-2). This gauge

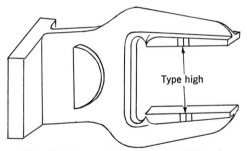

FIG. 44-2. A type-high gauge, 0.918 inch.

measures the height of any part of the cut. If one corner is too low, one or more thicknesses of paper are pasted in overlapping fashion on that corner. If the whole cut is low, these underlays of paper cover the whole bottom of the block.

If only the center of a cut is too low, the metal plate may be removed from the wooden block and the necessary paper put between the plate and the block. This is often called an *interlay*.

Unit 45. Standard Methods of Make-ready

Most printing forms need more than the flat impression you used in Unit 43, page 117. Some letters may be low, or rules may press too hard and cut into the sheet. Very dark and heavy areas in illustrations may need more impression to print clearly. For these reasons and others, pressmen usually prepare what is called a *make-ready sheet* and place it under the tympan.

If you set in type either the one-color place card or the bookplate suggested in Unit 40, this is your opportunity to print one of them. Carefully lock up the job in a chase. (For a review of this operation see Unit 27, "Locking Up Forms for the Job Press," pages 77–79.)

Put a new tympan on the platen (see Unit 41, page 112), check the grippers, ink the press lightly, put the chase in the press, put an impression on the tympan, mark the guide edges, and insert the gauge pins as described in Unit 42, page 116. If you used a cut in your job, be sure that it is type high (see page 121).

When you have adjusted the packing under the tympan and the press so that you have the flat impression as even as possible, you may find that the rules in your job have a tendency to press too

hard and actually cut into the sheet. The make-ready sheet, which you will learn how to prepare in this unit, will help to make the impression of the form even.

Procedure

1. Pull two or three proofs on make-ready tissue or lightweight (40-pound) book paper. Be sure that the sheets are fed up to the gauges.

2. Use the last proof sheet as the basis for the make-ready. This sheet is called an *overlay* or *underlay* sheet, or a *hanger*. With a sharp knife, cut out of this sheet all rules, leaders, or other sharp details that press through the sheet too hard.

3. From another proof sheet cut out letters or parts of a cut that need more impression and paste them on the overlay in their proper positions. You may need still another thickness on some parts. Sometimes four or five thicknesses of make-ready tissue are used for the built-up parts of an overlay.

4. When the overlay is complete, place it in position on the platen up to the gauge pins.

5. With the sharp point of a knife, make two L-shaped cuts through the overlay into and through the top tympan. One of these cuts should be made in each of the corners nearest you (see Fig. 45-2).

6. Take the overlay off the tympan and make the cuts larger so that you can fold back the triangular pieces as shown in the circle in Fig. 45-2.

7. Lift the top bail and raise the top tympan until you see the L-shaped cuts.

Fig. 45-1. Overlay sheet with make-ready patches.

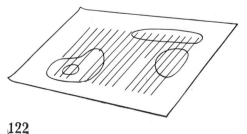

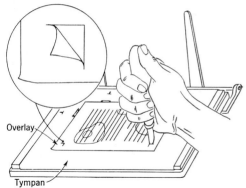

Fig. 45-2. Making two L-shaped cuts through the overlay into and through the top tympan.

Fig. 45-3. Placing a make-ready sheet under tympan on a small commercial press.

8. Lay the overlay in position between the upper and the lower tympan as follows:

a. Look through the triangular openings to place the L-shaped cuts of the overlay exactly on those of the lower tympan. In other words, use the stab marks to place the overlay under the tympan exactly where it was on top of the tympan. If the three gauge pins go through both tympans, as they usually do, you may need to cut a strip off the lower edge and left side of the overlay before you can put the overlay in place.

b. Use paste to attach the corners of the overlay firmly to the lower tympan. Do not put any paste on or under the printed areas.

9. Draw the top tympan over the overlay and fasten it with the top bail.

10. Pull an impression on the stock that you are going to use for this job to check the effect of your make-ready. It may be necessary to add more patches to the overlay. To do this, you do not need to remove the overlay from the press. If the impression is too heavy, remove some of the packing from below the tympan.

11. Before starting the press, review the procedure for hand-feeding a press given in Unit 43, pages 118–119.

12. Print as many copies of the job as you need.

13. Wash the press as described in the last unit, pages 120–121.

14. Return the type to your galley for distribution and the furniture and chase to their proper places.

Discussion Topics

1. After you have put the overlay in place, you may have to take out some of the packing. Why?

2. Why must the overlay be placed accurately?

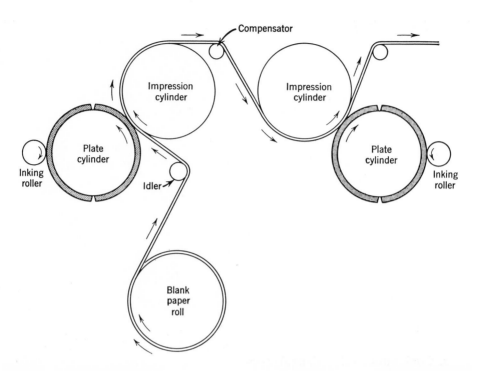

Compensator

Impression
cylinder

Impression
cylinder

Plate
cylinder

Plate
cylinder

Inking
roller

Inking
roller

Idler

Blank
paper
roll

FIG. 45-4. One of the large rotary presses used to print *The Reader's Digest*. This press can print up to five different colors on both sides of a roll of paper and deliver folded sections of the magazine. The drawing shows how a rotary press works. (*Graphic Arts Production Yearbook*, copyright 1948 by Colton Press, Inc.)

Other Kinds of Presses

Printing jobs such as large magazines or the mail-order catalogues require elaborate equipment and large organizations. It would be impossible to print such jobs on platen presses or flat-bed cylinder presses. It would take thousands of presses and thousands of skilled men to operate them.

Big printing jobs are produced on *rotary presses* that turn out complete folded sections of 16 pages or more. These sections are printed on both sides in as many as five colors. More than fifteen thousand sections an hour may be printed by a single press of this kind. Rotary presses fed from a continuous roll of paper are called *web presses*.

Other kinds of automatic presses are capable of printing tickets on both sides in several colors, number them in half a dozen places, and perforate them at rates of over one hundred thousand tickets an hour. What kind of tickets might be printed on such a press?

Unit 46. Make-ready and Register of Book Pages

Now you will make-ready, register, and print the individual or group project that you set in Units 19 to 26 and locked up in Unit 28.

Procedure

1. Take from the rack the two- or four-page forms that you locked up in Unit 28.

2. Get the press and the first form ready. See Unit 42, "Getting Ready for the Press," pages 114–116, for a review of this procedure. This form prints one side of the sheet. The other side is printed by the second two- or four-page form to make four or eight pages. The lines on one side of a sheet must print exactly on the back of the lines on the other side of the sheet. This is called *register* of pages. When you hold a sheet that has been printed on both sides up to a bright light and see that all the lines are printed exactly back to back with each other, the job is said to be *in register*.

3. Center the printing on the sheet as shown in your paste-up dummy of the job.

4. Test the register by turning printed sheets over end for end and pulling an impression on the other side. When you hold a sheet up to the light, not only the lines of type but the folios at the bottom of the page or the folio and the running heads (if any) at the top of the page must register.

5. Re-check, even if the lines seem to register, by printing another sheet and turning it over so that the top edge is fed to the two bottom gauges.

These tests will show you the following:

   a. If your gauges are set correctly.

   b. If the pages are made up right and are all the same in length.

   c. If the form is locked up right, has equal margins, and is square.

6. When the sheet is in register, check the impression.

7. Pull the make-ready sheets and go ahead with the preparation of an overlay as described in Unit 45, pages 122–123. If the folios push through, cut them out of the overlay. Paste a sheet of make-

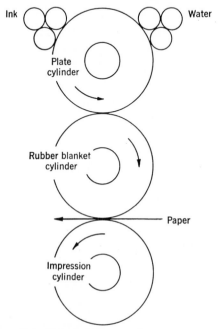

Ink   Water

Plate cylinder

Rubber blanket cylinder

Paper

Impression cylinder

Fig. 46-1. Below, a large offset rotary press used for printing newspapers and magazines. The above drawing shows the principle of offset printing.

ready tissue over lines of big type, for example, the title of the project. This helps to print the lines that need more ink than the text matter.

8. After you have hung your overlay (pasted it between the tympans), pull an impression on the paper stock cut for the job and look carefully at the back of the sheet. All letters should push through the sheet just a little. Any that push too hard should be cut out of one or more thicknesses of the overlay. Letters that do not push through as much as the others should be given more impression by the addition of a thin piece of make-ready tissue.

9. Show your final result to the instructor.

10. Print the desired number of sheets.

11. Clean and replace the first form by the second form of the project.

12. Remove the overlay prepared for the first form.

13. Prepare a new overlay for the second form as described above.

14. Check the register by feeding through two or three of the printed sheets.

15. Show your final result to the instructor.

16. Print the other side of the sheets.

17. Clean the form and the press.

18. Return all type to your galley for distribution and the furniture and chases to their proper places.

19. Store the printed sheets in a safe place. You will have an opportunity to bind them in Unit 60.

Discussion Topics

1. Do the pages of this textbook register?

2. Do newspaper pages register?

3. Make-ready tissue is one-thousandth of an inch thick. Lightweight book paper is two-thousandths of an inch thick. How thick is tympan paper? (Pile up several sheets of book paper and measure them.)

LITHOGRAPHY OR OFFSET PRINTING

One hundred and fifty years ago a man named Aloys Senefelder was experimenting with some sandstone. The story relates that his mother asked him to write down a laundry list as she called it out. He did not have a piece of paper handy, so he wrote the list with a wax crayon on wet sandstone. By accident he spilled some greasy ink on the wet stone and found that the ink stuck to the wax but not to the wet stone. From this fortunate accident came *lithography,* which means stone printing.

In place of stones we now use grained metal plates covered with a film of light-sensitive gelatin. The image to be printed is transferred to the plate by the photographic method. Where bright light has fallen on the plate, it repels water and receives the greasy printing ink. The image on the plate is printed on a rubber roller. From this roller the image is printed on paper (Fig. 46-1). This is called *photo-offset* or *offset* lithography.

The metal plates are thin enough to be curved around the cylinders of a cylinder press (see Fig. 46-1).

Nearly a third of all the printing done in the United States is now done by offset lithography.

Unit 47. Mixing Colored Ink and Printing Colored Stationery

Personal stationery is usually made from colored paper or has colored borders with envelope lining to match. The ink used to print the stationery may contrast with the color of the paper or match the colored lining.

Ultramarine blue is widely used for printing stationery. Chocolate brown and dark green are two other good colors for this purpose. If a lighter color of ink is needed, you can mix it yourself to suit your own taste.

Now you may print the personal stationery for which you set the type in Unit 34 and obtained the paper. If the design of your stationery has rules or an ornament that you wish to print in silver or gold, you should separate the rules or ornament as you did the two-color job in Unit 39, pages 102–104. After you have printed the lettering part of the stationery, you may add the silver or gold to it as described in the next unit.

Mixing Colored Inks

Printing inks are like water colors or other paints. Blue and yellow make green, red and yellow make orange, and so on. The important thing in mixing them is to keep from getting ink smeared over yourself and everything else. You can "keep it clean" by working the way experienced printers do.

Procedure

1. On an ink slab, or the back of a galley, put small amounts—not more than a teaspoonful—of each color you expect to use.

2. Squeeze the amount you want of each color from the tube. Use an ink knife to remove it from the mouth of the tube to the side of the slab. Scrape *all* the ink from the mouth of the tube before you re-cap it.

3. Clean off the ink knife with a rag and solvent each time you use it.

4. When you have all the inks on the slab, scrape up about two-thirds of the lightest color and put it in the center of the slab.

5. Now add other colors to the light color. Add only a very little bit at a time. Each time you add a bit of ink, mix the inks thoroughly with the ink knife.

6. Remember that the color will look darker on the slab than it will on the paper. To test a color, take a very little bit of it on the edge of the ink knife and spread it out in a thin layer on a sample piece of the paper on which you are going to print.

7. A white ink is the basis for most tints. To mix a tint, take a tablespoonful of the white and add color to it in tiny amounts. A light yellow ink is good for mixing light green tints.

8. When your ink is ready, scrape up all the little dabs of ink you have not used and wipe them off on a piece of scrap paper. Wrap up this paper carefully and throw it in the waste can.

9. With a clean ink knife remove the ink you have mixed from the slab or galley onto a small square of tympan paper.

10. Wash the ink slab or galley and knife off thoroughly.

Printing Stationery

Since the sheets of stationery paper that are to be printed should rest in the center of the platen as they are printed, the sheets, not the type form, should be centered in the chase. If the sheets are to be folded after printing, remember this in positioning the type form. See Fig. 34-1, page 93, for examples of personal stationery.

Procedure

1. Center a sheet of the stationery paper in the chase and place the type form on top of it in the desired position.

2. Lock up the type form.

3. Unfold the sheets if they are folded. Do not try to print on two thicknesses because the impression will mark the undersheet.

4. Get the press and form ready as described in Unit 42, pages 114–116. Use as little ink as possible. If you have prepared a special color of ink, use it on the press.

5. Show the instructor a proof of each job before you print it.

6. Open the flaps of the envelopes as shown in Fig. 47-1 before printing them.

7. Print the sheets and envelopes.

8. As you print the sheets and envelopes, let them dry for 15 to 20 minutes before putting them back in the box.

9. Clean the type and the press.

10. If you wish to add gold or silver rules or an ornament to your stationery, store the form on your galley. If you do not wish to add gold or silver to your stationery, distribute the type. Return the chase and furniture to their proper places.

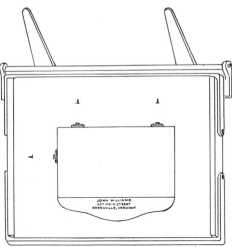

Fig. 47-1. Printing an envelope. Open the flaps of the envelope before printing.

Discussion Topics

1. Why do we always put a dark ink into a lighter one?
2. What is a complementary color?
3. Why unfold sheets before printing?

Unit 48. Thermography and Bronzing

Thermography means printing with heat. It is done by sprinkling a powder on freshly printed sheets and then heating the sheets. The powder, which is a mixture of rosin and metal dust or rosin alone, adheres to the wet ink. The heating swells the rosin, and the printing is thus raised up. This process gives the printing a shiny appearance. It is sometimes called *plateless engraving*. Virkotype is a commercial use of thermography (see pages 99–100).

THERMOGRAPHY

In this unit you may print the personal cards for which you set type in Unit 18 and locked up in Unit 27. You may also add the gold or silver rules or an ornament to the stationery that you printed in Unit 47. See Fig. 48-1 for the five basic steps in thermography.

Raised-letter Procedure

1. Get out the type for the personal card that you set in Unit 18 and locked up in Unit 27. Is the job in the center of the chase as it should be?

2. Ink up the press with job black. Use very little.

3. Place the form in the press and make the job ready the same way you do for ordinary printing.

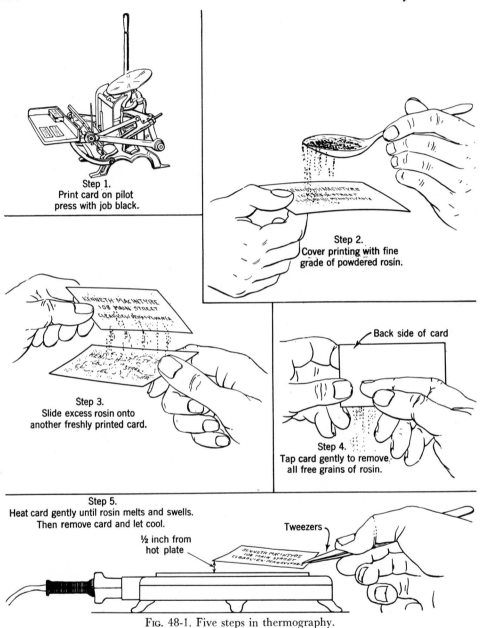

Step 1.
Print card on pilot
press with job black.

Step 2.
Cover printing with fine
grade of powdered rosin.

Step 3.
Slide excess rosin onto
another freshly printed card.

Back side of card

Step 4.
Tap card gently to remove
all free grains of rosin.

Step 5.
Heat card gently until rosin melts and swells.
Then remove card and let cool.

Tweezers

½ inch from
hot plate

FIG. 48-1. Five steps in thermography.

4. Pull a proof and take it to the instructor for his approval.

5. Spread out a big sheet of paper on the table where it will catch any rosin that you may spill.

6. Print 10 cards at a time. The ink should be wet when you apply the powder.

7. Cover the ink on one of the printed cards with about half a teaspoonful of a fine grade of powdered rosin made for this purpose.

8. Tip the card so the rosin slides off onto another printed card. You will have to tap the card to remove the last grains of rosin that are not sticking to the ink.

For each batch of 10 cards, pour the powder onto the top card and then slide the pile of rosin onto the next card, then onto the next, and so on, until you reach the tenth one. After you have reached the tenth card, put the rosin on a piece of cardboard until you are ready for the next batch of 10 cards.

9. Heat one card at a time over an electric hot plate. Hold it with tweezers about half an inch from the heat. When you see the rosin melt and swell, take the card away quickly. Process all 10 cards with rosin and heat before you print the next 10 cards.

10. If you wish to try bronzing a few cards, clean off the press and type with type wash and proceed as outlined below under "Bronzing a Job."

Raised-gold or -silver Design Procedure

1. Lock up the rules or design that you wish to add to the stationery printed in Unit 47. If you are adding rules that require exact positioning, or register, see Unit 52, pages 141–142, for detailed instructions.

2. Make the job ready and check the register by running through a few printed sheets of stationery. Use very little regular printing ink for this purpose.

3. Show a proof to the instructor for his approval.

4. Clean the press and type with type wash.

5. Ink the press with *gold size*. This is a kind of yellowish varnish. Use very little of it. You will not be able to see the gold size on the ink disk.

6. Print about ten sheets at a time.

7. Cover the printing with a teaspoonful, or more, of Virkotype fine gold powder, or similar powder.

8. Slide the excess powder off onto the next sheet as you did the rosin. Tap the sheet to remove the powder that is not sticking to the gold sizing.

9. Heat the sheets over an electric hot plate. Be careful not to burn your fingers or the paper while heating it.

10. Dust some of the sheets of stationery with gold bronze powder as described below.

11. Clean the press and the type.

12. Return the type to your galley for distribution and the chase and furniture to their proper places.

Bronzing a Job

On can labels and in other places you often see plain gold or silver printing. This is done by a process called *bronzing*. This process requires no heat. The powder used may be made of brass or aluminum.

Procedure

1. Ink the press with gold size. Use very little of it.

2. Print about ten cards.

3. Take a piece of clean absorbent cotton and dip it lightly in the bronzing powder; then put it over the printing.

4. Lay the sheets aside to dry for 15 or 20 minutes.

5. Dust off the excess powder with a clean piece of the cotton.

Discussion Topics

1. Why does gold or silver printing get dull or dark after a year or so?
2. What is Virkotype?

3. Thermography is used only for printing cards, personal stationery, and wedding announcements. Why not for books and advertisements?

EMBOSSING

Sometimes a printed design or parts of it will appear to be raised. When we look at the back of the sheet, we find that the paper has been pressed into the shape of the design. The process used to do this is called *embossing* (Fig. 48-2).

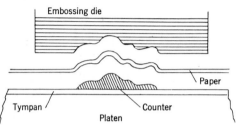

FIG. 48-2. Cross section of counter and embossing die used for embossing a sheet of paper.

A die is made first. This is of hard metal cut out in a pattern that is the opposite, or reverse, of the design.

The die is locked up in a chase and placed on a press with rollers removed. The die is then pressed into a soft plastic material on the platen. The plastic hardens in the shape of the sunken parts of the die. This is called a *counter*.

When a sheet of paper or cardboard is placed between the die and the counter and the press is closed, the sheet is pushed up into the die by the counter. This molds the paper or cardboard into the raised design desired. The die is often heated to help mold the paper or cardboard.

Unit 49. Printing Work-and-whirl Forms

In Unit 31 you set a rule job in two parts: the cross rules were in one form, the up-and-down rules in another. One way to print this job would be to feed the sheets through the press twice. For 500 cards there will be 1,000 press impressions.

There is a way to print a job of this kind complete with rules both ways, with only 500 impressions for 500 cards.

Procedure

1. Cut the paper stock double size. This job is 3 by 5 inches. Therefore, the stock will be cut 5 by 6 inches, or a little larger to permit trimming after printing.

2. Figure 49-1 shows you how to paste proofs of each part on the double card. How much space will you need to put between the two forms when you lock them up?

3. Slide both parts of the job onto the stone. Put them head to head as shown in Fig. 49-1. Check the spacing between them with the pasted double card and lock up.

4. Make the job ready as for ordinary

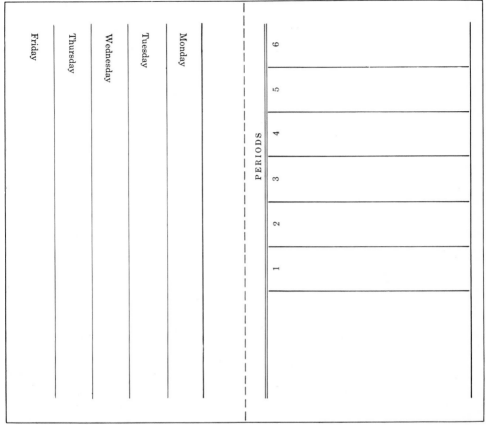

Fig. 49-1. Correct position for pasted proof of Figs. 31-1 and 31-2 on double card (5 by 6 inches).

printing. Use the pasted double card to position the printing on the press.

5. Test lockup and press position by printing one double card and then turning it halfway around and printing it again. The rules should fit together as they do in Fig. 49-2.

6. Show the proof to the instructor for his approval.

7. Feed the cards through the press once and let the cards dry overnight.

8. Clean the type and the press.

9. The next day, ink the press and turn the cards halfway around and feed them through the press again.

10. Clean the type and the press.

11. Return the type to your galley for distribution and the furniture and chase to their proper places.

12. After the ink on the double cards is thoroughly dry, cut them in half. Trim them to 3 by 5 inches. Turn all cards the same way before cutting. If you are going to use the cutting machine for this operation, read Unit 56, "Cutting Paper," pages 150–152, first.

For 500 finished cards you will have 250 double cards. To run them through the press twice takes 500 impressions. A great many ruled jobs are printed in this

PERIODS						
	1	2	3	4	5	6
Monday						
Tuesday						
Wednesday						
Thursday						
Friday						

Fig. 49-2. Printed card.

way. They are called *work-and-whirl* jobs.

Discussion Topics

1. What happens if a card is not fed up to the side gauge when you are feeding a work-and-whirl job?

2. Would it be possible to photograph a job that has been printed by the work-and-whirl method, then make a line cut, and re-print the job on single cards, using the cut?

3. Why not use 3 by 10 inch stock?

STEREOTYPE AND ELECTROTYPE PLATES

Newspapers use a process called *stereotyping* to make solid flat or curved plates from type forms. They also use this process for duplicating pictures and advertisements.

After the type has been cast, checked, and corrected, it is made up into pages. These pages include both the type and the illustrations. Each page is locked up in a chase and the type form given to the stereotype platemakers.

Figure 49-3a and b show the platemakers making a mold, or *matrix*. This is sometimes called a *mat*. Flat or curved plates can be made from the matrix. The type of plate made depends on the kind of press that is to be used. To make curved printing plates for a rotary press, they place the matrix in a curved iron box. Then they pour hot melted type metal into the box. Figure 49-3c shows a dried curved matrix used to make a semicircularly curved plate. This plate fits perfectly onto the large rollers of the rotary press as shown in Fig. 49-3d.

Electrotyping is a process (Fig. 49-4) for making more accurate and longer-

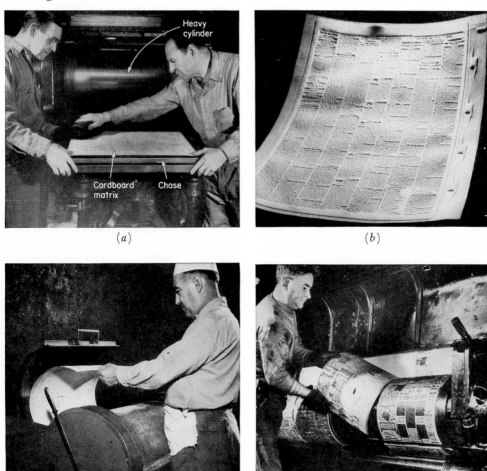

FIG. 49-3. Making a stereotype plate: (*a*) Here a soft cardboard-like sheet has just been forced down over the type page by the heavy cylinder in the background. The type is pressed into the sheet, forming a mold, or matrix. (*b*) The front side of the matrix shows the impression made by the type. (*c*) Roasting, or drying, the matrix to remove moisture before casting curved printing plate. (*d*) A curved plate is put in place on a rotary press.

wearing plates. The type forms or engravings are molded in wax or plastic. Then the mold is coated with graphite or another conductor of electricity and plated with copper or nickel in an electroplating bath. The thin shell of copper or nickel is carefully removed from the mold. Hot melted type metal is poured into the back of the shell to reinforce it.

The reinforced plate, or cast, is trimmed and cleaned, and a proof is pulled. Then all dead metal is routed off (Fig. 49-4*h*). The finished plate may be either trimmed, beveled, and mounted on the bed of the press or, if it is to be used with type, be mounted on a block of wood to make it type high (0.918 of an inch).

Any number of duplicates can be

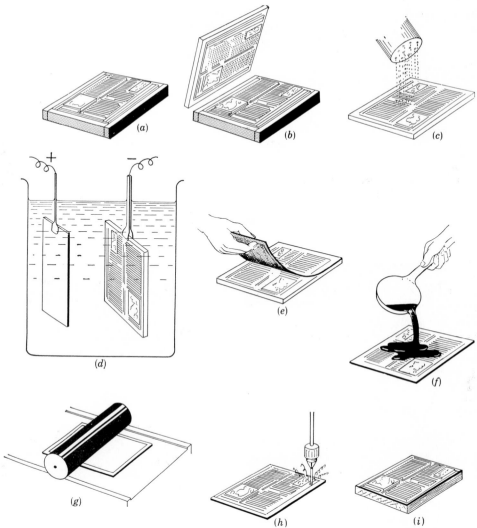

FIG. 49-4. Electrotyping process: (*a*) type form; (*b*) wax mold; (*c*) mold sprinkled with graphite; (*d*) mold placed in electroplating solution; (*e*) metal shell removed from wax mold; (*f*) type metal poured into back side of shell to strengthen it; (*g*) proof pulled of unmounted plate; (*h*) dead metal being routed off plate; (*i*) trimmed plate is mounted on a block of wood to make it type high when it is to be used with type. The finished electroplate in (*h*) may be trimmed, beveled, and mounted directly on the bed of a press for printing.

made from a single type form. By using duplicate plates, 2, 4, or even 10 or 20 copies of small jobs can be printed at one time.

Electroplating is used frequently for reproducing halftone engravings. It is commonly used in textbook printing. This book that you are now reading was printed from plates prepared by the electroplating process.

Unit 50. Printing and Perforating a Scratch Pad on the Press

Now you are ready to print and perforate on the press the scratch-pad job that you set in Unit 37 and stored on your galley.

Procedure

1. Ask the instructor to show you how to place short brass rules at the ends of the perforating rule to keep it from cutting the press rollers.

2. Lock up the scratch-pad job in a chase.

3. When you set the gauge pins, do not put one where the perforating rule will hit it.

4. Make the job ready and get the instructor's approval before you start the press.

5. If the rule does not cut through the paper enough, put a narrow strip of tympan paper or cardboard under the top tympan where the rule strikes.

On runs of several thousand sheets, printers stick a narrow strip of adhesive surgical tape the full length of the rule on top of the top tympan. This holds the tympan together, and the rule cuts cleanly to the end of the press run.

6. If a sheet sticks to the perforating rule and pulls off the platen even when you have both grippers holding it, tie two strings across and between the grippers above and below the sheet being printed and tie two other strings between these strings up and down on each side of the perforating rule (Fig. 50-1).

7. Print 50 sheets for each pad you wish to make. You will have an opportunity to bind these pads in Unit 58.

8. Clean the type and the press.

9. Return the type to your galley for distribution and the furniture and chase to their proper places.

FRISKET

When sheets are perforated on a press, a *frisket* is often used to pull the sheets off the perforating rule. To make a frisket, glue or paste a sheet of tympan paper across and between the grippers

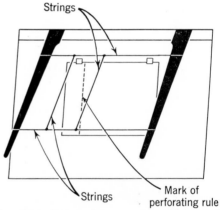

FIG. 50-1. Strings between grippers keep the paper from sticking to the perforating rule.

FIG. 50-2. A frisket fastened to the grippers with a narrow slot in it through which perforating is done. The frisket helps to pull the perforated sheet off the rule.

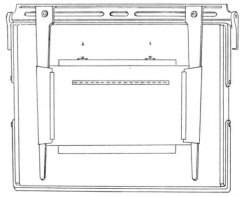

on the side next to the tympan (Fig. 50-2). In this sheet cut narrow slots for the perforating rules to print through.

A frisket is sometimes used to keep words or parts of cuts from printing. Holes are cut through the frisket to permit the other parts to be printed.

Perforating on Press Without Printing

Sometimes jobs are perforated on presses *blind,* that is, without ink. In such cases, the perforating rule is locked up without type and the rollers are removed from the press.

Discussion Topics

1. For a job that calls for 500 finished pieces, the printer usually cuts 525 pieces. The extra 25 cards or sheets are for *spoilage.* What percent of 500 is 25?

2. The full sheet of paper from which the scratch-pad job is to be cut measures 17 by 22 inches. The sheets for the pads measure 4¼ by 5½ before trimming. How many full sheets will be needed for 25 pads, 50 sheets to the pad, allowing 5 percent for spoilage?

Line Engravings

Fig. 50-3. Line engraving: (*a*) photograph of a cut; (*b*) proof of same cut; (*c*) sketch of cross section of line cut showing high and low parts and block on which it is mounted.

(*a*)

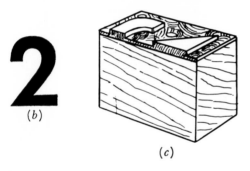

(*b*)

(*c*)

Line drawings are made into plates by etching them on a metal called *zinc.* A line engraving is like a linoleum cut, that is, the lines of the drawing are raised. When the press rollers pass over these raised lines, they leave a coating of ink on them. The press then prints the lines just as it does type (Fig. 50-3).

Line engravings may also be called *line cuts, zinc etchings, line etchings,* and *line blocks.*

Line drawings like the ones in this book are first photographed. Then photographic prints are made from the negatives on zinc in a hard material that acid cannot eat away. When the zinc plate is put into a tub of acid, the bare parts on the zinc plate are eaten away by the acid and the lines of the drawing are left. The etched plate is then mounted on a wooden block to make it type high (see page 121).

Line drawings that have no shading can be made into printing plates in this way. Copper also may be used for making line engravings, but it is much more expensive than zinc.

Unit 51. Linoleum Block Printing

Perhaps you have already made some linoleum block cuts. In art classes these are printed by rubbing or pounding a piece of paper laid on the block. It is much easier to print a linoleum cut on a platen press.

Linoleum is a mixture of solidified linseed oil, gums, and cork dust or wood flour or both. It is usually pigmented to give it color. The mixture is laid over burlap or canvas to give it more strength.

Procedure

1. Lock up a linoleum block in a chase. If the linoleum block is to be printed with type matter, print each separately. Linoleum blocks need a great deal of ink of a different kind from that used for type. If you run type in the same form with a block, the type will get too much of the soft ink and the printing will be smeared.

Linoleum is soft and will be crushed if the press squeezes it too hard. For this reason, it is printed with what is called a light, *kiss,* impression. The block just touches the paper lightly.

The ink for a linoleum cut may be any color. The secret of getting the ink to transfer from the block to the paper with very little impression is to mix the ink with cornstarch—half ink and half cornstarch.

2. Make the linoleum block type high (see page 121). Measure it with a type-high gauge (Fig. 44-2, page 121). Paste paper or cardboard on the back of the block if necessary.

3. Prepare the ink for printing the linoleum block as follows:

a. Take the ink from the tube and place it on the ink slab.

b. Put a pile of powdered cornstarch about the same size as the gob of ink on the slab alongside the ink.

c. Mix the cornstarch into the ink with the ink knife a little at a time.

4. Put only a little ink on the ink disk at first.

5. Level up the impression of the block and make it ready on the press.

6. Cut away the light portions from your overlay, and add a sheet of book paper to the solids (Unit 45, page 122).

7. Add ink on the disk until the cut prints clearly. The solids may break just a little, but this is all right. If the cut is a large one, you will need to add ink every few sheets.

8. If you want the back of your sheets to be clean, place sheets of paper between the printed sheets. This is called *slip sheeting.* Clean unprinted newspaper, or newsprint, makes good slip sheets. *Do not use newspaper.*

9. Clean the linoleum block and the press.

10. Remove the linoleum block from the chase and return the furniture and chase to their proper places.

Discussion Topics

1. From what is linoleum made?
2. Linoleum blocks are used only for simple designs and for a few copies. What kinds of cuts are used for longer runs and for drawings that have a great deal of detail?
3. Can prints of more than one color be made with linoleum blocks?

139

HALFTONE ENGRAVINGS

Look at a photograph in a newspaper. It is made of a lot of very small dots. The dots in printing plates that are made from photographs stick up just like the lines in a line engraving.

The dots are not all the same size. In the dark parts the dots are larger than the dots in the light or whitish parts. Middle-sized dots print gray tones (Fig. 51-1c).

This kind of plate is called a *halftone*. It is made by photographing the original photograph through a fine screen, which makes the dots.

The screens used for magazines and other printing on very smooth papers are finer than the screens used for newspapers. The dots in the newspaper photographs can be seen without a magnifying glass, but the dots in magazine photographs are so small that some magnification is needed to see them.

Halftones and line cuts are made by *photoengravers*. This part of the printing industry employs highly skilled men.

(a)

(b)

(c)

Fig. 51-1. (a) Photograph of a halftone. (b) Proof of same halftone. Note circled area. (c) Enlargement of circled area of halftone to show the dots that make it up. In the dark area of this halftone the dots are so large that they have run together. As a result the white areas between these large dots have been reduced to small white dots.

Unit 52. Two-color Printing American Flag
Rules Card, and Place Card

In all printing with two or more colors, register is very important. This means that the feeding of the sheets must be perfect, as in Unit 46, where you learned how to register pages.

AMERICAN FLAG

The instructor will supply you with two little cuts (Fig. 52-1) cast in type molds like type. Together these two cuts make an American flag. The field of stars and flagstaff are the blue cut (a). The stripes are the red cut (b).

Print the flag in the center of a sheet of paper, near the top. Later these printed sheets may be used as stock for a program for some patriotic occasion.

Procedure

1. Set a composing stick at 15 picas and justify each cut at the left-hand end of a line. Use metal furniture or quads to fill out the lines.

2. Place the blue cut in the chase so that the sheet will be centered on the platen when printing. Then lock up the job.

3. Ink the press with ultramarine blue. Place the chase in the press and print an impression on the tympan.

4. Moisten a sheet of the paper stock to be printed with a little solvent to make it transparent, and lay it over the blue impression on the tympan. This will help you to locate the correct position for the gauge pins.

5. Set the gauge pins firmly so that they cannot move.

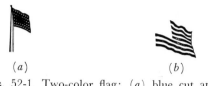

(a)   (b)

FIG. 52-1. Two-color flag: (a) blue cut and (b) red cut.

6. Feed every sheet carefully to the gauge pins.

7. Run off the blue and put the sheets in the rack to dry.

8. Clean the type and press. Remove the gauge pins.

9. Remove the blue cut and lock up the red cut in the place of the blue one. Now you are ready to print the red.

10. Ink up the press with flag red and print an impression on the tympan. Does it register perfectly with the blue impression?

11. Moisten the back of a blue-printed sheet with a little solvent and lay it on the platen over the impression of the red cut. This will help you to fit the two colors together exactly.

12. Mark the edges of the sheet for setting the gauge pins and set the pins firmly. The red must register perfectly with the blue.

13. Show the instructor a proof of the flag for his approval when you have it ready to run on the press.

14. As you feed off the red, throw out every sheet that is out of register. This will show how well you fed the sheets when you ran the blue.

15. Clean the press and the cuts and return both cuts to the instructor. Return the chase and furniture to their proper places.

141

RULES CARD

The two-color rules card that you set in Unit 39 may now be locked up and printed in the same way you printed the flag.

Procedure

1. Lock up the black form first and run it off.

2. Clean the type and the press.

3. Remove the black form from the chase carefully and put the red form in the same place in the chase. If you have made up this form correctly, the red will register with the black when you put it on the press. Check the register as you did for the red part of the flag.

4. Print the red form.

5. Clean the type and the press.

6. Return the type forms to your galley and the chase to its proper place.

7. Distribute the type.

PLACE CARD

If the place card that you set in Unit 40 is a two-color job, you may print it now. It is printed in the same way as you printed the flag.

Procedure

1. Separate the job by colors into two forms as you did the rules card in Unit 39, pages 102–104.

2. Lock up the black form first and run it off.

3. Clean the type and the press.

4. Remove the black form from the chase carefully and put the second color form in the same place in the chase.

5. After the first color is dry, ink the press with the second color and check the register. Then run off the second color form.

6. Clean the type and the press.

7. Return the type to your galley for distribution and the chase and the furniture to their proper places.

Discussion Topics

1. What two colors might be used for printing programs for these occasions?

> Christmas
> Fourth of July
> Halloween
> Thanksgiving
> Easter
> Washington's Birthday

2. What is register in pages? In printing two-color jobs?

COLOR PRINTING

Today, many people take colored snapshot pictures. More and more motion pictures are in color. The magazines print dozens of photographs in full color. Television in color is now a reality.

To print photographs in four colors, the photoengraver makes four halftones of the same picture—one for each color—by a process known as *color separation*. Each halftone is then printed in its own color in register with the others.

Under a magnifying glass the dots in a four-color halftone can be seen. They are yellow, red, blue, and black. They are of all sizes. A green lawn will be made up of big yellow and blue dots. It will also have small red and black dots. A brown coat will show big red and black dots and small blue and yellow ones. Each color is a different combination of these four colors. It is possible to reproduce almost any color in this way.

On the press the yellow halftone is printed first; then the red is printed over the yellow; the blue is printed over the red and the yellow; and the black is printed over the blue, red, and yellow. On small presses each color is a separate press run, but on high-speed magazine presses all four colors are printed one right after another. What does this tell you about the printing inks used?

Unit 53. Printing a Die-cut Greeting Card

In Unit 38 you set the type and made a cutting die for a greeting card. Now you can complete the job.

You will need, in addition to the regular press packing, a sheet of brass or hard aluminum. This should be a little smaller than the platen. It should be 20- or 22-gauge metal.

Procedure

1. Place each type form and the cutting die in a separate chase. (*a*) The card should be centered on the platen of the press. (*b*) The two type forms and the die should register correctly according to your pasted proof prepared in Unit 38. (See Fig. 38-1, page 100.)

2. Lock up the two type forms and the form containing the cutting die.

3. Make ready and run off the type forms. Use appropriate colors of ink. Mix a color as described in Unit 47, page 128, if the inks from the tubes do not seem just right.

Let each color dry before you start to work on the next color. Since wet inks smear and rub off on the back of other sheets, lay your cards out carefully as you print them.

When the type forms are finished and dry, you are ready for the die cutting.

4. Clean the type forms and the press.

5. Return the type forms to your galley for distribution and the furniture and chases to their proper places.

6. Take the rollers off the press and stand them on end in a safe place. Do not lay them down, because the soft rollers will become flattened.

7. Put the regular double tympan on the press.

8. Use the sheet of 20- or 22-gauge brass or hard aluminum in place of the packing.

9. Glue the tympans together and glue the bottom tympan to the metal sheet. The die will cut a hole through both tympans. The two center pieces will fall out if you do not glue them properly. If you try to feed over a hole in the tympan, the cards will catch on the edges of the hole.

10. Set the gauges in the usual way.

11. Feed only one sheet at a time when die-cutting on a press. The center pieces that are cut from the cards may fall out onto the platen and drop down into the press. To prevent this, file a

Fɪɢ. 53-1. Greeting cards for all occasions—Valentine, Christmas, wedding, sick-friend, Easter, bon voyage, new home, birthday, present, St. Patrick's Day, Thanksgiving, Mother's Day, Father's Day, congratulations, and anniversaries—are available. (Courtesy Hallmark Cards)

small nick in one or two of the cutting rules. The center pieces will then stay in the holes in the cards. After you have finished the run, you can stack the cards and push the center pieces all out at once.

12. Remove the cutting die from the press and replace the rollers. Unlock the die and return the furniture and chase to their proper places. (Store the cutting die on your galley.)

13. Remove the tympan and metal sheet from the platen and put a new tympan on the press and replace the packing.

Discussion Topics

1. Lots of things are die-cut. How about an envelope? Is a paper doily die-cut? How are the metal house numbers and automobile gaskets made? What other things are die-cut?

2. Which is harder, the cutting die or the material to be cut? Why?

3. Why must the ink rollers be removed from the press before die cutting is done on the press?

4. Why is a sheet of metal used in place of the packing?

Tʜᴇ Gʀᴇᴇᴛɪɴɢ-ᴄᴀʀᴅ Iɴᴅᴜsᴛʀʏ

Millions of dollars' worth of greeting cards are printed and sold every year. This industry employs many artists, engravers, and writers.

In cities where greeting cards are made, there are opportunities for young people who have artistic abilities to be regularly employed in creating designs for greetings.

Most greeting cards are sold to stores for re-sale. Figure 53-1 shows the wide variety of greeting cards available. Printing the name of the sender on these cards is done by commercial printers.

Unit 54. Color Tint Block Printing

With a flat linoleum block and a special ink mixture you can print a light colored tint on a sheet or card. This tinted paper can then be used as a background for type matter or a design.

A linoleum block design looks more finished if you add a tint background to it. The tint should be larger than the linoleum cut—enough larger to make a tinted margin about an eighth of an inch wide all around the design.

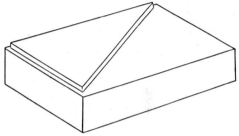

Fig. 54-1. Linoleum tint block.

Procedure

1. Take a plain linoleum block as large as the card you are going to print.
2. Draw a diagonal line on the linoleum from corner to corner.
3. Cut away all the linoleum on one side of this line as shown in Fig. 54-1.
4. To mix the tint, take white lake or tint base and color it with any printing ink. Add the color a little at a time.
5. Test your tint before you put it on the ink disk. Take a very little bit of it on the edge of the ink knife and spread it out in a thin layer on a sample piece of the paper that you are going to use.
6. Lock up the linoleum block in a chase and prepare the press for printing in the usual way.
7. Print as many cards as you need with the tint and a few extras to allow for later spoilage when printing the linoleum block and type matter. Clean the press and linoleum block. Allow the tinted cards to *dry thoroughly*. This may take a week or so.
8. Print your type matter or linoleum block on top of the tint. Clean the type or linoleum block and the press.

Discussion Topics

1. What is a tint?
2. Why should the printed tint be thoroughly dry before printing over it?
3. Why does it take several days for a linoleum-block print to dry?

COLOR IN MAGAZINE PRINTING

All the big magazines are printed on rotary presses that run paper from a roll, print the paper on both sides, and fold it to page size. These presses use curved plates made from the flat type forms. Many of them can print four or five colors on each side of the sheet to make the beautiful colored pictures you see in the magazines.

Some trade magazines and small publications are printed directly from flat type forms on large sheets of paper. To print two sides, the paper must go through the press twice. Each color is printed separately, which means that for four colors the paper must be run through the press four times.

Many of the jobs in magazine plants are like those in newspaper plants. Editors and writers get the copy ready for the typesetting machines. Under the direction of foremen, the type is set, proofread, made up into pages, and locked up. Plates are molded from the type forms and curved to fit around the press cylinders. Skilled pressmen, with their assistants, operate the big presses. They see to it that the color is correct and in register. The binding of magazines is done by automatic machinery.

Unit 55. Paneling a Printed Card

Paneled cards, which are often used for special types of announcements, are made by pressing down the center part of each card. The outer edges of the card make a wide, plain, raised border. This type of paneling can be done on a platen press. The card should be printed before it is paneled.

If you wish to panel some of the personal cards that you have already printed, make a layout of the appropriate size for your cards and ask the instructor to approve it before you begin to make the rule box for it.

Fig. 55-1. Cross-section view to show how cards can be paneled in a printer's rule box.

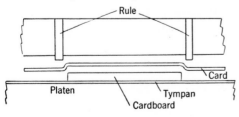

Procedure

1. Cut and trim a dozen cards 4 by 5 inches.

2. Make a layout on one of the cards to show the size of the sunken part, or panel. Use a pica line gauge and make the panel 17 by 23 picas (or the size required for the card that you have already printed).

3. Get a case of 12-point full-face rule. This is a rule that prints a line 12 points wide.

4. Take two pieces of this rule 25 picas long and two pieces 17 picas long. If you do not have a case of 12-point rules, ask the instructor to cut the pieces you need from strip materials.

5. With these rules make up a rule box that measures 25 by 19 picas outside and 23 by 17 picas inside. Fill in the inside of the box with the necessary leads and furniture. Tie up the job.

6. Center the rule box in a chase and lock it up for the press.

7. Take the rollers out of the press and stand them on end in a safe place. Do not lay them down because the soft rollers will become flattened.

8. Before you put the rule form in the press, ink the corners with a brayer.

9. Put the rule form in the press.

10. Pull an impression on the tympan. The inked corners will help you to center the rule box on the card.

11. When the position of the card is satisfactory, pull an impression on a piece of six-ply cardboard.

12. Carefully cut out the center of the six-ply cardboard (inside the rule) with a sharp knife and a metal ruler.

13. Paste the cutout piece exactly in place on the top tympan.

14. Now pull an impression on one of the cards. The rules will push the card down over the six-ply centerpiece as shown in Fig. 55-1.

15. Insert the gauge pins in the tympan. If you are paneling some of your printed personal cards, make sure that the cards are large enough so that the grippers and gauge pins do not interfere with the rule box.

16. Panel your cards.

17. Remove the rule box from the press.

18. Return the rules, chase, and furniture to their proper places.

19. Replace the tympan that you have been using with a new one.

20. Put the rollers back in the press.

Discussion Topics

1. What will be the result if the centerpiece is not pasted exactly in the right place?
2. What uses can you see for paneled cards?
3. Is paneling like embossing?
4. Why should a card be printed before it is paneled?

XEROGRAPHY

Industries are changing all the time as new machines and new methods are being developed. Industries are always looking for ways to reduce the selling prices of their products or to make them better or easier to use.

The printing industry is moving forward, also. Printers are finding methods that make printing better and cheaper.

A relatively new process called *xerography* was invented and introduced to the printing industry by Chester F. Carlson of New York in 1948. The word *xerography* means *dry* printing. Xerography is a quick, easy process of reproducing, or duplicating, original letters, forms, and documents. The whole process can be done in less than 5 minutes. Figure 55-2 tells the story. (*Turn page.*)

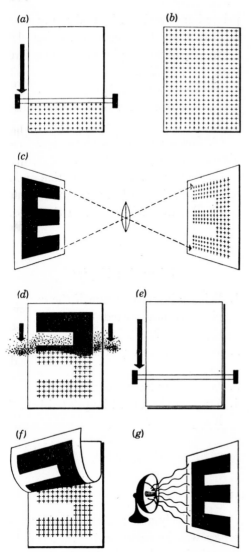

FIG. 55-2. Xerography: (*a*) The surface of a specially coated, nonmetallic plate is electrically charged as it passes under the wires indicated. (*b*) The coating of the plate is now completely charged with positive electricity. (*c*) The copy (E in this case) to be printed is projected through the lens of a camera. The plate is discharged in the white areas by the light, leaving the positive charge in the area of the image. (*d*) A very fine negatively charged printing powder is dusted gently over the plate. The powder adheres only to the positively charged image on the plate. (*e*) A sheet of paper is carefully placed over the plate and is charged positively by passing under the same wires used in (*a*). (*f*) The positively charged paper attracts the negatively charged powder from the plate to form a direct, positive image on the paper. (*g*) The paper with the image is heated for a few seconds to fuse the powder. This produces a permanent print.

Lyman is drilling the holes in his binding project.

Section *IV*. ELEMENTARY BOOKBINDING

Unit 56. Cutting Paper

Printers use paper-cutting machines that make smooth cuts through hundreds of sheets of paper at one stroke of the cutting blade. Some big cutters will cut through a stack of paper six inches thick and more than four feet wide. Small paper cutters used in schools are worked by a hand lever (Fig. 56-1). Larger cutters have electric motors to operate them. These are called *guillotine* cutters.

SAFETY RULES

The knife in a cutter is very sharp. You must be *very careful* in using this machine. Before you use the paper cutter, read the following rules.

1. Do not let anyone help you when you use the cutter. Be sure that everyone else stays away from the machine. Be sure that no one is in the way of the lever when you swing it down to make a cut.

2. Put both hands on the lever when making a cut as shown in Fig. 56-1.

3. Keep your hands out from under the clamp when you turn the clamping wheel.

4. Be sure the knife is up as far as it will go safely before you take your hands off the lever. Most cutters have safety devices to keep the knife from falling.

5. Be sure that the safety device is in working order.

6. The knife and its bar should be locked in the "up" position when the cutter is not in use (Fig. 56-2).

7. Handle paper carefully. Paper sheets have sharp edges.

CUTTING PAPER

Plan your cutting carefully. You cannot put a sheet of paper back together again after it is cut.

Fig. 56-1. A two-hand paper cutter.

Fig. 56-2. Lock paper-cutter knife and bar in "up" position when the cutter is not in use.

Procedure

1. Figure out the right number of sheets for each job. To do this, get a full sheet of the paper to be cut and make a layout on it showing how many pieces of the desired size can be cut from each full sheet.

The layout in Fig. 56-3 shows how 8 pieces 5½ by 8½ inches can be cut from a 17- by 22-inch sheet.

If you want 1,000 pieces this size, you divide 8 into 1,000 and get 125. This is the number of full sheets you will need to cut.

2. Set the *back gauge* of the cutter to 11 inches. Read this measurement on the steel tape or other measuring indicator. It is well to measure it with a yardstick also. Measure from the back gauge to the front edge of the clamp.

3. Put the 125 sheets in the cutter against the back gauge and against the right-hand side of the machine. Be sure

all sheets are even and snug against the back gauge and the side of the cutter.

4. Place a piece of chip board or scrap binder board on top of the pile to protect the top sheets. The clamp has feet that interlock with the back gauge, and these feet will cut into the top sheets unless they are protected in some way.

5. Place a piece of chip board or scrap binder board under the stock where the knife will cut.

6. Clamp the stock firmly.

7. Make your first cut.

8. Now stack the two halves on top of each other. Always double up in this way when you can. It saves extra cuts.

9. Set the gauge to 8½ inches and make the second cut.

If the knife is sharp and the paper thin, you can double up again. (How many sheets will there be in the stack after this second doubling up?)

10. Make the final cut at 5½ inches.

You may wish to store this cut paper for use in Unit 57, "Making Paper Pads," pages 152–156.

Fig. 56-3. Layout for cutting 8 pieces 5½ by 8½ inches from a 17- by 22-inch sheet.

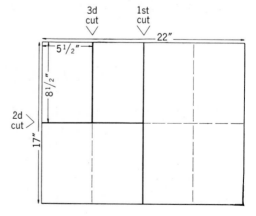

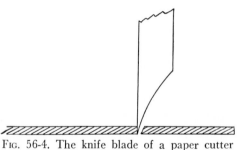

FIG. 56-4. The knife blade of a paper cutter is beveled like a chisel. It leaves a bevel on one side of the paper cut. The beveled side should be away from the edge you wish to keep when trimming.

TRIMMING PAPER

The knife blade of a paper cutter is beveled like a chisel. This makes the edges of the cut sheets straight and smooth on the straight side of the knife and rough on the beveled side, as shown in Fig. 56-4. The edges of cardboard cut in the beveled side of the knife will be very rough; they will show a feathery, beveled edge.

To have smooth edges all around on all sheets, you will need to trim off the rough edges. To do this, you trim off a very narrow piece, not more than the thickness of a piece of cardboard. When you are trimming paper or cardboard, be sure to jog each pile well, to push each pile up into the square corner made by the back gauge and the side of the cutter, and to clamp each pile firmly before making the cut.

TO KEEP THE BACK GAUGE FROM MOVING

When you put a pile of paper in place, you push it firmly against the back gauge. The gauge will move back a little each time you do this. To hold the gauge in the position at which you set it, screw down the thumbscrew under the table. You will find the thumbscrew behind or under the handwheel that moves the gauge.

Discussion Topics

1. A paper-cutter knife is hollow-ground (see Fig. 56-4). Is a pocket knife hollow-ground? Are scissors? Is a chisel?

2. Why is it necessary to clamp paper tightly before cutting it with a guillotine cutter?

3. Why is it necessary to trim some paper after it is cut?

4. Why should you measure from the back gauge to the front edge of the clamp before each cut?

Unit 57. Making Paper Pads

To make paper pads, you will need paper cut to size and some way of holding the piles of cut paper firmly while you apply a flexible cement to one edge of each stack. The school mimeographing department usually has waste sheets that can be made into pads. They have typing on one side, but the other side may be used for writing. The paper cut in Unit 56 may be cut again to make 2¾- by 4¼-inch pads. Each pad usually contains 25 to 50 sheets with a piece of chip board or binder board for a back.

Two procedures for making pads are given in this unit. The first procedure is for small pads and uses binder's rubber cement. The second procedure is for larger pads that require a stronger cementing and uses a wide-weave bookbinder's cloth, called *super*, with paste or glue.

Procedure for Small Pads

1. Cut the chip board to the size of the full sheets that you are going to use.
2. Insert a chip board after each group of 25 or 50 of the full sheets.
3. Cut the sheets with chip boards inserted to the size desired for the pads.
4. Put sheets of wastepaper along the edge of the table that is to be used during the cementing of the pads and on the floor under the edge of the table.
5. Stack the pads 4 or 5 inches high along the edge of the table with the edge to be cemented facing outward (Fig. 57-1).
6. Put some kind of weight on each pile to keep the pile from moving. The cement holds better if the weight is not too heavy. Large clamps may be used to hold the piles in place.
7. Even up the edges that are to be cemented and make each stack of pads square up and down.
8. Apply a thin coat of binder's rubber cement with a brush. In about five minutes apply a second coat.
9. Clean out the rubber-cement brush as soon as you have finished with it. Never let the rubber cement dry on the brush. If the brush is part of the lid of the rubber-cement jar, return it to the

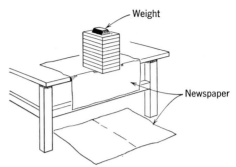

Fig. 57-1. Stacking small pads in preparation for rubber cementing.

jar each time you use it. Do not lay it down on the table. Such a brush need not be cleaned.

10. Wipe off every bit of rubber cement from the mouth of the jar before you screw the cap on. If you do not, the cap will be hard to remove.
11. Let the pads dry overnight on the table.
12. Separate the pads by cutting them apart with a thin, dull wide-blade padding knife. A chip board should be on the *back* of each pad. This is particularly important if you are using paper that has already been used on one side.
13. Trim the pads on the three sides that are not cemented. Use the paper cutter.
14. Turn every other pad halfway around. This gives the stacks a candy-stripe pattern.
15. Wrap 5 or 10 pads together in a package for convenience in storing (Fig. 57-2).

Procedure for Cloth-back Pads

1. Cut the chip board to the size of the full sheets that you are going to use.

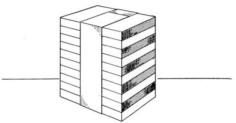

Fig. 57-2. Wrapping or banding pads up before storing.

2. Insert a chip board after each group of 100 of the full sheets.

3. Cut the sheets with chip boards inserted to the size of pad desired.

4. Stack pads 4 or 5 inches high along the edge of a table that has been carefully covered with sheets of wastepaper.

5. Even up the stacks of pads and put a weight of some kind on each pile to keep it from moving.

6. Cut pieces of super that will cover the ends of the stacks of pads.

7. Brush on a thin coat of paste or glue. Before it dries, put the super over it and brush more paste or glue over the super.

8. Clean the brush.

9. Let the stacks of pads dry overnight on the table.

10. Separate the pads with a thin, dull wide-blade padding knife.

11. Trim the pads on the three sides that are not glued or pasted. Use the paper cutter.

12. Turn every other pad halfway around.

13. Wrap 5 or 10 pads together in a package for convenience in storing.

Discussion Topics

1. Why do we call them *scratch pads?*
2. Why do we use a chip-board back?
3. Why do we trim the pads?
4. Would pads of 100 sheets be more convenient to use than pads of 25 to 50 sheets?

How Paper Is Made

Most of the paper we use is made from cellulose fibers obtained from trees. These tiny fibers can be seen along the edges of a torn sheet of paper. Some papers contain cotton or linen fibers.

Not so many years ago all paper was made by hand, one small sheet at a time. Now it is made by machine in rolls that are miles long and many feet wide. Some of the machines that make newsprint, for example, make continuous sheets 24 feet wide and 15 miles long for each hour that they run.

Figure 57-3 shows the principal steps in the manufacturing of paper. The *pulp logs* are lifted by a *jack-ladder* type of conveyor to the *wood room.* Here they are fed into a horizontal rotating *drum de-barker* to loosen and remove the bark from the wood. Large logs are split by the *splitter.* At this time a high-speed drill may be used to remove the knots from the debarked logs. The logs are next fed to the *chipper,* which changes the logs into thousands of tiny uniform chips. The chips are transferred to a *vibrating screen* through which only chips of the correct size pass. The sorted chips are now ready for the *digester.* The chips and chemicals used are

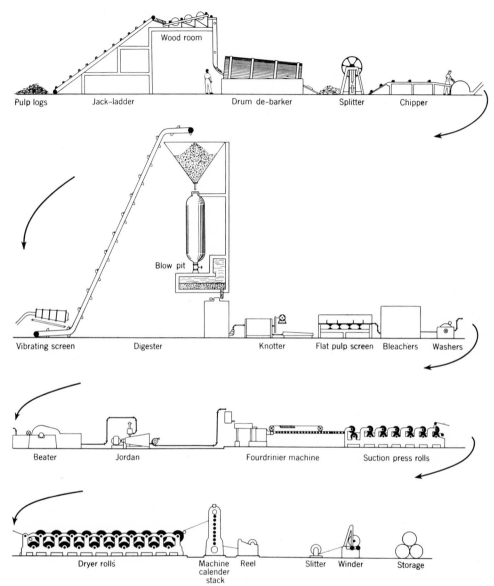

Wood room

Pulp logs · Jack-ladder · Drum de-barker · Splitter · Chipper

Blow pit

Vibrating screen · Digester · Knotter · Flat pulp screen · Bleachers · Washers

Beater · Jordan · Fourdrinier machine · Suction press rolls

Dryer rolls · Machine calender stack · Reel · Slitter · Winder · Storage

Fig. 57-3. Principal steps in the manufacture of paper. (See text for a description of each step shown.) In most papermaking operations today, pulpwood chips are cooked with chemicals, using either a sulfite or sulfate process. There are various modifications of these basic processes, depending on the kind of paper or paper board to be made. The ground-wood-pulp process is used in making newsprint.

heated with steam. They are maintained at a set temperature and pressure for a controlled period of time. After the wood has been digested, the slurry that is formed in the digester is discharged into the *blow pit.* Here it is diluted with water. Knots that have not been completely removed or digested are separated from the pulp by a vibrating screen in the *knotter.* Following another dilution with water, the pulp flows onto a *flat pulp screen* for further separation of the undesirable materials. Next the pulp is bleached in the *bleachers* and washed in the *washers.* It then goes into the *beater.* Here the pulp passes beneath a heavy beater or grinder wheel which further tears the fibers apart. Rosin and alum are added to give the paper greater strength. Pigments or dies are added to give the paper color. Other materials such as clay may be added to improve the paper's printing characteristics. After this treatment the pulp slurry goes into the *Jordan.* Here the fibers in the slurry are cut to the correct size for the type of paper being made. Then more water is added to the pulp fiber, and this solution flows onto a finely woven endless screen in the *Four-*

drinier machine. As the water drains through the screen, a sheet of tightly tangled fibers is formed. Here the sheet passes under the dandy roll, which leaves a mark, called a *watermark,* in the paper. This sheet is carried by means of an endless felt blanket to the *suction press rolls.* Here more water is squeezed out of the sheet. This prepares the sheet, now paper, for the heated *dryer rolls.* After the paper is dry, it is given a surface sheen by passing it between the chilled rollers of the *calender stack.* The finished sheet of paper is wound on a *reel.* From here it goes to the *slitter,* which cuts it to the proper size. The finished sheet of paper is then rolled up on shipping spindles on the *winder.* The paper is now ready for *storage* or shipment.

It takes a ton of water to make a pound of paper. The cooking and washing use most of this. For this reason, paper mills are usually located where there is an unlimited supply of water.

Cardboards may be made in a way similar to paper, or they may be made by pasting several sheets of paper together. The latter process is known as *lamination.* How is chip board and binder board made?

Unit 58. Wire-stitching and Stripping Pads

In this unit the scratch pads that were printed and press-perforated in Unit 50 will be fastened together (see Fig. 37-1, page 99).

Procedure

1. Cut binder-board backs the same size as the printed perforated sheets.

2. Each pad should consist of 50 sheets and binder-board back. Count the sheets for one pad and then use this pad to measure the others. Just put a small pile of sheets alongside the counted stack and press down on both stacks with your thumb.

3. Insert the binder-board backs as you measure the pads.

4. Ask the instructor to show you how to set the wire stitcher. He may stitch a pad to show you how.

5. Stitch each pad with two stitches in the narrow strip above the perforation. Be sure to jog the sheets evenly. Place the stitches about three-quarters of an inch from each side edge and halfway between the perforations and the top edge of the pad (Fig. 58-1).

6. Trim the top edge, or head, of each pad after it is stitched. This will make a smooth edge for the binding tape.

7. Cut as many pieces of *gummed cloth* (binding tape) as you have pads. Each tape should be about 1½ inches wide and long enough to go across the head of the pad.

8. Moisten the glue on the tape with a small brush or a damp sponge.

9. Cover the top edge of the pad with this tape. It should cover the front of the pad down to the perforation, the trimmed edges, and a strip of the binder board on the back (Fig. 58-2).

10. Rub the tape down as smoothly as possible.

11. Trim the pads on the three free sides after the tape is put on.

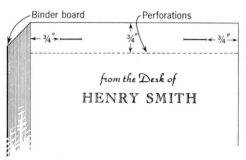

Fig. 58-1. Wire stitching of pads.

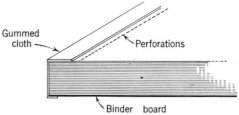

Fig. 58-2. Stripping pads with gummed cloth or binding tape.

Discussion Topics

1. Why do we stitch the pads? Why not cement or glue them as the ones you did in Unit 57?

2. What is the purpose of the cloth strip?

3. This kind of wire stitching is called *flat,* or *side, stitching.* What is *saddle stitching?*

Some Physical Characteristics of Paper

Paper has a grain like wood. It folds easily in the direction of the grain. It may crack if folded across the grain.

The thickness of paper cannot be measured directly because there is a variation from sheet to sheet of the same stock. For this reason the thickness is given by the *weight* of a ream (500 sheets). For example, sheets of 60-pound paper are thicker than sheets of 50-pound paper.

Paper that contains rag fibers (cotton or linen) is stronger than paper containing no rag fibers. For this reason, most writing paper contains some rag fiber.

The edges of some kinds of book papers are irregular and ragged. These are called *deckle edges*. A deckle edge is an imitation of the edge of handmade paper.

Papers are made in a limited number of standard sizes. Special sizes may be made to order. Printed pieces should be planned to be cut without waste from standard sizes of paper.

Unit 59. Making a Blotter Holder and Framing a Picture

In this unit you will have an opportunity to make a blotter holder and to frame a picture with gummed cloth.

MAKING A BLOTTER HOLDER

A blotter holder is a piece of heavy cardboard with corner pockets that hold the blotter in place. The blotter can be easily changed.

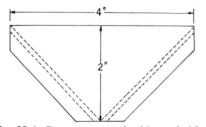

FIG. 59-1. Corner pattern for blotter holder.

FIG. 59-2. Covering blotter corner with gummed cloth.

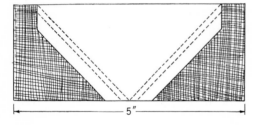

Procedure

1. Cut a piece of dark-colored heavy illustration board 9¾ by 12 inches. If you do not have illustration board, heavy binder board or chip board may be used.

2. Cut out (with scissors) four pieces of medium-weight cardboard with the dimensions given in the pattern shown in Fig. 59-1.

3. With a ruler and pencil draw the dotted lines on each piece, or card, as shown in Fig. 59-1.

4. Score the cards with a bone folder on the dotted lines. The distance between the two dotted lines should equal the thickness of the illustration or binder board that you are using.

5. Fold the cards on each of the four scored lines. Then lay the cards out flat again.

6. Cut four pieces of gummed cloth 2 inches wide and 5 inches long.

7. Lay a piece of the gummed cloth on the table glue side up and moisten it.

8. Put one of the cards on the moistened gummed cloth in the position shown in Fig. 59-2. Have the scored side of the card up.

9. Press the card down until all of it is stuck to the piece of gummed cloth.

10. Lay one corner of the illustration board on top of the card. The corner should match the nearest scored lines (Fig. 59-3).

11. Fold the ends of the gummed cloth up and over the edge of the illustration board. The ends of the gummed cloth should meet neatly on top of the illustration-board corner and stick to it. Repeat the same procedure for the three other corners. Turn over the binder board with the four corners attached. It is now ready for a blotter.

12. Cut the blotter 9½ by 11⅝ inches. Bend it a little to slip its corners under the corner pockets (Fig. 59-4).

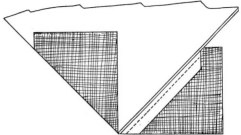

FIG. 59-3. Fastening gummed cloth of corners to illustration board.

FIG. 59-4. Placing a blotter in a blotter holder. Cut the corners off the blotter about an inch from the corners. This will permit the blotter to lie smoothly in its holder.

FRAMING A PICTURE

If you have a picture you want framed, here is a simple way to do it (Fig. 59-5).

Procedure

1. Take a piece of mat board that is 4 inches wider and 4 inches longer than the picture you are to frame (Fig. 59-5a).

2. Cut a hole a little smaller than the picture just above the center of the mat board (Fig. 59-5b). Since this hole should have straight, clean edges, use a sharp knife.

3. Indent a line with the bone folder 1 inch from the outside edges of the mat board all around (Fig. 59-5b). Use a ruler.

4. Cut a piece of binder board to the same size as the mat board.

5. Lay the mat board over the binder board and mark the edges of the hole on the binder board.

6. Place the picture on the binder board so that it covers the outline of the hole drawn in the last step (Fig. 59-5c).

7. Put the mat board over the picture on the binder board.

8. Cut four strips of gummed cloth each 2 inches wide: two strips the same length and two strips the same width as the mat board.

9. Moisten one of the long strips. Lay it down carefully along the scored line along one side of the mat board and even with the ends of the board.

10. Holding the two boards together with your fingers, draw the tape over the edge of the two boards and stick it

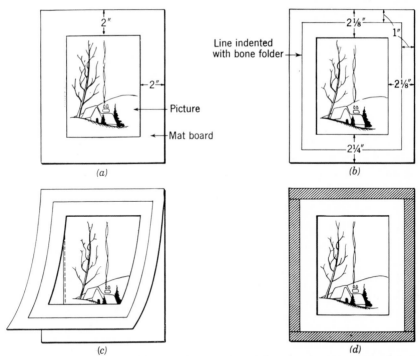

Fig. 59-5. Framing a picture: (*a*) measuring mat board for picture; (*b*) cutting hole in mat board and indenting a line with bone folder; (*c*) assembling mat, binding board, and picture; (*d*) fastening mat and binding board together with gummed cloth.

down on the back of the binder board (Fig. 59-5*d*).

11. Do the same on the three other edges.

12. Rub down the corners.

Discussion Topics

1. The adhesive substance on gummed cloth is glue. What other kinds of adhesives do you know about?

2. Will gummed cloth stick to glass?

How Paper Is Packaged and Sold

Printing papers are wrapped in packages. In most cases a package contains 500 pieces. This is called a *ream*. For large printings paper is bought by the skid. A skid is about 3,000 pounds. Cardboards are wrapped in packages of 100 sheets.

The printer does not have to buy full packages. He can buy any number of sheets from one sheet up. If he buys several packages of one kind of paper or cardboard, the price is usually less than for single packages.

Most paper is sold by the pound. Cardboards and cover papers may be sold by count, that is, by the number of sheets.

Envelopes and cut cards are sold by the box. Announcements and personal stationery are also sold in boxes.

Wrapping papers come in rolls and are priced by the pound.

Unit 60. Pamphlet Binding

The group or individual project that you began in Unit 19, locked up in Unit 28, and made ready and printed in Unit 46 will be bound as a pamphlet in this unit. If you wish to add a cover to the project, you may saddle-stitch the sheets together and trim them as described in this unit and add a cover as described in the next unit.

Procedure

1. Fold the printed sheets as you did your folded paper dummy, or imposition sheet. Fold each sheet carefully and press each fold down with a bone folder (Fig. 60-1).

2. Fold each section, if more than one, separately—one sheet at a time. If the folding is not well done, the pages will be out of line.

3. Gather the folded sections, one inside the other, in order.

4. Check the page numbers to see if you have folded and gathered the sheets correctly.

5. Ask the instructor to show you how to set the wire stitcher for saddle stitching (Fig. 60-2).

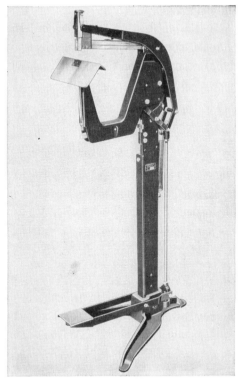

Fig. 60-2. Wire stitcher for saddle-stitching pamphlets.

6. Put two wire stitches in each pamphlet so that they are about 1½ inches from each end. If you are going to add a cover, one stitch just above center will be sufficient.

7. Count off the pamphlets in piles of 10.

Before using the paper cutter, review the safety rules given in Unit 56, page 150.

8. Set the paper cutter to trim ¼ inch off the head of the pamphlets.

9. Put a pile of 10 in the cutter at the *right-hand side* with the backs to the right.

10. Trim the head of each pile in this way.

Fig. 60-1. Folding a printed sheet with a bone folder.

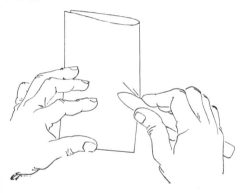

11. Trim the side of each pile. Cut off about one-quarter inch.

12. Finish the job by trimming the bottoms of each pile. For this trim, put the piles against the *left* side of the cutter with the backs to the right.

1. What is the difference between a wire-stitching machine and a hand stapler?

2. Why is the heavy wire used for binding thick pamphlets?

PAPER-FOLDING MACHINES

Pamphlets of 8 pages or more, like books and magazines, are not printed in single pages. Sections of 8, 12, 16, 24, 32, or even 64 pages are printed on large sheets of paper with half the pages on one side and half the pages on the other side of each sheet. Then the sheets are folded into sections by machines.

In a folding machine the center of the sheet is pushed between a set of two rollers that presses the fold together. The sheet then goes on to another set of rollers that folds it again. It may pass through several of these folding units. In the end it comes out folded to page size.

Folding a sheet once makes 4 pages. A second fold makes 8 pages. Folding it again makes 16 pages. Four folds make 32 pages. It is said that no matter how big the sheet, it is not possible to make more than eight folds in it.

Unit 61. Binding Programs and Booklets by Lacing

School programs and small booklets usually are saddle-stitched. Saddle stitches are neat and strong. For some jobs though, the wire stitches may seem a little unfinished. You can dress up a job of this kind by tying the sheets and cover together with silk cord, ribbon, or linen thread.

You may wish to add such a cover to the individual or group project that you saddle-stitched and trimmed in Unit 60. If you do bind your individual or group project in this unit, you may wish to select your binding paper so that you can add an appropriate photograph to it later (Section VII, "Photography," pages 226–266).

If you wish to print a title or ornament on the binding, you should do this before you fold it.

Since the cover of a program or booklet is usually a little larger than the inside pages, the resulting overhang (about one-quarter inch) must be taken into consideration when you are lacing and tying the job. In this unit three procedures for lacing and tying are given: with cord, with ribbon, and with linen thread.

LACING WITH CORD

The cut ends of silk cord have a tendency to unravel if not carefully handled. A little moisture on the end of the cord will help to hold the loose threads of the ends together and make lacing easier. Do not put the ends in your mouth.

Procedure

1. Fold the inside pages and trim them to size if not already folded and trimmed.

2. Fold the covers and trim them to size.

3. Ask the instructor to show you how to set the paper punch so that it will punch three half circles out of the folded edges of the inside sections. Use ⅛-inch punches. Set the punches so that the holes are an equal distance apart, with the middle hole in the center of the binding edge (Fig. 61-1).

4. Re-set the paper punch for the cover punching so that the holes will line up with those of the inside sections and so that the cover will overhang equally top and bottom (Fig. 61-1).

5. Cut a cord about fifteen inches long for a regular knot or about twenty-five inches long for a bowknot, and make a test tying before cutting all the cords required. You may need a longer or shorter cord than the one used for the test.

6. Study the phantom view in Fig. 61-2. It shows how the cord will be put through the holes. One end is pushed up through the middle hole from the inside. The other end is taken through an end hole to the outside. Then it is taken along the back to the other end hole and is pushed down through this hole to the inside again. This same end is then pushed through the middle hole alongside the first end. The ends outside

FIG. 61-1. Correctly punched-in side of sheet and cover. Holes are an equal distance apart, and the middle hole is in the center of the binding edge.

FIG. 61-2. How to put the cord through the holes in two-loop saddle sewing.

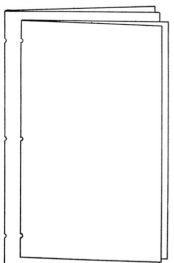

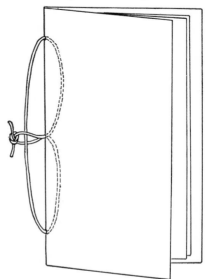

the middle hole must be on opposite sides of the piece of the cord that runs along the back.

7. Pull on these ends until the cord is tight and the ends are the same length.

8. Tie the ends in a square knot or bowknot. Let the ends hang loosely or trim them off as close as you like.

If you have used a silk cord, you can tassel the ends by tying a knot about three-quarters of an inch from each end and unraveling the cord.

LACING WITH RIBBON

The ribbon used for lacing and tying a program or booklet should be ½, or not more than ¾, inch wide.

Procedure

1. Fold the inside pages and trim them to size.

2. Fold the covers and trim them to size.

3. Set the paper punch so that it will punch three half circles out of the folded edge of the inside sections. Use ¼-inch punches. Set the punches so that the holes are an equal distance apart, with the middle hole in the center of the binding edge (Fig. 61-1).

4. Re-set the paper punch for the cover punching so that the holes will line up with those of the inside sections and so that the cover will overhang equally top and bottom (Fig. 61-1).

5. Cut a ribbon about fifteen inches long for a regular knot or about twenty-five inches long for a bowknot and make a test tying before cutting all the ribbons required. You may need a longer or shorter ribbon than the one used for the test.

6. Use a stick with a small rounded end to push the ribbon through the holes. One end is pushed up through the middle hole from the inside. The other end is taken through an end hole to the outside and along the back to the other end hole. It is pushed down through this hole to the inside again. Then this same end is pushed through the middle hole alongside of the first end. The ends outside the middle hole must be on opposite sides of the piece of the ribbon that runs along the back.

7. Pull on these ends until the ribbon is tight and the ends are the same length.

8. Tie the ends in a square knot or bowknot. Let the ends hang loosely or trim them off as you like.

LACING WITH LINEN THREAD

If you have many booklets to sew with linen thread, it will make the work easier if you fasten the covers and sections together with a single wire stitch before you start to sew. This stitch must be placed a little above or below the center of the program, booklet, or pamphlet so that it will not get in the way of the threads that pass through the center hole.

If it is desirable to have the finishing knot on the inside of the pamphlet or program being laced with linen thread, the procedure given below, starting with step 5, is reversed, that is, the needle is pushed through the center point from the inside to the outside, leaving a 2½-inch end on the inside.

Procedure

1. Fold the inside pages and trim them to size.

2. Fold the covers and trim them to size.

3. Mark the center point and two points about three-quarters of the distance from the center point to the top and bottom edge on the back edge of an inside section. Push a needle through these three points. Place this inside section in a cover and push a needle through each one of the three holes and through the cover, too. Using this cover and inside section as guides, mark the remaining covers and inside sections with a sharp pencil.

4. Thread your needle with about seventeen inches of linen thread. After you have laced the first pamphlet or program, use a longer or shorter thread as needed.

5. Holding a section firmly in place in its cover, push the needle through the cover and section from the outside at the middle point on the back.

6. Pull the needle through, leaving about 2½ inches of thread on the outside (Fig. 61-2).

7. Push the needle through the point below the center point to the outside.

8. Push the needle through the point above the center point to the inside.

9. Push the needle through the center hole alongside the thread already there.

10. Remove the needle from the thread.

11. Pull on the two ends until the thread is tight and the ends are the same length. The ends should be on opposite sides of the piece of the thread that runs along the back.

12. Tie the ends in a square knot and trim off the ends.

Discussion Topics

1. Can you think of a way to use your school colors for a program, with the covers in one color and the cord or ribbon in another?

2. Time yourself while you are tying a job. How many minutes does it take you to tie one program or pamphlet? How much would tying cost per program or pamphlet if you paid yourself $3 an hour?

OTHER BINDERY MACHINES

Book binderies use paper cutters, wire stitchers, and folding machines. They also use many other kinds of machines for fastening sheets of paper together and for making various things from paper, paper boards, cloth, and adhesives.

There are two types of machines for making holes in paper: *paper punches* and *paper drills*. The latter can bore holes through a thousand sheets at a time. The holes made may be round or they may be shaped to fit special binders.

Round-cornering machines cut the corners off cards or sheets.

Perforating machines are of two kinds. One makes round-hole perforations like those in stamps. The other makes slits like little knife cuts. Bank checks are usually perforated this way.

Sewing machines are used to fasten

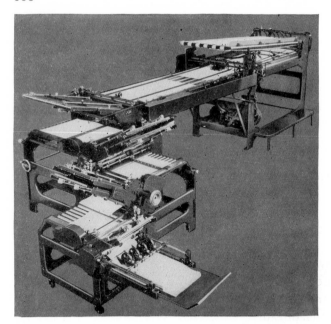

Fig. 61-3. Machine folding signatures of a book.

Fig. 61-4. Machine sewing signatures of a book.

the pages of books together. Linen thread is used for sewing through each section; this is done in a way similar to saddle stitching.

Millions of books are printed every year. Most of the hand labor formerly used in binding books is no longer needed. Today machines do most of the binding operations required in bookbinding.

Unit 62. Making a Pocket Notebook with Removable Filler

In this and the next three units you will use paste or glue to fasten paper or cloth to binder board. Paste and glue are kinds of *adhesives* and are used in many bookbinding jobs.

When you paste or glue paper or cloth on one side of binder board, you must paste the same kind of paper or cloth on the other side. If you do not, the board will curl up and you will not be able to flatten it out.

When you spread paste or glue on paper or cloth, do not use too much. Use a brush to apply paste or glue and spread it evenly. If the paste, or glue, does not spread evenly and seems to be too thick and sticky, add a little water to it. Always put sheets of old newspaper or similar scrap paper under the cloth or paper that you are covering with paste or glue, and then throw the sheet away as soon as you have used it. This will accomplish three things: (1) It will enable you to paste or glue the edge of the cloth or paper. (2) The clean unglued or unpasted side of your job will remain clean. (3) The table top upon which you are working will not require cleaning during or after your gluing or pasting job.

The pocket notebook described in this unit is made in two stages: first the cover and then the tongue-back fillers that are to be used in the cover.

NOTEBOOK COVER

For this cover you should use a good grade of cotton cloth called *book cloth*. It has been treated to prevent the glue

or paste that is used on it from showing through on the unglued or unpasted side.

Procedure

1. Cut the pieces of book cloth and medium-heavy binder board listed below for each cover you wish to make. Use the paper or table cutter.

1 piece of book cloth 6 by 9½ inches
1 piece of book cloth 4¼ by 6½ inches
2 pieces of binder board 3 by 4½ inches
1 piece of binder board ⅜ by 4½ inches

2. Lay the larger of the two pieces of cloth face down on a piece of newspaper on the table.

3. Draw a penciled line on the cloth ¾ inch from the lower and left-hand edges (Fig. 62-1). Draw another penciled line 2 inches from the right-hand edge.

4. Cover all the cloth except the 2-inch strip at the right-hand end with paste.

5. Lay one of the two larger pieces (3 by 4½ inches) of binder board on the pasted cloth. Place it even with the pen-

FIG. 62-1. Pattern for pocket notebook.

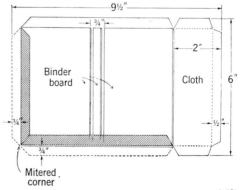

ciled lines along the left-hand and the lower edges.

6. Lay the other large piece of binder board on the pasted cloth ¾ inch to the right of the first piece and even with the line along the lower edge (Fig. 62-1).

7. Lay the narrow strip of binder board exactly in the middle between the two other pieces (Fig. 62-1).

8. Press down on the binder-board pieces to stick them to the cloth.

9. With scissors, miter the corners and notch the cloth as shown in Fig. 62-1.

10. Use a bone folder to turn the cloth over the boards on the left-hand side and at the top and bottom edges. Press the cloth down with the bone folder until the cloth sticks tightly.

11. Cover the other piece of book cloth (4¼ by 6½ inches) with paste and lay it over the whole cover. This piece lines the inside of the cover. This lining will extend to within ⅛ inch of the edges all around.

12. Press down on both sides of the narrow center strip with the bone folder so that the lining will become pasted to the book cloth on the outside of the binding.

13. Notch and miter the unpasted right-hand piece of the cloth, as shown in Fig. 62-1, if not already done. This is the part of the cloth that forms the pocket into which the tongue of the paper pad is inserted.

14. Score the right-hand edge of the cloth along the dotted line ½ inch from the edge with the bone folder.

15. Put a little paste on this ½-inch strip and fold it over. Rub it down with the bone folder until it sticks.

16. Score the end strips with the bone folder.

17. Fold the end strips over and paste the *top side* of the flaps only.

18. Put a small piece of wax paper inside the pocket to keep it from sticking shut and fold the flap over onto the right-hand side of the cover to which it is attached. The top and bottom flaps will stick to the right-hand cover.

19. Lay the cover between two sheets of wax paper to keep it from sticking to anything while the paste is drying.

20. Put a board on top of the cover and a 10-pound weight on top of the board. Press it overnight or until the cover is dry.

Tongue-back Fillers

Now you are ready to make the tongue-back fillers to be used in your notebook cover. Make 6 or 10 for each cover you have made. If you wish to print and perforate these pads, follow the procedures outlined in Unit 37, "Preparation for Perforating on the Press," pages 98–99, and Unit 50, "Printing and Perforating a Scratch Pad on the Press," pages 137–138.

Procedure

1. Cut 30 sheets for each filler 2¾ by 4¼ inches.

2. Perforate the sheets about one-half inch from the edge. Perforate along the longer edge (see procedure on pages 99 and 137). If you are printing these sheets as you perforate them on the press, be sure that the perforations are to the left of the printed matter.

3. Cut binder-board backs 2¾ by

4¼ inches and taper each board so that it will slip easily into the pocket in the cover. This is done with scissors.

4. Count off the sheets in pads of 30 and put a binder-board back under each pad. Be sure that the straight edge is under the perforations and the tapered edge points to the right (see Fig. 62-2).

5. Fasten the pads together with two wire stitches.

6. Trim the pads (see page 157).

7. Add a strip of gummed cloth along the back to cover the stitches. (See Figs. 37-1, 58-1, and 58-2 on pages 99 and 157 for a similar pad.)

Now you are ready to insert your tongue-back pad in the notebook cover you have made.

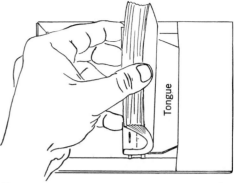

FIG. 62-2. Inserting a tongue-back pad in finished cover.

Discussion Topics

1. What is paste made from?
2. What is glue made from?
3. What is binder board made from? Tear a piece apart and examine it.

BOOKBINDING MATERIALS

Book cloths are made in many colors and with various weaves and surface finishes. Some book cloths are waterproof. Heavy book cloth is called *buckram*. Both book cloth and buckram are sold in rolls 36, 38, 40, and 42 inches wide.

Imitation-leather book coverings are cloths that have been coated with a plastic substance and then grained to look like leather. Cowhide, pigskin, and alligator skin are imitated in this way.

Real leather is used for fine bindings. Almost any kind of leather can be used. The thicker kinds like cowhide are split into thin sheets. The soft inner split layers are called *skivers* and are used for cheaper bindings. Leather book covers must be pared thin where they go around the edges of books.

A stiff, coarse cheesecloth, called *super* or *grass cloth,* or a kind of flannel is used inside the backs of books to reinforce the bindings.

Unit 63. Making a Portfolio

In this unit you will be using bookbinders' flexible glue for the first time. The glue is made from bones and hides of animals. It is a crude form of gelatin.

Some kinds of glue must be soaked in cold water before they are heated.

The pot used for heating glue is a kind of double boiler. Most bindery

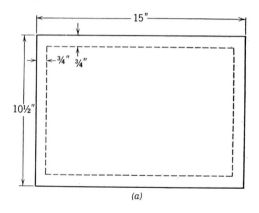

(a)

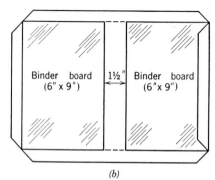

Binder board (6" x 9")   1½"   Binder board (6" x 9")

(b)

FIG. 63-1. Making a portfolio: (*a*) Marking off a piece of book cloth. (*b*) With both binder boards in place, miter all four corners.

gluepots are heated with electricity. They have electric controls that shut the current off when the right temperature is reached. If glue gets too hot, it burns and must be thrown away.

The glue in the pot should be heated to about 140 degrees Fahrenheit. This is not hot enough to burn you, but it would be uncomfortable if you spilled some on your hand.

The glue should "take hold" right away when you put it between two pieces of paper or cloth. If it "lets go," it contains too much water and it is necessary to heat it longer until some of the

water is driven off. If the glue in the pot is too thick to spread with a brush, add a small amount of water to it.

The portfolio you will make in this unit would be a good present for one of your friends. It can be used to hold stationery or small papers.

Procedure

1. Start heating the bookbinders' flexible glue.

2. Cut the following pieces of book cloth and binder board on the paper or table cutter:

1 piece of book cloth 10½ by 15 inches
1 piece of book cloth 8½ by 13 inches
2 pieces of book cloth 5 by 12 inches
2 pieces of binder board 6 by 9 inches

3. Draw lines on the largest piece of cloth (10½ by 15 inches) to show where the boards are to go, that is, ¾ inch from top and bottom edges and ¾ inch from right- and left-hand edges (Fig. 63-1*a*).

4. Spread bookbinders' glue evenly and thinly all over the piece of cloth.

5. Lay the two pieces of binder board on the glued side in the center and about 1½ inches apart. Use a ruler to space the boards correctly and to get them on straight.

6. Miter all four corners and turn over the edges with a bone folder (Fig. 63-1*b*). Press the turned edges down with the folder.

7. Make two pockets in the following way: Use the bone folder to score the 5- by 12-inch cloth piece ½ inch from one long edge, 1½ inches from the

other long edge, and 1½ inches from each end, as shown in Fig. 63-2*a*.

8. Miter all four corners (Fig. 63-2*b*).

9. Put a little glue along the ½-inch scored side of each piece, fold it over, and press it down tightly (Fig. 63-2*b*). This forms the finished edge on each pocket.

10. Fold in the three other flaps (Fig. 63-2*c*).

11. Cover the *outside* of these three folded flaps carefully with glue.

12. Put the two pockets in place. They fit right up to the inside edges of the cover (Fig. 63-3). Use the bone folder to press the glued flaps down. Be sure that the pockets themselves are not glued shut.

13. Put glue over the entire lining (8½- by 13-inch book cloth).

14. Open the pocket at one end and slip the glued lining, glue side down, into the pocket as far as it will go, as shown in Fig. 63-3*b*. Hold up the other end of the lining while you do this.

15. Lay the lining down a little at a time and smooth it over the board.

16. Slip the other end of the lining into the other pocket (Fig. 63-3*c*) as far as it will go, and smooth the whole lining down firmly on the boards and the back strip (Fig. 63-3*d*).

17. Put pieces of wax paper in the pockets and over both sides of the portfolio.

18. Put a board on top of the portfolio and a 10-pound weight on top of the board.

19. Press it overnight.

20. Turn off the heat on the gluepot.

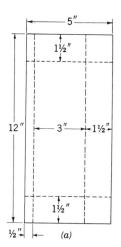

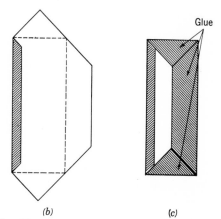

(b)   *(c)*

Fig. 63-2. Steps in making pockets: (*a*) Mark off binding cloth with correct measurements. (*b*) Miter all four corners and glue down the ½-inch scored side. (*c*) Glue the *outside* of the three remaining flaps of the pocket.

Discussion Topics

1. Why have you more time to work with a glued sheet than with a pasted one before it dries?

2. Is there a right and a wrong side to book cloth? Does it make any difference which side you use?

3. In what ways is book cloth better than paper for binding purposes?

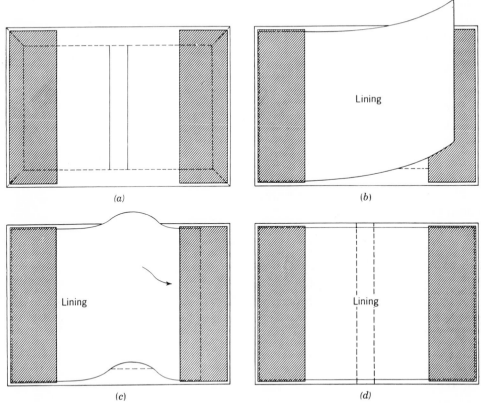

FIG. 63-3. (*a*) Put the two pockets in place. (*b*) Insert lining in left pocket of portfolio. (*c*) Insert lining in right pocket of portfolio. (*d*) Finished portfolio.

STAMPING BOOKS

Gold leaf or very thin sheets (foil) of other metals and opaque colored inks are used in stamping the covers of books. This stamping may be just the title of the book and the author's name, or it may include decorative treatment, such as a rule border.

A piece of the gold leaf or of the metal foil is laid on the cover and then pressed with hot type. An adhesive that has been placed between the metal and the cover is melted where the type touches and sticks these parts of the metal to the book. The rest of the metal, not touched by the hot type, is brushed off.

The same process is used to mark pocketbooks, purses, and luggage with the names or initials of their owners.

Bookbinders have big presses for hot stamping. Most of the type used for this purpose is made of brass.

Unit 64. Making a Photograph Album
or a Scrapbook

This is to be a loose-leaf book 11 by 14 inches in size. Photographs or clippings may be pasted on the pages. When all the pages are full, more pages can be added.

You may wish to make a photograph album or a plain loose-leaf book for the paper scrapbook that is suggested in Unit 67, "Preparing a Paper Scrapbook," pages 179–180. Whichever you make, the photograph album or scrapbook, the procedure is the same.

Procedure

1. Start heating the bookbinders' glue.

2. Cut the following pieces of paper and cloth on the paper cutter or on a board cutter:

2 pieces of book cloth 13 by 16 inches
2 pieces of book cloth 10½ by 13½ inches
1 piece of gummed cloth 3 by 11 inches
1 piece of heavy binder board 1¼ by 11 inches
1 piece of heavy binder board 12½ by 11 inches
1 piece of heavy binder board 11 by 14 inches

3. Draw a line 1 inch from all four edges of one of the 13- by 16-inch pieces of book cloth (Fig. 64-1a).

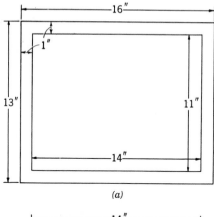

(a)

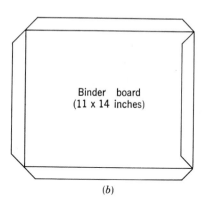

Binder board
(11 x 14 inches)

(b)

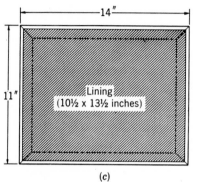

Lining
(10½ x 13½ inches)

(c)

FIG. 64-1. Back cover for scrapbook: (a) Dimensions. (b) Covering binder board. (c) Lining.

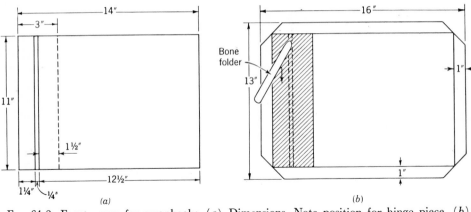

FIG. 64-2. Front cover for scrapbook: (*a*) Dimensions. Note position for hinge piece. (*b*) Hinge piece in position. Press down hinge with bone folder, miter corners of book cloth, turn the edges over, and press them down firmly.

4. Place a piece of large scrap paper or newspaper under this piece of cloth and spread glue evenly all over it. This is called *gluing off*.

5. Lay the 11- by 14-inch binder board in the center of this glued piece of cloth along the penciled lines, miter the corners, turn the edges, and press them down firmly (Fig. 64-1*b*).

6. Line this board with one of the 10½- by 13½-inch pieces of cloth (Fig. 64-1*c*). How far from the edge of the board will the lining be?

7. Put this covered board in a press between two pieces of wax paper. This is to be the back cover of your loose-leaf book.

8. The front cover of your loose-leaf book must be hinged. Use the 3- by 11-inch piece of gummed cloth to fasten the 1¼- by 11-inch strip of binder board to the 12½- by 11-inch piece, with ¼-inch space between them (Fig. 64-2*a*). (The total length will be 14 inches, like the back.) The gummed cloth will cover the narrow strip and extend 1½ inches onto the bigger piece.

9. Mark and glue off the other 13- by 16-inch piece of book cloth as you did the first piece in steps 3 and 4.

10. Lay the hinged board with the gummed-cloth hinge facing up in the center of the glued piece of book cloth. Press the gummed cloth down into the hinge until it is stuck to the book cloth.

11. Miter the corners of the book cloth, turn the edges, and press them down firmly.

12. Line the front cover with the other 10½- by 13½-inch piece of book cloth and put it in a press between two pieces of wax paper.

FIG. 64-3. Pattern for scrapbook pages.

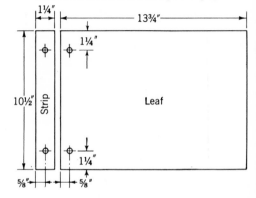

13. Cut the following pieces of black paper if you are making a photograph album, or heavy cover paper or heavy kraft paper if you are making a scrapbook:

20 pieces of 10½ by 13¾ inches (for leaves)
20 pieces 10½ by 1¼ inches (for strips)

Fig. 64-4. Assembled scrapbook.

14. Set the paper punch to punch two ¼-inch holes in the leaves and in the narrow strips, as shown in Fig. 64-3.

15. Put the strips between the leaves. They help to keep the book flat by allowing for the thickness of your pasted clippings or photographs on the leaves.

16. Take the covers out of the press and punch holes in them to match those in the strips and sheets. How much do the covers overhang the leaves on each side?

17. Assemble the covers, leaves, and strips as shown in Fig. 64-4.

18. Tie the book together with a strong shoelace or use binding-post fasteners.

Discussion Topics

1. Why is it necessary to hinge the front cover?
2. What is the purpose of the narrow strips between the pages?

EXTRA CASE BINDING

Most books are *case-bound.* This means that the covers are made up separately and then attached to the books with paste or glue. Today the making of the covers and the attaching of them to the book pages, a process called *casing in,* are usually done by machines made for that purpose.

A few books are bound in real leather or other fine materials, and all the work of binding is done by hand. Each cover is made on the book and is attached to it by tapes or cords that are part of the sewing. These tapes or cords are laced into the cover boards. These books usually are hand-stamped in real gold. The leather may be hand-tooled or inlaid with other leathers.

This hand binding is what is called *extra binding.* It is done as a hobby by artists and amateur binders. There are also a few professional binders who do extra binding of rare volumes or of valuable books.

Unit 65. Making a Large Envelope

A heavy paper suitable for the covers of pamphlets is called *cover paper*. An 11- by 15-inch envelope can be made from a sheet of 20- by 26-inch cover paper. Double-thick cover paper will be best for this purpose. An envelope like this is handy for the storing of maps and other sheets that are too large to go into a binder.

Procedure

1. Cut the cover paper 20 by 20 inches square.

2. Cut a piece of binder board 11 by 15 inches.

3. Draw a light dotted line on the cover paper diagonally from corner to corner as shown in Fig. 65-1a. If the cover paper is two-sided, that is, has a

FIG. 65-1. Making a large envelope. (*a*) Marking the diagonals. (*b*) Indicating center point of both 15-inch edges of binder board. (*c*) Marking the corners of the binder board on the cover paper. (*d*) Cut away pieces marked *X* and fold in all four flaps.

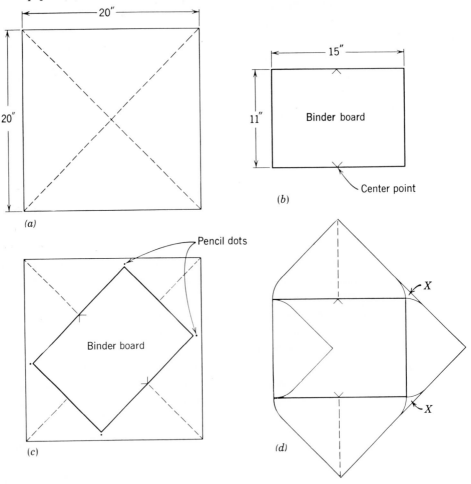

special finish on one side, draw the line on the wrong, or unfinished, side, which will become the inside of the envelope.

4. Mark the center of both 15-inch edges of the binder board (Fig. 65-1*b*).

5. Lay the binder board in the center of the cover (Fig. 65-1*c*). The center of the binder board should be straight with the diagonal line on the paper.

6. Mark all four corners of the binder board on the cover paper with a penciled dot.

7. Draw lines from the dots to the edges of the paper like those shown in Fig. 65-1*d* and cut away the pieces marked *X*.

8. Lay the binder board on the paper again with the corners touching the dots.

9. Fold over all four of the flaps with the bone folder and press them down firmly on the binder board.

10. Open the flaps and remove the binder board. You may use this same piece of binder board to make as many envelopes of this size as you need.

11. Put a small amount of glue or paste on the top side of the side flaps, and fold them over, glue side up.

12. Bring the bottom flap over and glue it down on the side flaps. Do not get glue anywhere except on the flaps. A piece of 11- by 15-inch wax paper placed inside the envelope while the glue is drying will prevent any possible sticking together of the sides of the envelope.

13. Keep the envelope under a weight until the glue is dry.

14. Remove the piece of wax paper. The envelope is now ready for use.

Discussion Topics

1. Steam a regular commercial envelope open. Is it cut like the one you have made?

2. The gum on the flap of a commercial envelope that is moistened to seal the flap is usually made from wheat or potato starch. Why is regular glue not used?

CARE OF BOOKS

Books are made to be used. They are made to be read, not to lie on a shelf. Bookbinders try to make books strong enough to last a long time. But paper and cloth are not strong materials. Anyone can spoil a book by careless handling.

Books are tools. They are tools for learning. Read them.

Book covers are like the clothes we wear. They can be torn or soiled or scuffed. Handle them with care.

Anyone who has ever helped to bind a book will be more careful of all books that he handles.

He will keep them dry and clean.

He will not drop them or throw them around.

He will not scratch the covers or tear or mark or fold down corners of pages.

Unit 66. Marbling Paper

For this project you will need a large square baking pan or photodeveloping tray. It should be 11 by 14 inches or larger and at least 2 inches deep. You will also need five small empty glasses and six flat sticks 8 inches long and ½ inch wide.

Procedure

1. Cover the table that you are going to use with old newspapers to protect it.

2. Put the pan on the newspapers and pour an inch or so of water into the pan.

3. Add 3 or 4 tablespoons of hot glue and stir the mixture. (Fish glue, mucilage, or dissolved gelatin may be used in place of the hot glue.)

4. Squeeze ½ inch of yellow printing ink from its tube onto one of the flat sticks.

5. Put the stick with the ink on it into one of the glasses.

6. Fill the glass about half full of benzol or naphtha solvent. *Be sure that the room is well ventilated.*

7. Stir the solvent with the stick until the ink is all dissolved.

8. Take the stick out of the glass and lay it aside for use later. (If you leave the stick in the glass, you may tip the glass over.)

9. Dissolve red, blue, green, and purple printing inks in the same way in separate glasses. Use a different stick for each color.

10. Cut a dozen pieces of white 8½- by 11-inch bond paper in half to make 5½- by 8½-inch sheets. Now you are ready to start marbling this paper.

11. Dip the yellow stick into the yellow solution. Then sprinkle about twenty drops of the yellow solution on the water in the pan. The drops will spread out on the surface of the water.

12. Do the same with each of the other colors.

13. Use a clean stick to move the drops into some sort of pattern (Fig. 66-1a). Perhaps you will move the stick in circles. Or you can move it in one direction with a wavy motion.

14. After you have a pattern, pick up a sheet holding it by diagonal corners, and lay it carefully on the water (Fig. 66-1b). Wet only one side. When you lift the paper, the pattern of the colors will be on it (Fig. 66-1c).

15. Lay a sheet of old newspaper on the water and take up any ink that is left.

16. Sprinkle more drops and make another pattern, and so on. Each sheet will be different. Use only one or two colors for some of the sheets. Try using more of one color than of the others. You can get all kinds of effects.

17. After the marbled sheets are partially dry, stack them in a pile.

18. Put a flat board on top of the pile and a weight on top of the board. This will hold the marbled sheets flat until they are thoroughly dry.

19. Let them dry at least overnight.

Discussion Topics

1. Look at the edges of the pages and the front and back pages of the big dictionary in the library. How was the pattern on them done?

2. Can you think of some uses for marbled sheets?

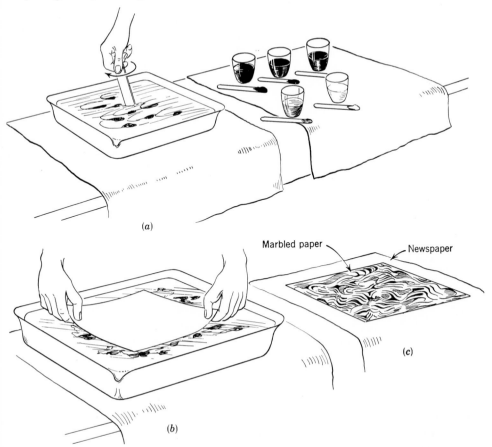

FIG. 66-1. Steps in marbling paper: (*a*) Use a clean stick to move the dots of color into some sort of pattern. (*b*) Hold sheet to be printed by diagonal corners and lay it carefully on the water. (*c*) Lift paper off water and lay it on a piece of newspaper.

Unit 67. Preparing a Paper Scrapbook

You may use the scrapbook you made in Unit 64, or you may wish to make another scrapbook for this unit.

In the print shop or graphic-arts laboratory you will find many different kinds of paper and cardboard. At home you can collect many kinds of wrapping papers, labels, and bags. You can also save the various sizes of envelopes that come in the mail to your home.

Places where they sell paper, such as wholesale paper houses or stationery stores, may give you samples of paper if you ask for them.

You will be surprised how many papers and things made of paper you can collect in a short time. A scrapbook with your collection will be fun to make.

Procedure

1. Divide your collection into sections. For instance, you can have a page or more for each of the following:

Writing papers
Papers used for printed advertising
Cellophane
Tags
Cover papers
Paper bags
Corrugated boards
Binder board
Blotting paper
Business cards
Heavy carton boards
Paper labels
Envelopes
Sealing tapes

2. Letter a heading for each page. If you have time, set up the headings in 24-point type and pull a proof of them on paper. Paste these headings at the top of the pages.

3. Paste the specimens firmly to the pages with library paste.

4. Put each page under a weight and leave overnight to dry.

5. Letter or print a label for the front cover of your scrapbook. It may read *"Scrapbook of Papers—made by* (your name)," or some other, similar wording.

Discussion Topics

The first paper in Europe was made in the late 1100s, or about 800 years ago, during the Crusades.

1. What do you think they did before they had paper?
2. What did they write on?
3. What were books made of?

Paper-ruling Machines

The lines on school tablets and binder paper and the lines on bookkeeping sheets are drawn by a *ruling machine* (Fig. 67-1). This machine has rows of

Fig. 67-1. Paper-ruling machine.

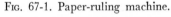

pens which are fed with inks of various colors. The paper is carried on a moving thread belt under these pens.

Machine ruling is a branch of the bookbinding industry.

Cards are ruled by machines that have circular disks in place of pens. The disks revolve in an ink bath and roll the ink onto the cards.

How is graph paper ruled?

Unit 68. Side Binding of Loose Sheets

Loose sheets or magazines made up of sections and loose sheets can be bound together by *side wiring, side stitching,* or, as it is sometimes called, *flat stitching.* This can be done on a wire-stitching machine.

U-shaped staples are usually used to bind thick jobs. Many stitchers are adjustable and can accommodate from 2 sheets up to 2 inches or more.

Loose sheets that are bound in this way need a cover of some kind. Heavy cover paper is recommended for this purpose.

You may have a collection of stories from magazines, or your mother may have pages of recipes from magazines that you could bind in this unit. Before binding, remove any pins, paper clips, or staples from the sheets to be bound.

Procedure

1. Cut two pieces of cover paper to the same size as the sheets to be bound. (Set the type and print the front cover before binding.)

2. Score the front cover with a bone folder ¾ inch from the binding edge.

3. Jog the sheets and the covers to the back and head.

4. Wire-stitch the job if the sheets and covers together are less than ½ inch thick, and proceed with step 13 below. If the sheets and cover are more than ½ inch thick, they will have to be stapled together as outlined in steps 5 to 12.

5. Put a piece of heavy cardboard under the pile.

6. Clamp the covers, sheets, and heavy cardboard together in a bookbinding press so that you can stab holes along the binding edge. Place the clamp about 1½ inches from the back edge.

7. Use a shoemaker's awl to put two holes ⅜ inch from the edge through the sheets at the center of the back edge. These holes must be as far apart as the legs of the U-shaped staples to be used. If a bookbinding setup is available (Fig. 69-1, page 183), these holes may be drilled (Fig. 69-2, page 184).

8. Stab another pair of holes 1½ inches from each end and ⅜ inch from the edge.

9. Lift the edge without unclamping the pile and put a staple in each of the sets of holes.

10. Turn the ends of the staple down toward each other.

11. Tap the staples down tightly with a flat hammer.

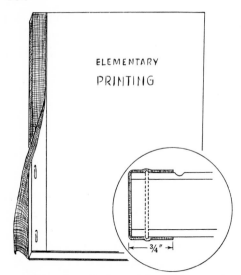

ELEMENTARY

PRINTING

← ¾″ →

Fig. 68-1. Side binding of loose sheets, wire-stitched or stapled, and back covered with a strip of gummed cloth.

12. Take the book out of the press and tap the staples down on both sides until they are smooth.

13. Trim the back with the paper cutter. Cut off only enough to make the surface straight and smooth.

14. Cut a strip of gummed cloth as long as the book and wide enough to cover the back and ¾ inch on each side (Fig. 68-1).

15. Moisten this strip and lay it glue side down on the front cover up to the scored hinge.

16. Turn the book over and draw the gummed-cloth strip smoothly along the back and over onto the back cover (Fig. 68-1).

17. Rub the cloth strip until it is smooth.

18. Trim the book on the paper cutter on the top, bottom, and front edges.

19. Print a label for the cover if you have not already printed it, or letter the title on the cover by hand.

Discussion Topics

1. Is the type of binding presented in this unit stronger than the binding on ordinary books?

2. Side-wire binding will not open out flat. Is this always satisfactory?

3. Why is it necessary to hinge at least the top cover?

Some Occupations in the Printing Industry

The young man who likes printing and who wishes to make it his life work can plan his school studies so that it will help him to succeed in this work.

He will need to concentrate on English composition, spelling, grammar, and punctuation. He should take algebra, chemistry, economics, and public speaking. Drawing, both mechanical and free-hand, would be very helpful to him. Art courses, such as drawing, design, color, and lettering, are useful in many kinds of printing work.

He should learn all the printing he can while he is in school. When he gets through school and is ready to go to work, he will have to serve an apprenticeship—this usually is from four to six years. The time spent in the school printshop or graphic-arts laboratory does not usually count toward this apprenticeship.

The young man may have a choice of work. If he gets into commercial printing, he may be apprenticed in the composing room, in the pressroom, or in the bindery. If he goes into newspaper printing, he may be apprenticed in the composing room, in the pressroom, or in the mail room.

Apprenticeships are not always easy to find. The young man or his parents should start early to make inquiries of employers and union officials about possible openings. For further information see pages 196 and 268–270.

Further information on printing occupations may be had by writing for the BLS Bulletin No. 1126, Government Printing Office, Washington 25, D.C. This bulletin describes the printing industry and its major occupations.

Unit 69. Side Sewing with Thread and Making a Square-back Case

If you and your family have been saving some favorite magazines, this is your opportunity to bind them into books. You may wish to remove the covers that are now on them and any of the opening or closing pages that have advertisements but no text material on them.

Hand-bookbinding equipment such as that shown in Fig. 69-1 is needed for the type of binding described in this unit.

SIDE SEWING WITH THREAD

Side sewing with thread will make a book that opens out more easily than

FIG. 69-1. Hand-binding equipment: (1) trimming shelf; (2) drilling jig; (3) drill backstop; (4) backing metals; (5) sewing-frame board; (6) sewing frame; (7) clamp.

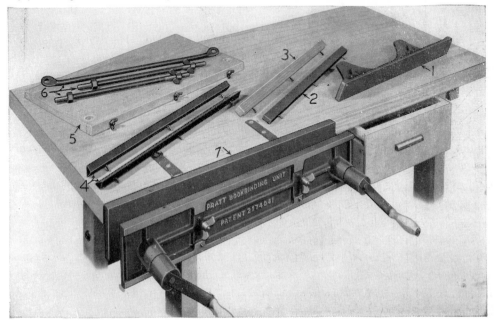

one bound with side-wire stitching or staples.

Procedure

1. Cut two end sheets of medium-weight cover paper the same size as the magazines and put one on top and one on the bottom of the pile of magazines to be bound.

2. Draw a line parallel to the back edge and ¼ inch from it on the top and the bottom sheets.

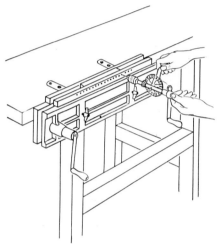

FIG. 69-2. Drilling holes with a hand drill.

3. Starting ¾ inch from one end, make penciled dots on this line ½ inch apart. These are the places where you will drill holes.

4. Put the pile in a binder's press with ½ inch of the binding edge showing (Fig. 69-2).

5. Drill the holes with a hand or electric drill using a No. 48 drill. Go slowly when you drill. Keep the drill holes straight. A clamping device with guide holes for the drill, called a *drill jig,* helps to keep the holes straight (Fig. 69-2).

6. Remove the drill jigs but leave the drilled pages in the binding press. Be careful to keep the holes aligned.

7. Thread a needle with linen thread about 3 feet long.

8. Push the needle down through the first hole and up through the second hole.

9. Pull the thread through until the end is just long enough for you to tie a knot in it as shown in Fig. 69-3*b.* This will fasten the end of the thread and keep it from pulling out of the first hole.

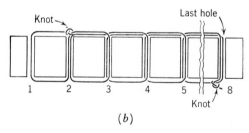

(*b*)

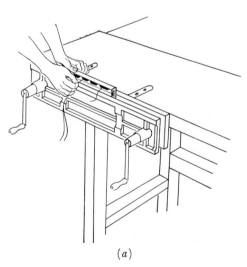

(*a*)

FIG. 69-3. Side sewing: (*a*) Drilled sheet being sewn together. (*b*) Method used when sewing by hand.

10. Put the needle down through the third hole and bring it up through the second hole (Fig. 69-3*b*). Pull the thread taut each time you put the needle through a hole.

11. Jump over the third hole and push the needle down through the fourth hole.

12. Bring it up through the third hole.

13. Continue to jump over a hole and come back and up through the hole you jumped until you reach the last hole.

14. Put an extra turn of thread through the last hole and then push the needle under this turn.

15. Tie a knot.

16. Trim the back of the book very lightly. Do not cut off more than the thickness of a thin cardboard. This may be done with a book-edge trimming chisel (Fig. 69-4).

17. Trim the three other sides on the paper cutter to make them smooth and even.

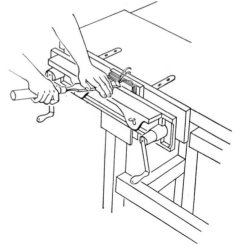

Fig. 69-4. Trimming back of book with a book-edge trimming chisel.

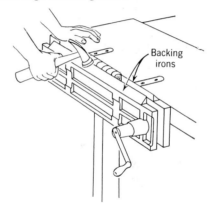

Fig. 69-5. Rounding with backing hammer. Note position of backing irons.

MAKING A SQUARE-BACK CASE

After the magazines are sewn together and trimmed, they are fastened in what is known as a *square-back case*. A *case* is a book cover. It is made in a separate operation. *Casing in* is the process of gluing a book inside its covers, as mentioned before. There are round- and square-back cases. The book you are now reading is bound in a round-back case. Notice the curve of the backbone, or spine, and of the front edges of the pages. This is done by the process of rounding. Figure 69-5 shows the rounding process. For this operation, backing irons are used. They are placed in the same position as the drill jig. This is not done when a book is cased-in in a square-back case as you will be doing.

Procedure

1. Cut two cover boards from heavy binder board the same width as the trimmed book and ⅜ inch longer.

2. Cut another piece of binder board for the back, or spine, of the book. To measure this piece, lay both cover boards on the book and measure the combined thickness. This will be the width of the piece for the spine. The length of this

INSIDE VIEW

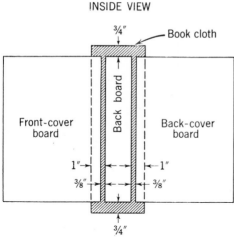

FIG. 69-6. Fastening back board, or spine, to front and back covers.

piece will be the same as that of the cover boards.

3. Cut a piece of book cloth to cover the back board of the book. It should be 1½ inches longer than the cover boards and 2 inches wider than the back board, as shown in Fig. 69-6.

4. Glue off this backstrip.

5. Place the back board in the middle of it.

6. Place a cover board on each side of the back board, leaving exactly ⅜ inch on each side (Fig. 69-6). Use a case gauge if you have one (see Fig. 70-2, page 190).

7. Fold over the top and bottom of the cloth and smooth it down into the grooves between the boards (Fig. 69-7).

8. Close the case. A part of the cloth strip now covering the back board will show on each of the cover boards.

9. Decide how much of this strip is to show on the finished case, and make a light mark across the top edges to show where the overlap of the cloth for the covers is to stop.

10. Open the case again and draw light penciled lines at these points on each side of the cloth strip parallel to the front edges of the cover boards.

11. Cut two pieces of cloth large enough to cover the sides, with ¾ inch to turn over on three sides (Fig. 69-7).

12. Glue off one of these pieces and lay it on the outside of one cover. Be sure to touch the penciled line all along its length.

13. Turn the case over, miter the corners (Fig. 69-8), and turn over the edges.

INSIDE VIEW

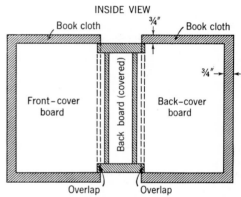

FIG. 69-7. Covering front and back covers with book cloth.

FIG. 69-8. Outside view of binding.

OUTSIDE VIEW

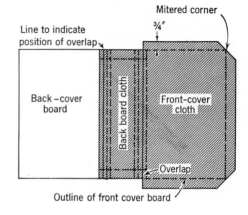

14. Cover the other cover in the same way.

15. Put the case under a light weight until you are ready to use it on the book. Do not line the case you have made.

16. Make two double end sheets by folding two sheets of strong paper in the center and trimming them to the size of the trimmed sewn book.

17. Paste a strip ¼ inch wide along the folded edge of each of the double end sheets (Fig. 69-9).

18. Paste these end sheets on each side of the book flush to the back edge.

19. Cut a piece of super 3 inches wide and 1 inch shorter than the book.

20. Attach this strip to the back and sides of the book (Fig. 69-10) in much the same way that you apply a backstrip of gummed cloth. Use as little paste as possible.

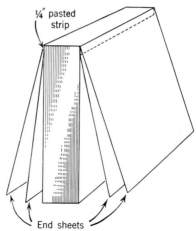

Fig. 69-9. Pasting on end sheets.

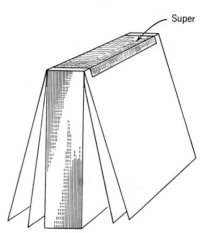

Fig. 69-10. Adding super to backbone.

CASING-IN THE BOOK

Now you are ready to case-in the book you have sewn together.

Procedure

1. With a brush, cover one of the end sheets and the super on it with a smooth coat of thin paste.

2. Open the case.

3. Turn the book over and lay the pasted side down on the inside of the case (Fig. 60-11a). Lay it so that about three-sixteenths of an inch of the case shows on all three sides.

4. Turn the book over and paste the other end sheet.

5. Draw the other half of the cover up and over the stitched book and lay it down on the pasted end sheet so that it projects about three-sixteenths all around as did the other side of the cover (Fig. 69-11b).

6. Use a bone folder to push the cloth down into the grooves at the back.

7. Insert wax paper between both the front and the back covers and the book. This paper keeps the moisture in the paste from penetrating into the pages of the book.

8. Use brass-bound boards if you have them for pressing the back and

End papers

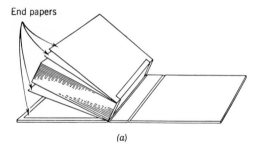

(a)

End paper

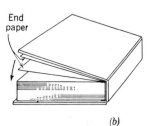

(b)

FIG. 69-11. Casing in: (*a*) Placing the pasted front end paper in position on the front book cover. (*b*) Laying the back book cover onto the pasted back end paper.

forming the hinges. If you use flat boards, lay a piece of ⅛-inch brass welding rod in each of the grooves and press the book with these rods in place.

9. Put the cased-in book in the press between wax paper and leave it until it is dry. This will take about twenty-four hours.

10. Paste a paper label on the cover if you wish. Set in type and print the label or letter it carefully by hand.

Discussion Topics

1. Does this book open flatter than the one you made in Unit 68? Does it open as flat as the book you are now reading?
2. What holds a book in place in the case?

OCCUPATIONS IN LITHOGRAPHY

Making a lithographic plate requires exact scientific methods. Instruments are used for measuring light, temperature, humidity, and quantities or volumes. Chemical processes must be carefully carried out.

A young man who wants to make lithography his life work should at least plan to graduate from high school. He should have good grades in all his studies, but especially in mathematics, chemistry, and physics. Courses in photography and art, particularly lettering and color, are excellent preparation.

Few schools offer courses in lithography. The high school or college graduate who wishes to enter this field of employment will have to serve an apprenticeship of four or five years. In some large cities the employers and unions cooperate in providing training schools for apprentices in connection with their shopwork.

There are four main groups of lithographic workers: the cameramen, the artists and letterers, the platemakers, and the pressmen and assistants. The cameramen photograph the copy to be printed. The artists and letterers re-touch the negatives after they have been developed; correct colors in the final press plates; draw posters or other pictures on stone, metal plates, or special paper; and do all the hand lettering. The platemakers in photolithography transfer the negatives and positives prepared by the cameramen onto press plates. The pressmen and assistants in offset lithography do work similar to that of the letterpress and gravure men.

In lithography, as in printing, a young man should start early to seek an apprenticeship.

Unit 70. Telephone-book Cover

A heavy cover for a telephone book, a school catalogue, or some other book that is changed from time to time may be made in this unit. The book or catalogue is held in the cover firmly, but it can be taken out easily and a new one put in.

Most telephone books are made in a standard size. They are 8¾ inches by 11 inches. The cover you make must be 1 inch longer than the book and ½ inch wider.

For this job you will need heavy binder board, buckram, or book cloth, and two strips of 20-gauge galvanized iron that have been cut and formed as shown in Fig. 70-3. A case gauge (Fig. 70-2), if available, may be used but is not essential.

Procedure

1. Cut two pieces of heavy binder board 9¼ by 12 inches.

2. Cut another piece of binder board for the backstrip. Make the backstrip 12 inches long and ⅜ inch wider than the thickness of the telephone book that is to go in the cover. This allows for the thickness of the cover boards and also for expansion. Each new telephone book usually has a few more pages than the last one; therefore, the cover must be big enough to fit the new, thicker books.

3. Cut a piece of book cloth or buckram 14 inches wide and long enough to turn over an inch on each edge. To find out how long to cut this:

    a. Lay out the boards on the table.

    b. Allow ⅜ inch on each side of the backstrip for the hinge.

    c. Measure across the three boards and add 2 inches for the turnovers. This will be 21¼ inches plus the width of binder board for the backstrip (Fig. 70-1).

4. Glue off the cloth and lay the boards on it. Use a case gauge (Fig. 70-2), if one is available, in laying the boards straight on the cloth. It may also be used to measure the distance to be left on each side of the back board.

5. Miter the corners and turn the edges of the cloth in all around (Fig. 70-3).

FIG. 70-1. Layout for a telephone-book cover.

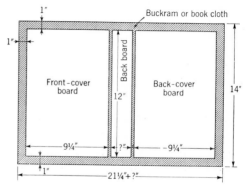

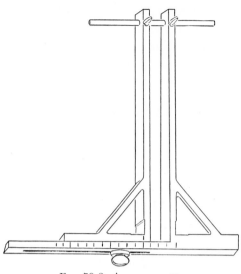

Fig. 70-2. A case gauge.

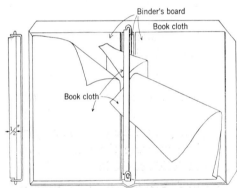

Fig. 70-3. At left, a detailed view of metal centered strip. At right, assembling telephone-book cover and metal strip.

6. Take the two strips of 20-gauge galvanized iron and glue the strip that has the bent ends in the center of the backstrip inside the cover.

7. Cut a piece of buckram 11⅛ by 1½ inches plus the width of the backstrip.

8. Glue this down across the metal strip and press it into the hinges and over onto the cover boards on both sides, as shown in Fig. 70-3.

9. Cut two pieces of cloth for lining the covers. These will be 8¾ by 11½ inches.

10. Glue these two pieces off and lay one on the inside of each cover. There should be ¼ inch between the lining and the edges of the cover on three sides.

11. Print or letter a label and glue it on before you press the book.

12. To press the cover:

  a. Get two pieces of wood ¾ by 10 by 12 inches.

  b. Lay the cover out flat on another board or on a table.

  c. Place wax paper on both sides of the cover to keep it from sticking to the boards and table.

  d. Put the 10- by 12-inch boards on each side of the metal strip.

  e. Put the cover and boards in a press or place a heavy weight on top of the boards. Leave them overnight.

13. To put the telephone book in the cover:

  a. Remove the free strip from the glued-in metal bar.

  b. Open the book at about the center and lay it on the opened cover.

  c. Spring the free metal strip into the two holes in the metal strip fastened to the cover.

14. Close the book carefully.

Discussion Topics

1. Why are the corners of the book cloth used to cover the outside of a cover always mitered?

2. How is a telephone book bound? What holds the pages together?

Occupations in Photoengraving

The requirements for photoengraving workers are much the same as those for lithographers. Photography and chemical processes are used in both industries.

By the photoengraving process, metal plates of illustrations and other material that cannot be set in type are prepared. The printing surfaces on these plates stand out in relief above the nonprinting spaces in the same way as the letters do on a piece of type.

A high school graduate who has had good instruction in chemistry and photography will find uses for this type of knowledge in various ways in photoengraving. Color sense and good eyesight are also very important.

In addition to the courses desirable for all printing workers (page 182), courses in chemistry and metallurgy will be helpful to the photoengraver. A six-year apprenticeship is generally required for one to become a journeyman.

The student who wants to make his life work in this or allied fields must expect to wait his turn for an apprenticeship. He or his parents should visit engraving shops and talk with the management and with union representatives well before the time he is graduated and starts looking for a place.

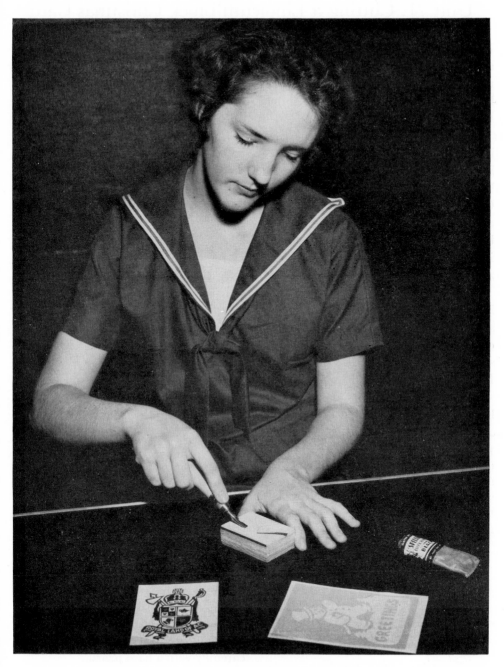

Marcy is cutting a linoleum block to make a personalized card.

Section V. CUTTING LINOLEUM BLOCKS

Unit 71. Cutting a Linoleum-block Christmas Card

If you have ever made a linoleum cut, or seen one made, you know that it is not hard to do. All you need is a type-high linoleum block and a few simple tools.

If you have a ready-made block, use it. If you do not have the ready-made kind, get a piece of brown battleship linoleum about 6 by 10 inches in size. Glue the linoleum to a board with fish glue. The thickness of the linoleum and board together must be type high (0.918 inch). After gluing, put the block under a heavy weight to dry.

The kit of tools for linoleum cutting includes a thin, sharp-pointed knife and some small V-shaped and U-shaped chisels. Any tool that you use should be sharpened carefully on an oilstone before you begin to cut with it.

A small board, like a carpenter's bench hook (Fig. 71-1), is a help in

Fig. 71-1. Cutting a linoleum block. A carpenter's bench hook is being used here to hold the block in position during cutting. In the circle is a cross section of the linoleum block in which the grooves have been cut correctly.

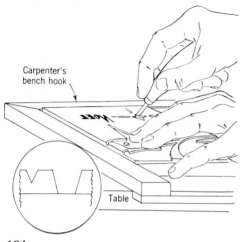

Carpenter's
bench hook

Table

194

holding the block from slipping when you are cutting it. Keep your free hand back of linoleum cutter while cutting.

Procedure

1. Lay a piece of thin paper or tracing paper about eight inches square over the design in Fig. 71-2a, or any other design you prefer, and trace the lines carefully with a soft, sharp pencil. If you select or make a design of your own, be sure to reverse it. The design in Fig. 71-2a is reversed already.

2. Turn the tracing over and rub a soft pencil over the back of each of the lines of the design. This will leave a thin coating of black, which will act like carbon paper when you trace the lines.

3. Cut a type-high linoleum block the size of the design. The one in Fig. 71-2 is 2½ by 3⅛ inches.

4. Place the tracing face down on a table.

5. Place the block linoleum side down on the design. The line around the drawing will be your guide for placing the block.

6. Hold the block on the paper firmly and fold the sides of the paper up and over onto the back of the block.

7. Fasten the folded edges down on the back of the block with cellophane tape. This will keep the tracing from slipping. Turn the block over.

8. Go over the lines of the design carefully with a hard pencil.

9. Take the paper off. You will find the lines of the design drawn on the surface of the linoleum. If you are very careful, you may be able to cut the block without rubbing out any lines. You will

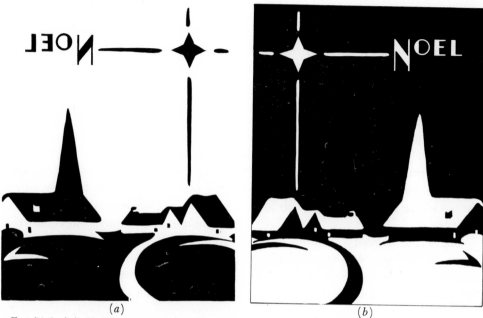

Fɪɢ. 71-2. (*a*) Christmas-card design that may be used in cutting a linoleum block. (*b*) How this design will appear when printed. Why is the drawing in (*a*) backward?

be wise, however, to spray the linoleum with a little fixative (a thin coat of shellac) to protect the lines.

10. Cut the block. The narrow lines of the design are cut V shape. If you use a knife, make a series of stab marks all along each line on each side. Stab toward the middle of the line with the blade held slantwise. Then remove the V-shaped piece (see insert, Fig. 71-1). You can do this job more easily with a V-shaped chisel.

To cut out larger areas, make slantwise cuts all around them and remove a V piece with a knife or V chisel. Then gouge out the rest down below the surface with a large gouge or with a U chisel.

Work carefully and leave clean, sharp edges. Avoid undercutting your design.

11. Test your work by pulling a proof of the block from time to time as you cut. Nᴏᴛᴇ: You cannot pull a test proof unless you have protected the design with fixative.

12. When you finish the block, lock it up for press and print it on book paper according to the instructions in Unit 51, "Linoleum Block Printing," page 139.

13. When the prints are dry, trim them right up to the design all around.

14. Mount each print on a piece of brown or gray cover paper. If you have used the design in Fig. 71-2, this should be about 4½ by 5⅜ inches. Use a little paste in the upper corners only to attach the prints to the mounts.

You can follow this same method to cut designs for program covers, for booklet covers, and for blocks to print on cloth. You may wish to combine a linoleum block print and photograph for the cover of your group or individual project.

Discussion Topics

1. Would you call a linoleum cut a line engraving? (See Fig. 50-3, page 138.)

2. Blocks of hardwood can be used in place of linoleum for making printing cuts. Why is linoleum better for school use?

OTHER OCCUPATIONS IN THE GRAPHIC-ARTS INDUSTRY

With a good education and some basic knowledge of printing methods and printing processes, a young man may find employment in divisions of the industry where he does not have to learn a trade.

The words *a good education* usually mean a college education. This is needed for jobs in management, for the better selling jobs, and for many of the jobs in the editorial and advertising professions.

Some of the courses that the student may take in college are business administration, accounting, sales management, journalism, advertising, and commercial art.

For jobs requiring special skills see "Some Occupations in the Printing Industry," pages 182–183.

Ann finds silk-screen printing very fascinating and rewarding.

Section VI. SILK-SCREEN PRINTING

Unit 72. Silk-screen Equipment
Preparation of Frames and Drying Racks

By the silk-screen process you can print in color a variety of useful things: glassware, T shirts, scarves, aprons, tea sets, greeting cards of all kinds, game boards for checkers or chess and darts, and so on. By a process called *flocking,* which is described in Unit 76, pages 222–224, you can add a feltlike finish to a silk-screen-printed surface.

In this section you will learn the basic techniques of the silk-screen process. Later you may wish to set up your own silk-screen printing shop at home where you and your friends can continue it as a hobby. Printing family and friends' Christmas cards has become a very profitable hobby for some silk-screen club groups. Drinking glasses and scarves with monograms or pictures silk-screen-printed on them make very pretty gifts.

Fig. 72-1. Equipment necessary for silk-screen printing.

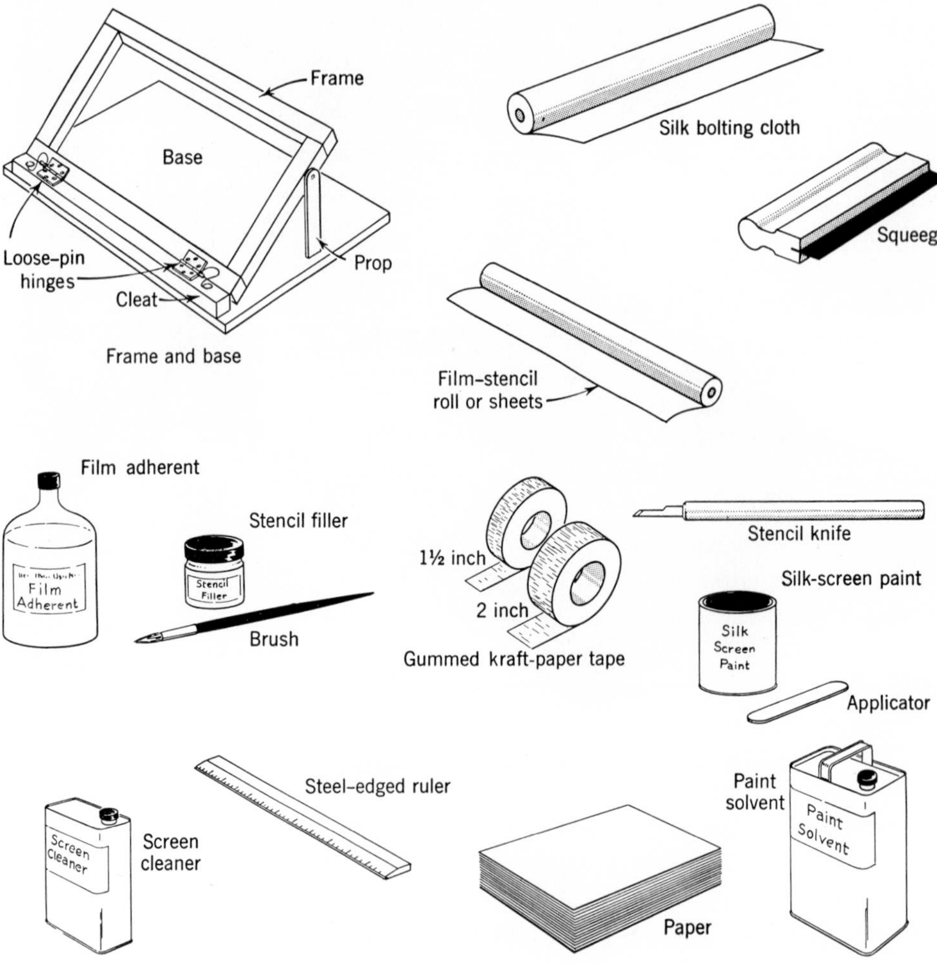

198

You may make your own printing frames for this process or purchase a complete standard silk-screen unit that includes one or more frames. Even if you do have silk-screen frames available, it may be necessary or desirable to make an additional frame or a special frame for a particular job. Small jobs may be printed with a large screen by blocking out the unused parts of the screen with screen filler or with a sheet of paper taped down on the silk around a small stencil.

EQUIPMENT

For silk-screen printing, you will need the following: a silk-screen frame and base, a sharp knife for cutting the stencils (special stencil knives are made for this purpose), 1½- and 2-inch gummed-kraft-paper tape, synthetic rubber squeegee for drawing the paint across the screen, No. 10 mesh silk bolting cloth or cotton organdy (silk is recommended), Nu-film for stencils, adherent for sticking the Nu-film stencil to the silk screen, stencil filler for filling in around the stencil, waterproof silk-screen paint, and kerosene or the solvent recommended for the particular paint being used to remove the paint from the screen after the printing, and lacquer thinner for removing the stencil and cleaning off the screen after the job is done (Fig. 72-1). A steel-edged ruler or steel ruler will be needed in this unit as a guide during the cutting of the stencil for the checkerboard.

Because the rather heavy paint used for the silk-screen process is relatively slow in drying, it is not possible to stack or to slip-sheet the printed sheets as they come from the silk-screen press. Two types of racks that might be made in the school workshop are suggested here. The rack shown in Fig. 72-2 is a series of shelves built on a frame mounted on casters. The rack in Fig. 72-3 is a base mounted on casters on top of which simple frames are placed. After each frame becomes filled with printed sheets, another frame is laid in position on top of it.

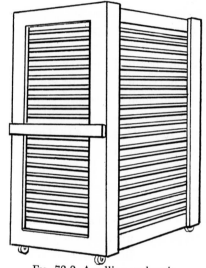

FIG. 72-2. A rolling rack unit.

FIG. 72-3. A loose rack on a truck.

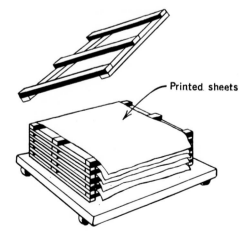

Printed sheets

MAKING A SILK-SCREEN FRAME
AND BASE

The dimensions for the silk-screen printing frame and base given here will print a 15- by 15-inch checkerboard with a 1½-inch border in two parts, each 7½ by 15 inches. The screen frame is made of strips of wood 1½ to 2 inches wide and ¾ inch thick put together like a picture frame. (Grooved lengths of wood mortised at both ends for quick assembly are available in any desired length from some suppliers of silk-screen equipment for this purpose.) The frame can easily be made in a woodworking shop. The corners may be mitered or square and joined together with corrugated wood fasteners or with angle or straight irons (Fig. 72-4). The inside measurements of the frame should be 12 by 18 inches (Fig. 72-5). The base is made of ⅜-inch plywood 16 by 25 inches in size. The frame is hinged to a cleat (Fig. 72-1) that is as thick and as long as the frame. The cleat is fastened permanently to the base. Two 2- by 1½-inch loose-pin, or pushpin, hinges such

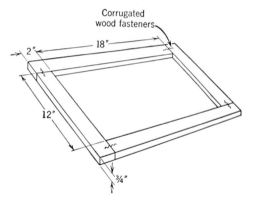

FIG. 72-5. Frame for silk screen.

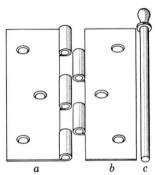

FIG. 72-6. Loose-pin, or pushpin, hinge.

as those used on doors (Fig. 72-6) are used to fasten the frame to the cleat. By removing the pins, the frame is easily detached from the cleat. Whenever you remove the frame from the cleat or base, be sure to put the pins back into that part of the hinge that is attached to the cleat. An additional precaution is to tie a piece of string to each of the pins and to thumbtack the loose ends to the cleat near the hinges, as shown in Fig. 72-7.

If the same base is to be used for several frames, divide the hinge so that the *a* and the *b* parts shown in Fig. 72-6 will both be on the cleat. When you put the hinge on the frame, be sure to match up the *a* and the *b* parts correctly as shown

FIG. 72-4. Frame corners: (*a*) mitered; (*b*) square.

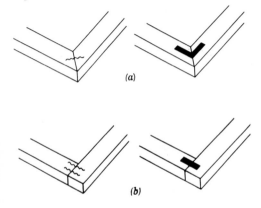

(*a*)

(*b*)

in Fig. 72-7. Such interchangeable frames are particularly useful when two or more colors are to be printed on the same base (see Unit 75, page 219).

Fasten a short movable leg to the screen at one end of the frame with a wood screw (Fig. 72-8). This is to hold the screen up when you work under it.

Small wooden guide blocks fastened to the base on each side of the frame will help to ensure the registry each time the frame is brought down on a job (Fig. 72-8). This is particularly important when you are printing a job in more than one color.

TACKING SILK ON FRAME

Stretching the silk and tacking it on the frame so that it is even and drum-tight is very important. A staple gun may be used to fasten the silk to the frame in place of tacks. The procedure is the same for the staple gun as it is for the tack method given here.

Procedure

1. Cut a piece of No. 10 mesh silk bolting cloth an inch larger than the outside dimensions of the frame that you are to cover.

2. Line up the silk with the vertical and horizontal threads parallel with the sides of the frame.

3. Lay the frame flat on a rigid table with the open parts of the hinges on the frame facing upward. With No. 4 carpet tacks, proceed as follows:

a. Put the first tack in the center of the hinge side of the frame. (You may wish to use strips of oilcloth or binding tape under the tacks to pro-

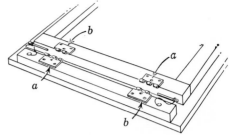

FIG. 72-7. Loose-pin hinges installed on frame and on cleat permanently attached to the baseboard. Each frame should have an *a* and *b* part of the hinge placed to match the *b* and *a* part on the cleat. (See Fig. 72-6.)

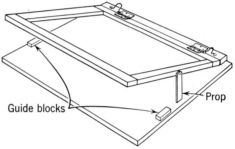

FIG. 72-8. Guide blocks on baseboard and movable leg, or prop, attached to screen.

tect the silk.) Tack the silk to the frame from the middle outward toward each end (Fig. 72-9*a*). Place the tacks about one inch apart. Be sure to drive the tacks all the way in so that the head of the tack and not the shaft is holding the silk. Make sure that the silk is smooth and the horizontal and vertical threads are parallel with the sides of the frame. Very little stretching is required when you are tacking down the first side.

b. Tack the opposite side. Again start in the middle and work toward the ends (Fig. 72-9*b*). Pull the silk outward from the center of the frame. This will stretch it taut with as few wrinkles as possible.

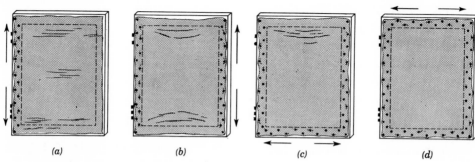

(a)   (b)   (c)   (d)

Fɪɢ. 72-9. Tacking silk on frame. Tack from the middle outward toward each end as indicated by arrows.

c. Tack the ends in the same way by starting in the center and working toward each side (Fig. 72-9*c* and *d*). If done properly, the tacking of the last end will remove the remaining wrinkles.

d. Wash the silk with warm water to remove the sizing. Let it dry thoroughly. This will help to smooth and tighten the silk on the frame.

4. Cover the tack heads with gummed-kraft-paper sealing tape 2 inches wide. Cover about a quarter of an inch of the silk screen as shown in Fig. 72-10.

5. Turn the screen over and apply folded strips of the gummed-paper tape 1½ inches wide to seal the edges where

Fɪɢ. 72-10. Cover tack heads (or grooves and fiber rope, Fig. 72-12) with gummed-kraft-paper sealing tape.

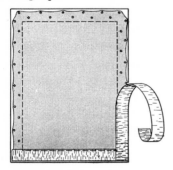

the silk and the frame join (Fig. 72-11). Half of the folded tape must be stuck to the frame and the other half to the silk. This prevents the paint from running between the silk and the frame during the printing process. When the paper strips are completely dry, a coat of shellac over the entire frame will help to make it even more paintproof. If any shellac gets on the silk screen, remove it immediately with alcohol.

6. Fasten the finished frame to its base by the hinges. You are now ready to make the stencil.

Sᴛʀᴇᴛᴄʜɪɴɢ Sɪʟᴋ ᴏɴ Gʀᴏᴏᴠᴇᴅ Fʀᴀᴍᴇs

The stretching of silk on the grooved frames is simpler and faster than tacking. For this procedure you will need a ball or spool of fiber rope.

Procedure

1. Cut a piece of No. 10 mesh silk bolting cloth an inch larger than the outside dimensions of the frame you are to cover.

2. Cut four pieces of fiber rope—one for each side—the length of each groove.

3. Line up the silk with the vertical

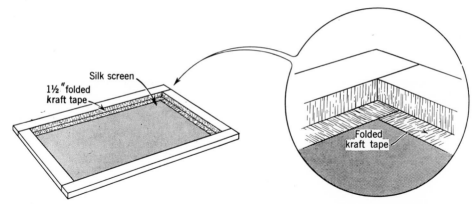

Fig. 72-11. Apply folded strips of gummed-kraft-paper sealing tape to edges where silk and frame meet.

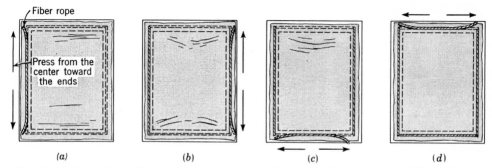

(a)   (b)   (c)   (d)

Fig. 72-12. Stretching silk on grooved frame with fiber rope. Start at the middle and press the fiber rope into the groove outward toward each end (see arrows).

and horizontal threads parallel with the sides of the frame.

4. Cover the tackheads with gummed-drum-tight is very important. To do this, lay the frame flat on a rigid table with the grooves facing upward and proceed as follows:

a. Start forcing the silk into the groove of the frame at the center of one of the long sides with the fiber rope and work toward each end (Fig. 72-12). You may need to use a hammer to force the fiber rope into the groove far enough for it to hold the silk firmly.

b. Stretch the silk over to the opposite long side and force the silk into the groove all around with a wedge fiber rope. Start from the center and work toward each end as before.

c. Repeat the process for each end.

d. Tap the fiber rope farther into the groove all around with a wedge and hammer, as shown in Fig. 72-13. This should make the silk drum-tight.

e. Wash the silk with warm water to remove the sizing. Let it dry thoroughly.

5. Cover the grooves and fiber rope with gummed-kraft-paper sealing tape.

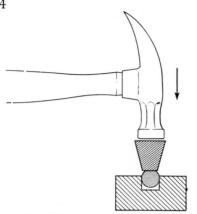

Fig. 72-13. With a wedge and hammer tap the fiber rope farther into the groove all around the frame. Be particularly careful at the corners. The silk can be easily broken.

Use tape that is the width of the frame (Fig. 72-10).

6. Turn the screen over and apply folded strips of the gummed kraft paper 1½ inches wide to seal the edges where the silk and the frame join (Fig. 72-11). Half the folded tape must be stuck to the frame and the other half to the silk. This prevents the paint from running between the silk and the frame during the printing process. When the paper strips are completely dry, a coat of shellac over the entire frame will help to make it more paintproof. If any of the shellac gets on the silk screen, remove it immediately with alcohol.

7. Fasten the finished screen to its base. You are now ready to make the stencil.

Discussion Topics

1. Why is the silk cut a little larger than the frame that it is to cover?
2. Why is it so important to stretch the silk evenly and drum-tight on the silk-screen printing frame?
3. What would happen if the paint used for silk-screen printing dried quickly?

TYPES OF SILK-SCREEN STENCILS

There are five different methods of making silk-screen stencils: block-out, paper, lacquer-film, tusche (or resist), and photographic. The method used depends on which is best suited to the particular job being done.

In the *block-out* method the part that is not to be printed is blocked out by painting it with a screen filler that is resistant to the type of paint to be used for printing. This type of stencil is particularly useful for simple designs such as single block letters and silhouettes. The procedure for making this type of stencil is given in Unit 75, pages 216–219.

The *paper* stencil method, like the block-out method, is used for printing simple designs, but it is good for only short runs. In this method the design or lettering is cut out of thin paper. The procedure for making a paper stencil is given in detail in Unit 74, pages 212–215.

The *lacquer-film* method is the one that you will find most useful. By this method the stencil is cut out of a thin film of colored lacquer that is laminated to a sheet of glassine paper. The glassine paper acts as a backing for the film and holds the pieces of the stencil together. After the stencil is adhered to the silk screen, the backing is removed. This method is described in the next unit.

The *tusche,* or resist, method is used by artists for making fine color prints and for creating a hand-brushed effect. In this method a different screen is made for each color by tracing each color on a separate screen with liquid tusche and grease pencil or tusche crayon. After the screen is thoroughly dry, a small amount of a cold solution of glue and water, with a few drops of glycerin added, is poured into one end of the screen and scraped across the entire screen with the edge of a piece of stiff cardboard. This process is repeated several times. The glue is used in this process as a filler. The tusche and the crayon are dissolved out of the screen by turpentine or kerosene. This leaves the screen open where the tusche and crayon tracing were painted and drawn in and permits the desired color to be printed through the screen.

The *photographic* stencil method is used to reproduce very fine, delicate detail. It is also used where photographic accuracy is required. It does not require a knowledge of photography, a camera, or any expensive equipment. The *Ektagraph* process film is used for making photographic stencils for line or halftone reproduction. With this type of stencil film even the amateur can prepare his or her own photoscreens. In this process the film is exposed under a positive (as opposed to a negative, or reverse) film using a simple photoflood bulb. Then the film is put through three baths: (1) to develop the exposed areas of the film, (2) to wash out the soft unexposed areas of the film, and (3) to fix the stencil so that further exposure to light will not affect it. The stencil is then transferred to the silk screen by simple contact adhesion.

Other types of film are available for this process. One such film is the *Gelatine Transfer Film,* which is made light-sensitive just before it is used by a special solution made for that purpose. After exposure, the soft unexposed areas of the film are washed away with hot water and the hardened portions of the film are adhered to the silk screen by contact adhesion.

Unit 73. Preparing Nu-film Stencil and Printing a Checkerboard

The Nu-film is one type of lacquer stencil film. The Nu-film silk-screen stencils may be used for many different types of silk-screen printing projects. Cutting and adhering a Nu-film stencil for a checkerboard will give you the experience you need to prepare more difficult stencils.

Cutting a Nu-film Stencil

With a little practice you will acquire the "feel" of the stencil knife and will be able to cut the lacquer film without cutting through the glassine backing (Fig. 73-1). If intersecting lines are overcut, these overcuts will be sealed during the adhering process. This means that you can cut each line of your checkerboard with single strokes from one side of the board to the other.

Procedure

1. Make a full-scale drawing of half of the checkerboard that you are going to print. If you are going to use the

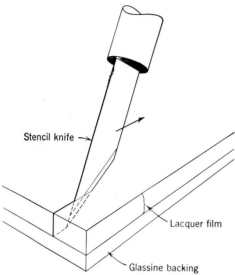

Fig. 73-1. Cutting of lacquer film (much enlarged) for making silk-screen stencil. Note: The backing of the lacquer film is *not* cut.

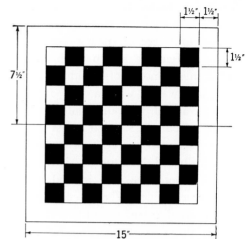

Fig. 73-2. Layout for checkerboard.

measurements given in Fig. 73-2, this will be 7½ by 15 inches with four rows of 1½-inch squares, 8 squares wide, and a 1½-inch border at the top and on each side. Be sure that the drawing is thumbtacked securely to the drawing board.

2. Cut a piece of the Nu-film slightly larger than your drawing (8 by 15½ inches), place it over the drawing with the lacquer side up, and hold it in place with cellophane tape.

3. Cut the straight lines of your checkerboard with a sharp knife. Use a steel-edged or steel ruler. Be careful not to cut through the glassine backing (Fig. 73-1).

4. Carefully remove from the backing the squares that are to be printed (Fig. 73-3). To do this, raise one corner of the square with the stencil knife and then gently pull the rest off with your fingers. If the outside border is to be

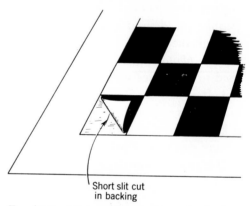

Fig. 73-3. After cutting, remove the lacquer film from the squares that are to be printed in black. After removing a square of the film, cut a short slit in the backing as shown.

printed, it should also be removed. The glassine backing should remain intact.

5. Cut a slit in the center of each glassine square from which you have removed the square of lacquer film. This slit will allow the air to escape from under the stencil during the adhering process.

6. Cut small crosses at the corners of the outer margins. These crosses will show on the final printed sheet and be your guide in trimming.

7. With a sharp knife cut the lacquer film around the cellophane tape holding the Nu-film to the original drawing. Be careful not to cut the glassine backing.

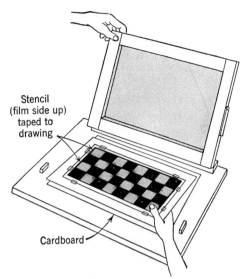

ADHERING NU-FILM STENCIL TO THE SILK FRAME

The drawing remains attached to the stencil until the adhering process is complete. The screen must be as close to the stencil as possible during the adhering process. To do this, put a sheet of cardboard under the drawing and stencil.

For the adhering process you will need a large and a small clean rag or a roll of absorbent cotton and adhering liquid (adherent). Before starting the adhering process, be sure that the silk screen is clean and free from dirt, lint, pieces of cut film, and paint.

Be sure that the room in which you are working is well ventilated.

FIG. 73-4. Placing the stencil in the position desired for printing. The stencil is still attached to the original layout, or drawing. The black squares of the original drawing show through the stencil backing. A piece of cardboard placed below the stencil helps to push it against the screen.

Procedure

1. Place the stencil, film side up with the drawing still attached, under the silk-screen printing frame in the position desired for printing, and lower the frame (Fig. 73-4).

2. Moisten the small rag or wad of absorbent cotton with adherent (not wringing wet). With the moistened rag in one hand and the large dry rag in the other, wet a small area of the screen over one corner of the stencil with a single stroke and wipe it dry immediately with the dry rag (Fig. 73-5). Repeat the process in a small area next to the first one. Continue in one direction to avoid wrinkles in the film. Wet the small rag or wad of cotton as often as necessary.

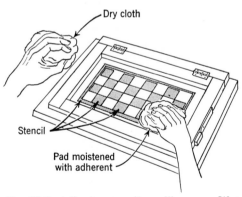

FIG. 73-5. Adhering stencil to silk screen. Wet small area with a single stroke and wipe dry immediately.

Continue the process until the entire stencil is adhered to the silk screen.

3. Raise the frame, cut the cellophane tape holding the original drawing to the stencil, and remove the drawing.

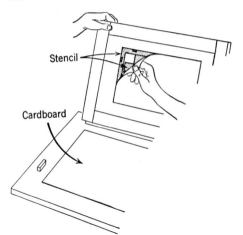

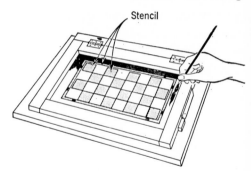

Fig. 73-7. Fill in between the checkerboard stencil and the edge of the silk-screen printing frame with filler.

Fig. 73-6. Slowly peel off the glassine back from the adhered film, or stencil.

4. Let the stencil and screen dry for several minutes with the screen raised.

5. Slowly peel off the glassine back from the adhered film and watch carefully for any portion of the film that may not be adhered to the silk (Fig. 73-6). If such places are found, lower the frame and repeat the adhering process in these places.

Filling In around the Stencil

The same printing frame may be used to print projects of a variety of shapes and sizes within its own size limits. It would be a waste of paint if more area were printed than was needed—for example, if the space around the design as well as the design were open and permitted the paint to pass through.

To fill in the open silk between the film and the frame, a liquid called a *filler* is used (Fig. 73-7). This filler, like the stencil, must be resistant to the paint being used for printing. Why? Since a lacquer stencil has been used, a lacquer screen filler may be used for this purpose.

The filling in between the stencil and the frame may also be done with paper. In this method a mask is cut slightly smaller than the whole frame. An opening is cut in the mask to permit the printing of the design stencil. The mask is held in place on the underside of the silk by gummed-paper tape at the edges (see Unit 74, page 214).

Printing the Checkerboard

The checkerboard may be printed as black on white paper or black on red paper. If you wish to have a red and black checkerboard and no red paper is available, a second stencil for the red would be 6 by 12 inches. Why? If two of you work together on this project, one could prepare the black and one the red stencil.

In silk-screen printing, as in letterpress printing, *register* is important. Finding the proper printing position and locating the registry guides are part of the printing process. The guides should be no thicker than the material being printed. Why? If the checkerboard is to be printed on cardboard, three pieces of the cardboard may be used as guides. If the checkerboard is to be printed on paper, gummed-paper guides folded in the middle and pasted to the base as shown in Figs. 73-8 and 74-3 (page 213) will be satisfactory.

Procedure

1. Locate the registry guides (Fig. 73-8) for the sheet on which the checkerboard is to be printed. The sheet should be a little larger than the black stencil (7½ by 15 inches), and the guides should be small enough not to interfere with the printing.

2. Place a piece of the paper to be printed against the registry guides. Lower the screen.

3. Pour about a quarter of a cup of black silk-screen paint onto one end of the screen.

4. Draw this paint evenly across the screen from end to end with the squeegee (Fig. 73-9).

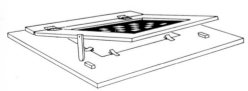

Fig. 73-8. Registry and press guides in position for printing. (See also Fig. 74-3.)

Fig. 73-9. Draw the paint evenly across the silk of the frame with the squeegee.

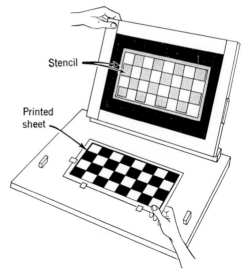

Fig. 73-10. Lift printing frame and remove printed sheet.

5. Raise the screen and remove the printed sheet (Fig. 73-10).

6. Feed another sheet to the guides. You will need to print two sheets for each checkerboard you wish to make. If you are printing both red and black squares, print the red squares first and let them dry overnight before printing the black squares on the same sheets.

7. After you have printed all the checkerboards that are desired, remove the silk-screen printing frame from the baseboard. With a cardboard, scoop up any paint that is left over and put it back into the paint can.

8. Clean off the squeegee, screen, and stencil with the proper solvent for the paint that you have been using. Either kerosene or turpentine is often used for this purpose.

9. Remove the stencil from the screen as follows:

   a. Lay the screen, stencil down, on newspaper.

b. Soak the stencil with film remover. This is a solution of lacquer thinner that will remove the particular lacquer film used. It is supplied by the film manufacturer.

c. After a few minutes pull the paper away from the silk. It will take most of the stencil with it.

d. Wet two clean rags or wads of absorbent cotton with film remover and wash both sides of the silk screen at the same time.

e. Dry the silk with a clean rag or wad of absorbent cotton.

10. Remove any paint that may have gotten on the baseboard.

11. Re-assemble the clean silk-screen printing frame and baseboard and return it to its proper place.

Finishing the Checkerboard

If you printed your checkerboard directly on cardboard, you will not need the binder board mentioned below. For mounting the checkerboard printed on paper, you will need two pieces of binder board 7½ by 15 inches. For binding, or finishing, either of the two types of checkerboards, you will need a 1-inch strip of black gummed cloth 15 inches long and a 16- by 16-inch piece of black

book cloth. You will also need a pot of bookbinders' glue.

Procedure

1. Start heating the bookbinders' glue.

2. Trim the printed sheets of the checkerboard so that each sheet is 7½ by 15 inches. Use the printed crosses indicating the outer corners of the border as guides. This should give you a 1½-inch border at the top and on each side of the printed checkerboard. The bottom of the checkerboard has no unprinted border.

3. Cut two pieces of binder board 7½ by 15 inches, a 1-inch strip of black gummed cloth 15 inches long, and a 16- by 16-inch piece of black book cloth.

4. Place the two pieces of binder board so that they form a 15-inch square with about an eighth of an inch space between them.

5. Join the two pieces together with the 1- by 15-inch strip of black gummed cloth, as shown in Fig. 73-11.

6. Glue off both halves of the printed checkerboard and lay one on each piece of the binder board (Fig. 73-12). They will cover up most of the 1- by 15-inch strip of gummed cloth. Let the glue dry thoroughly.

Fig. 73-11. Joining the pieces of binder board that are to be used for the mounting of the checkerboard.

Fig. 73-12. Both ends of the checkerboard mounted on binder board.

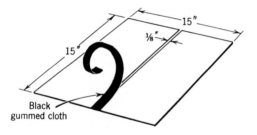

7. Mark a ½-inch border on the inside of the 16- by 16-inch piece of black book cloth.

8. Glue off the piece of book cloth and lay the checkerboard in the center of it. The marked ½-inch border should help you to center it correctly.

9. Place a 7½- by 15-inch piece of wax paper on top of one side of the checkerboard and close the board slowly (Fig. 73-13).

10. Gently force the book cloth into the hinge and open the checkerboard out flat again.

11. Miter the corners of the book cloth as shown in Fig. 73-14 and turn the edges in all around.

12. Put the finished checkerboard between sheets of wax paper and place it in a press. Leave the checkerboard in the press overnight or longer. It must be thoroughly dry before you use it or decorate it further.

Although the checkerboard itself is now complete, you may wish to decorate the outside of it with a linoleum block print or silk-screen design.

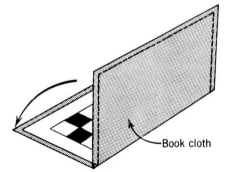

Fig. 73-13. After laying the checkerboard on the glued-up cloth, close the board slowly.

Fig. 73-14. Miter corners of the cloth and turn the edges in all around.

Discussion Topics

1. Why is it important not to cut through the glassine backing when you are cutting out a Nu-film lacquer stencil?

2. After the lacquer film has been removed from the areas of the stencil that are to be printed, why are slits cut in the glassine backing of these areas?

3. What happens to the edges of the stencil if you put on too much adherent?

4. What would happen if some of the lacquer filler splashed on an open area in your stencil? When and what would you do about it?

SOME USES OF SILK-SCREEN PRINTING

The silk-screen process is used for printing book covers; posters of all sizes from small announcements to billboards; and decorations and lettering on glass, fabrics, metal, wood, rubber, leather, and a variety of surfaces. It is also used to reproduce color prints of fine paintings. Silk screening is a very versatile color-printing process. The following are a few items you may use at home or in school that are often printed by this process: lamp shades, oilcloth tablecloths, shower curtains, dress goods, sportswear, glassware, decalcomanias, school banners, greeting cards, wallpaper, and gift wrapping paper.

The feltlike finish on greeting cards is produced by silk-screening an adhesive (a flexible, slow-drying synthetic or varnish-type paint) on the card and then spraying the card with finely cut cotton and wool fibers which stick to the adhesive. This process is called *flocking,* and the finely cut cotton, wool, or rayon is called *flock.* The process is described in Unit 76, "Flocking," pages 222–224.

Unit 74. Preparing a Paper Stencil and Printing a Silk-screen Poster

The silk-screen stencil for this project could be prepared by the Nu-film method described in Unit 73. The paper stencil is satisfactory for simple designs and is inexpensive. Whether you prepare a stencil for a school poster or a sign for some other purpose, such as "Please Keep Off the Grass" or just "Please," the procedure for preparing

the stencil is the same. If the sign or poster you make is to be used out of doors, be sure that you have a suitable type of paint for the purpose. Simple silhouettes cut out of paper may be used to decorate a poster.

In planning your sign or poster, remember that, when the individual letters of the poster are cut out of paper, the background of the poster will be the color of the paint used and the letters will be the color of the material on which you are printing. This is the simplest way of preparing a paper stencil. The letters may be cut out of newspaper headlines, or you may wish to draw them yourself on thin paper.

Fig. 74-1. Cover the baseboard with a piece of three-ply cardboard and thumbtack it in place.

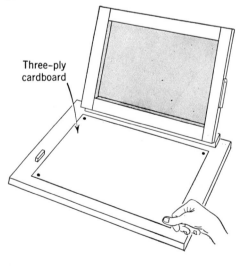

Three-ply cardboard

Procedure

1. Cover the baseboard of the silk-screen printing unit with a sheet of three-ply cardboard and thumbtack the cardboard in place (Fig. 74-1).

2. Cut out the letters carefully for the words of the poster that you are going to print and any decorative silhouette you may wish to use.

3. Arrange the letters of the words on a flat surface just as you wish them to appear on your poster. Measure the width of the widest line and the distance from the top of the tallest letter of the top line to the bottom of the bottom line. This is your printing area. Allow about a ½-inch printed border around this printing area and about a 1½-inch unprinted border. This means that your printed poster will be 4 inches longer and 4 inches wider than the printing area. How large a sheet of poster board do you need for your poster?

4. Cut the pieces of poster board that you are going to print.

5. Lay one of these pieces on the cardboard under the screen and in the center of the screen opening.

6. Mark the edges of the poster board on the cardboard (Fig. 74-2).

7. Prepare three gummed-paper press guides. A 6-inch piece of gummed paper, ¾ to 1 inch wide, folded in the

middle with one end folded back about an inch from this middle fold (Fig. 74-3), makes a satisfactory guide. The two free ends are stuck to the cardboard that covers the baseboard with the second fold on the line of the sheet to be printed (step 6 above). This will permit the sheets to be fed to the exact position indicated. If the poster board is $\frac{1}{16}$ inch thick or more, use three pieces of the poster board as press guides.

Stick the three register guides in position (Fig. 74-3).

8. Draw a rectangle the size of the printing area in the center of one of the sheets that is to be printed.

9. Lay this marked sheet on the baseboard up to the register guides.

10. Lower the printing frame and

FIG. 74-3. Prepare three folded gummed-paper press guides. Glue the press guides in the positions indicated by the line on the cardboard.

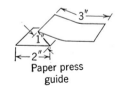

Paper press guide

FIG. 74-2. Firmly hold a piece of the poster board to be printed in the center of the printing area. Mark the edges of the poster board on the cardboard with a pencil.

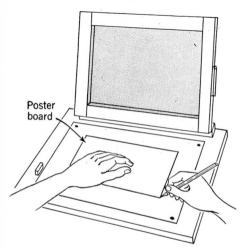

Poster board

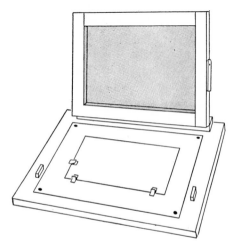

mark the corners of the printing area on the silk screen with a soft pencil.

11. Prepare a paper mask for the printing area.

  a. Cut a piece of smooth wrapping paper 1 inch smaller all around than the printing frame.

  b. Remove the printing frame from the baseboard.

  c. Use cellophane tape to fasten the masking paper at the corners to the underside of the printing frame.

  d. Turn the frame over and mark the corners of the printing area on the masking paper through the silk. Be careful not to damage the silk.

  e. Remove the masking paper from the frame. The opening in the mask should be ¼ inch larger all around than the printing area indicated. Join the four points marked and enlarge the rectangle by ¼ inch all around. Cut out the larger opening for the printing area.

  f. Place the printing frame over the paper mask and center the printing area. Hold the mask in place with cellophane tape at the corners.

  g. Turn the frame over and fasten the mask into place with gummed-paper tape all around the outside edges and around the opening for the printing area. When placing the gummed tape around the opening of the printing area, overlap the opening ¼ inch all around. If you crease the gummed-paper tape ¼ inch from one edge before moistening it, the crease may be used as a guide when covering the edge of the opening of the printing area.

  h. Put the printing frame back on the baseboard.

12. Place the letters that you have cut out on the marked sheet (step 9) within the printing area indicated. Lay the letters evenly and space them carefully. The letters and any decoration should be placed just as you wish them to be on the printed poster (Fig. 74-4).

13. Lower the silk screen carefully onto the lettering. Although the paint used for printing will adhere the paper letters to the silk screen, it is sometimes desirable to use dabs of glue or lacquer through the screen to hold the letters and decorative pieces in place. If used, be sure that none of the glue or lacquer gets on the open printing area of the silk screen. Why?

14. Pour about a quarter of a cup of screen paint of the color you have selected onto the screen at one end of the frame.

15. Draw the paint evenly across the screen from end to end with the squeegee. Be sure it crosses all the printing area.

16. Raise the screen. You will find the paper letters stuck by the paint to the underside of the screen. On the poster board will be your first print with white letters on a colored background (Fig. 74-5).

17. Take the printed sheet out and check the registry of the printing. Adjust the register guides if necessary.

18. Feed another sheet of the poster board to the register guides, lower the screen, and draw the paint across the screen from end to end of the frame with the squeegee. Lift the screen and

take out the printed sheet. Repeat this procedure until you have printed all the posters needed.

19. Lay the printed sheets out to dry. Do not pile them one on top of the other. A special drying rack is useful for this purpose (see page 199). Let the sheets dry overnight.

20. When the posters are dry, trim them so that there will be white showing all around the printed area.

21. Clean up the screen after you finish the job.

    a. Take any remaining paint out of the screen frame with two pieces of clean cardboard held in the shape of a V and put it back into the jar from which it came.

    b. Strip off the paper letters and the gummed tape and paper that were used to mask the printing area on the screen.

    c. Wash both sides of the screen with the solvent recommended for the paint you have been using. *Be sure that the room in which you are working is well ventilated.* If either glue or lacquer has been used, be sure that it is removed from the screen.

    d. Support the screen with the leg while it is drying.

F<small>IG</small>. 74-4. Position of cutout letters within the printing area.

F<small>IG</small>. 74-5. Printed sheet on baseboard. The paper letters are stuck to underside of the silk screen by the paint.

Discussion Topics

1. Why is thin paper used for paper stencils?

2. How could you have printed the poster you have just made in two colors?

3. Why is it important to clean the silk screen promptly and thoroughly after you are through with it?

C<small>OMMERCIAL</small> S<small>ILK-SCREEN</small> P<small>RINTING</small>

Until recently all commercial silk screening was done by hand at the rate of about 250 impressions an hour. Although most of the commercial silk-screen printing is still done by hand at the present time, new automatic screen presses are being used in some commercial plants. These automatic screen presses can produce 2,400 to 3,000 impressions an hour and can utilize any paint used by the hand operation.

You may now realize from your own experience with the silk-screen printing process that the printing inks that are easy to use in this process also take a long time to dry. How, then, you may well ask, do they dry hundreds and thousands of sheets? The answer to this question is in two parts: (1) Quick-drying inks for book cloth, paper, and board have been developed for this process, and (2) an infrared conveyor heater unit is used for drying the printed sheets as they leave the press.

The recent developments in the commercial silk-screen printing field mentioned here and the developments in allied fields together indicate a definite future use of the silk-screen process on a large commercial scale never before possible. Visit a commercial silk-screen printing plant if possible.

Unit 75. Block-out Stencil and Two-or-more-color Printing.   Silk-screening a Design on a T Shirt

Now you can make your intramural basketball or softball T shirt more attractive by printing a colorful initial or emblem on it. Other members of the team or club—airplane, radio, boy or girl scout troop, or other group—may wish to print for themselves the design that you have made on a T shirt. If each one in the class prepares a different design, you may wish to print more than one T shirt for yourself. If two or three work together, you can print a two- or three-color design by each one's preparing a stencil for one of the colors from the same master copy.

In this unit the procedures are given for the block-out stencil method of silk-screen printing which is used for simple designs and for the preparation of Nufilm stencils for printing two or more colors. Since you will be printing on cloth, you should know something about textile colors.

TEXTILE COLORS

Regular silk-screen paints may be used for printing on textiles, or cloth,

such as a T shirt or silk scarf, but they are not colorfast as dyes prepared for this purpose, called *textile colors*. The silk-screen paints also stiffen the cloth printed. If possible, use textile colors prepared especially for silk-screen printing. After the printed textile color has dried, it is ironed to make it washable and sunfast. Textile colors do not stiffen the cloth printed.

BLOCK-OUT STENCIL

This type of silk-screen stencil is inexpensive and easy to make. It is particularly useful for very simple designs such as a single block letter (Fig. 75-1) or a silhouette (Fig. 75-2). If you have decided to print your T shirt with a simple block letter or silhouette, use the block-out stencil method described here.

Procedure

1. Make a full-scale drawing of the letter or silhouette that you are going to print (Fig. 75-3). (If you use this method to prepare a stencil to print on paper or cardboard, draw your de-

A B C D E F G H
I J K L M N O P Q
R S T U V W X Y Z

Fig. 75-1. Block letters.

Fig. 75-2. Types of designs that you might use on a T shirt.

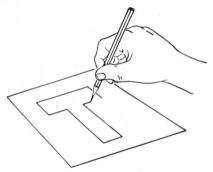

FIG. 75-3. Make a full-scale drawing of the letter or silhouette that you are going to print.

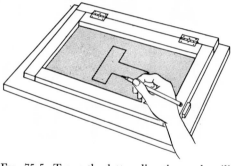

FIG. 75-5. Trace the letter directly on the silk with a soft pencil.

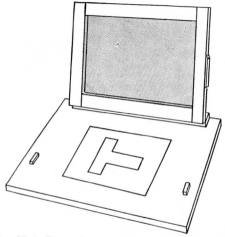

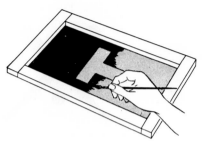

FIG. 75-6. To print the letter, paint out all but the letter with filler.

FIG. 75-4. Place the drawing on the center of the baseboard.

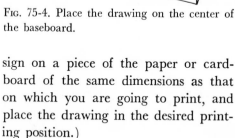

(Fig. 75-5). Be very careful not to damage the silk.

4. Remove the silk-screen printing frame from the baseboard of the printing unit.

5. Select the block-out, or screen filler, that is resistant to the paint or textile color that you are going to use.

6. Paint on the screen filler in either of two ways:

sign on a piece of the paper or cardboard of the same dimensions as that on which you are going to print, and place the drawing in the desired printing position.)

2. Place the drawing under the silk screen in the center of the baseboard of the printing unit (Fig. 75-4). If paper or cardboard is to be printed, put three register guides in position on the baseboard (see page 213).

3. Trace the letter or silhouette directly on the silk with a soft lead pencil

    a. If the letter or silhouette alone is to be printed, paint out all the rest of the screen except the letter (Fig. 75-6).

    b. If the letter or silhouette is not to be printed but is to be outlined by the color being printed, paint out the letter and the screen around the outline (Fig. 75-7).

7. Let the screen dry thoroughly before using it for printing.

8. Before printing on your T shirt, try out the stencil by printing it on a piece of paper. Make any necessary corrections with the stencil filler.

You are now ready to print a T shirt. For this procedure see "Printing on Textile," pages 221–222.

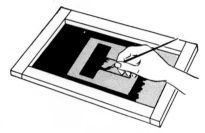

FIG. 75-7. To outline the letter with printed color, paint out the letter and the screen around the outline.

NU-FILM STENCILS FOR TWO OR MORE COLORS

A separate Nu-film stencil is prepared and mounted for each color to be printed in the same way as the Nu-film stencil was prepared for the checkerboard on pages 205–208. It is for this process that the interchangeable printing frames described on pages 200–201, are particularly useful. If several printing frames are available, a stencil for each color to be printed may be prepared before any printing is done. If only one frame is available, the first color stencil must be prepared and printed before the next color stencil is mounted and printed. In either case the problem of registry is the same.

If the registry of each color is not correct, you will have overlapping colors and unprinted areas in your design. Whether you are printing on cloth or paper, the procedure for registry is much the same. Cross marks are used at each corner of the master copy of the design, and corresponding crosses or dots are used on the stencil for each color to give precise registry of the stencil when you are printing. The point marks used to indicate the registry position on cloth, such as on a T shirt, must be erasable. When you are printing on paper or cardboard, cut the cross, registry, marks out of the stencil. They are printed in the margin that is trimmed off the sheet after the printing process is complete.

Since the placing of the registry marks for printing two or more colors on cloth is done during the printing process, this procedure is given under "Printing on Textile" on page 221. The following procedure is for preparing the color stencils for printing two or more colors on paper or cardboard. In this process the registry marks are part of the stencil, as mentioned above. The same process is used for preparing color stencils for printing on cloth except that the registry marks are not cut out of the stencil.

Procedure

1. Prepare a full-scale master copy in color of the design that you are going to reproduce. Leave a ¾- to 1-inch margin to be trimmed off after the printing process is complete (Fig. 75-8).

2. Draw cross marks in this margin in each corner as in Fig. 75-8. These are the marks that will be used to register each color stencil.

3. Thumbtack a clean sheet of cardboard to the baseboard of the printing unit.

Red squares
(1½" x 1½")

¼" Black border
on three sides

¾" to 1" margin
to be trimmed
off after printing

Black squares
(1½" x 1½")

Registry mark

FIG. 75-8. A checkerboard in two colors.

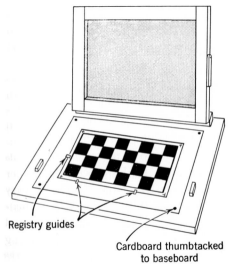

Registry guides

Cardboard thumbtacked
to baseboard

FIG. 75-9. Center the master copy below the screen and put registry guides in position.

4. Place the master copy on this cardboard and center it under the screen. Place the registry guides for printing in position (Fig. 75-9). The registry guides may be made of gummed-paper tape as described on page 213.

5. Cut a piece of Nu-film large enough to cover the entire master copy, and use cellophane tape to fasten it to the master copy of the design. Be sure that the lacquer-film side is up. Cut through the lacquer film around the edge of the tape but do not cut the glassine backing.

6. Cut the cross marks on the film exactly over those on the original drawing (Fig. 75-10). These cuts should remove thin strips of the lacquer film. This will permit the marks to print on the sheet being processed and will thus enable the operator to check the printing registry of each color. As mentioned before, the margin in which these registry guide marks are printed is trimmed off after the printing process is complete.

7. Cut the stencil for the lightest color first, for example, yellow, pink, or light blue. For the red and black checkerboard, cut the red stencil first. If the same frame is being used for each color, adhere this stencil to the silk screen of the printing frame as you did the one for the checkerboard described on pages 207–208. Remove the backing and prepare a mask to cover the area of the screen that is not to print (page 214) or paint in this area with screen filler.

8. Print the first color and lay out the sheets to dry overnight. The first color must be thoroughly dry before the second color is printed over it.

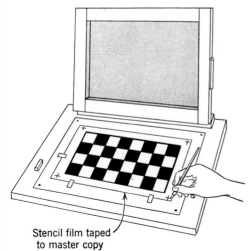

Stencil film taped to master copy

FIG. 75-10. Cut the cross marks on the film exactly over those on the original drawing.

9. Clean the frame and remove the stencil.

10. Repeat the process for each color. Print the darkest shade or color, such as dark blue, red, or black, last. Why?

Check the registry marks each time you print a new color. If the stencil is mounted properly, you should not need to move the registry guides on the base-board during the entire printing process.

PRINTING ON TEXTILE—PRINTING A T SHIRT

Now you are ready to print the T shirt. If the T shirt is new, it should be washed to remove any sizing from it. The stencil prepared by the block-out method or the stencils prepared for the two-or-more-color job may be used for this project.

Procedure

1. Place the T shirt on a drawing board and thumbtack it so that the cloth is stretched smoothly and tightly where the design is to be printed (Fig. 75-11).

2. Place a piece of tympan or wax paper inside the T shirt so that the textile color used in printing will not soak through to the back side of the shirt (Fig. 75-11).

3. Check the stencil and textile color by printing the design on a piece of thin transparent paper before you print the shirt. If it is satisfactory, print the shirt (Fig. 75-12).

4. If you are printing two or more colors, you will use the print on the thin paper to help you register the other colors as follows:

a. Lay the thin printed sheet over the master copy of the design and carefully trace the cross marks in each corner.

Tympan or wax paper

FIG. 75-11. Thumbtacking a T shirt smoothly to a drawing board.

FIG. 75-12. Position the design carefully before printing it on a T shirt.

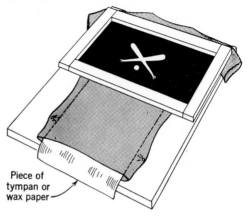

Piece of tympan or wax paper

b. After the first color on the T shirt is dry (it should be allowed to dry at least overnight), place the printed sheet carefully over the printed area. The print on the paper should register perfectly with that on the T shirt.

c. With a soft, sharp pencil pierce the point of intersection of the crosses in each corner and mark the T shirt. After the printing process is complete, these pencil marks can be erased.

d. Mark the registry marks on the next color stencil by turning the frame over, stencil side up, and laying the printed side of the paper next to the stencil. Hold the sheet and the stencil on the screen together up to the light and adjust the registry with your eye. With a soft pencil or a pen and india ink carefully mark the stencil with four points as you did the T shirt. Be very careful not to pierce the stencil.

e. Turn the frame over and with the thin sheet of paper in register print it with the next color. Is the registry correct? Is the color the right shade?

5. Place the stencil on the T shirt. Check the four points for registry and make the print.

6. Repeat the same process for each additional color.

7. After the printing is complete, do not remove the T shirt from the drawing board until the last color is completely dry.

8. Erase the four pencil marks on the T shirt.

9. If the textile colors such as those described on page 216 have been used, iron the design on the T shirt before wearing the shirt. This makes the colors washable and sunfast.

10. Clean the silk-screen printing frame or frames thoroughly with the proper solvent for the paint or textile colors used in printing and remove the stencil or stencils with the proper solvents. *Be sure the room in which you are working is well ventilated.*

11. Dry the screen or screens and return them to their proper places.

Discussion Topics

1. What are the advantages of using textile colors when printing on cloth?
2. Why should a new T shirt be washed before it is printed?
3. Why are the light colors printed first in the two-or-more-color silk-screen printing jobs?

Unit 76. Flocking

Flocking is the process by which a suède, velour, or texture finish is applied to any surface that can be silk-screened, brush-painted, or sprayed. It is used on greeting cards, jewelry boxes, artificial flowers, sportswear, posters, draperies, and a variety of other surfaces where a special texture effect is desired. The flock itself is made of finely cut ($\frac{1}{8}$ to $\frac{1}{64}$ inch long) rayon, cotton, or wool

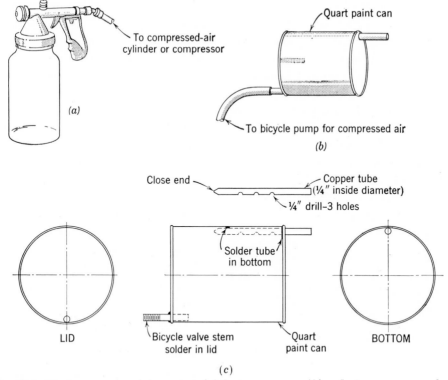

To compressed-air
cylinder or compressor

(a)

Quart paint can

To bicycle pump for compressed air

(b)

Close end

Copper tube
(¼″ inside diameter)

¼″ drill–3 holes

Solder tube
in bottom

LID

Bicycle valve stem
solder in lid

Quart
paint can

BOTTOM

(c)

Fig. 76-1. Flock spray gun: (a) commercial flock spray gun; (b) a flock spray gun made in a school shop; (c) details of flock gun shown in (b).

fibers. Rayon flock gives a velvet or velour-like finish, whereas cotton and wool give a dull, suèdelike finish. Flock can be obtained in a variety of colors and lengths, depending on the effect desired. Other types of flock are available that simulate frost and snow.

A special adhesive, or binder, which is flexible and slow-drying, is used to hold the flock to the surface being flocked. This adhesive, or binder, is silk-screen-printed onto the surface in the same way as any colored part of a design is printed. The binder should be the same color as the flock being used.

The flock may be applied with a specially constructed flocking gun (Fig. 76-1) or with an ordinary vegetable

Fig. 76-2. Using an ordinary vegetable strainer or sieve to sift flock on a surface already printed with adhesive.

strainer (Fig. 76-2). The strainer breaks up the fibers and gives an even dusting all over a small painted area. To achieve a uniform finish, the object that has been flocked is placed on a board which is tapped from underneath with a hammer or mallet for 15 to 30 seconds.

For this project you may use one of the stencils you have already prepared, for example, the block-out stencil, or you may prepare a new stencil. You may wish to print and flock your initials or those of a friend on the lid of a pretty box. A colorful flocked emblem on a jacket or T shirt may be done in this unit with one or two stencils.

Procedure

1. Prepare a full-scale drawing in color of the design you are using.
2. Cut a Nu-film stencil for each color (pages 205–207) and indicate the registry marks in the corners.

> *a.* If it is to be printed on paper, see pages 208–210, 219–221.
> *b.* If it is to be printed on cloth, see pages 221–222.

3. Adhere the plain-color stencil to the screen of the printing frame (pages 207–208) and block out the area around the stencil with screen filler (page 208) or prepare a paper mask (page 214).
4. If the design is to be printed on paper or cardboard, set the register guides on the baseboard of the printing unit (page 213).

5. Print the first color and allow it to dry overnight.
6. Prepare the stencil for that part of the design that is to be flocked in the same way, check the registry carefully, adhere it to the screen of the printing frame, and block out the area around the stencil with screen filler or a mask.
7. Select the right color of flock adhesive, or binder, and flock.
8. Print the flock adhesive.
9. Sift the flock onto the printed adhesive area.
10. Tap the undersurface of the flocked object for about half a minute.
11. Let the flocked object dry thoroughly before brushing off the excess flock.

Discussion Topics

1. Why should the plain color be printed before the flock adhesive, or binder?
2. Why should the flock adhesive be the same color or nearly the same color as the flock used?
3. After the flock has been sifted onto the printed adhesive, or binder, why should the object be tapped?
4. In what other ways besides the silk-screen printing process can the adhesive for flocking be applied to a surface?

COMMERCIAL USE OF FLOCK

Flock is applied to walls and large areas for acoustical purposes, that is, to help to deaden the sound. For large areas, the adhesive is sprayed on and then the flock is sprayed on top of the adhesive. Flock is also used on luggage, manikins, and turntables of record players. Some flock and adhesives are available in spray consistency so that both may be applied with one operation. Diamond dust, tinsel, sawdust, and many other materials are used as flock.

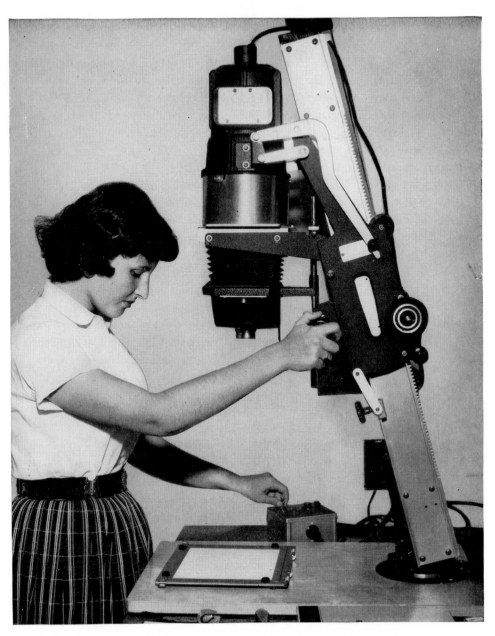

Mary is making a projection print from one of her own negatives.

Section VII. PHOTOGRAPHY*

* This section on photography has been prepared under the supervision of Alan Kellock of the McGraw-Hill Text-Film Department. The material for the units on developing film, contact printing, and projection printing has been adapted from *Develop, Print, and Enlarge Your Own Pictures* by Jack O. Flynn, Albert J. Rosenberg, and Alan Kellock, McGraw-Hill Book Company, 1952. For more complete instruction and detailed photographs showing step-by-step darkroom procedure, the reader is referred to that text.

Unit 77. Taking Good Pictures

Everyone enjoys looking at pictures. A photograph whether taken by a professional photographer or by an amateur is a permanent record that tells its own story at a glance. A family photograph album is always a source of pleasure and amusement for the family, friends, and relatives.

Now you shall have an opportunity to learn how to take good pictures and how to develop, print, and enlarge them yourself. You may take a few pictures that can be used in your school newspaper or added as illustrations to the group or individual project that you set, printed, and bound earlier in this course. You may wish to begin your own photograph album. You can use the album that you made in Unit 64, pages 173–175.

Taking good pictures is an art. Like any other art it requires a skill that can be acquired only through practice. Part of this skill is good judgment in the selection of the subject to be photographed, the position or angle from which to take the subject, the best lighting on the subject, and the best moment to take the picture.

THE CAMERA

To use a camera intelligently, you should understand the function of the lens, the diaphragm, and the shutter. You should also understand the principle of focusing the image of the object on the film in the camera. Then, too, you should know something about the different types of films used for taking different types of pictures.

The lens. Light rays traveling through air go in a straight line. But when a ray of light goes from one medium into another, for example, from air into glass or from glass into air, it is bent. This bending is called *refraction.*

Light passing through a glass prism is bent, or refracted, as it enters the prism and is bent, or refracted, again as it leaves the prism (Fig. 77-1). The greater the angle between the two surfaces of the prism, the greater the refraction of the light. A circular glass camera lens refracts the light passing through its outer edge more than that passing through it nearer its center (Fig. 77-2). The rays of light from a distant light source are parallel. Light rays parallel to the principal axis of a lens are bent toward the thicker part of the lens. As these rays leave the lens, they converge at a point called the *principal focus* (Fig. 77-3). The distance from the principal focus to the center of the lens is called the *focal length* of the lens.

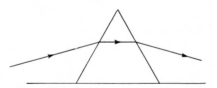

FIG. 77-1. Light passing through a prism is bent, or refracted, as it enters and as it leaves.

FIG. 77-2. A camera lens refracts the light passing through its outer edge more than the light passing through it nearer its center. What happens to the light passing through the center of the lens shown here?

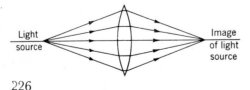

Light source — Image of light source

Using what you have just read about the refraction and the simple camera lens, answer this question: What happens to the light leaving a candle and passing through a simple lens? Make a diagram of what you think would happen and then check your answer with Fig. 77-4. The *image* of the candle is upside down, or inverted.

When you take a picture, the light entering your camera is distributed over the image of the object photographed. Therefore, with the same amount of light, a large image will take longer to photograph than a small image. The size of the image is determined by the focal length of the lens. The shorter the focal length, the smaller the image and the greater the speed of the lens. The amount of light passing through the lens is controlled by the size of the lens opening, or aperture. Therefore, the *speed* of a lens is determined by both the size of the lens opening and its focal length. If both the aperture and the focal length are doubled or cut in half, the speed of the lens would remain the same. Why?

The speed, or *f* value, of a lens is expressed in terms of the relationship between the diameter of the aperture and the focal length of the lens. For example, if the diameter of the aperture is one-fourth that of the focal length, the speed is given as *f*/4. What does *f*/16 mean? The *f*/2, *f*/3.5, and *f*/4.5 lenses are called *fast,* and the *f*/11 and *f*/16 lenses are called *slow.* Why? The *f* number or numbers for a particular camera are usually marked on the lens mounting. What *f* values are marked on the camera you are using?

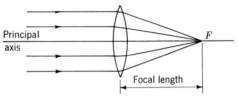

Fig. 77-3. Parallel rays of light passing through a lens are focused at a point called the *principal focus* (*F*).

The diaphragm. A diaphragm limits, or controls, the lens opening, or aperture. The diaphragm of a camera controls the amount of light that reaches the camera lens. As the opening is made smaller, a smaller diameter of the lens is being used. Since the focal length of the lens remains the same, reducing the lens opening increases the *f* value.

Cameras with adjustable diaphragms have the different *f* numbers marked on them for your convenience. Fixed-focus cameras, such as the box camera, usually have a slide with three different sizes of holes, or stop openings. The largest stop in the slide is in front of the lens when the slide is pushed all the way in. Either of the other two stops may be used by pulling the slide out until the desired one is in front of the lens. The last stop is the smallest. It is used for landscapes, groups, and street scenes. It is also used when the subject is in bright sunlight. The largest stop opening is used on cloudy days.

The shutter. A shutter is used to shut out light. The speed with which it opens and shuts controls the length of time that the camera film is exposed to light. A camera with a fast shutter and fast lens can take a picture of moving objects. Without a fast shutter and fast lens such pictures would be blurred.

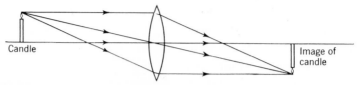

FIG. 77-4. The image formed by the camera lens is upside down, or inverted.

FIG. 77-5. A photoflash attachment makes it possible to take pictures indoors. It also enables you to take pictures whenever the outdoor light is not bright enough to take a regular photograph.

Just as some cameras have adjustable diaphragms, some cameras have adjustable shutter speeds. These speeds may range from 1 second to $\frac{1}{1000}$ of a second. Most inexpensive cameras have just one speed. However, such cameras, as well as the more expensive ones, may be adjusted so that the shutter remains open until released. In this way it is possible to take a picture that requires one, two, or more seconds or minutes to take. For example, an indoor scene by lamplight or a view of the city by night would require more time than the usual shutter speed would give. Taking pictures by this method is known as *time exposure*.

If the camera you are using has a photoflash lamp attachment (Fig. 77-5), the flash is set off by the shutter. This makes sure that the maximum flash of light takes place at the same instant that the camera shutter is opened.

View finder. With the view finder you can see the subject you wish to photograph. It helps you to compose the picture you wish to take. View finders are frequently located above or to one side of the lens opening. For this reason they do not show exactly the same field that is in front of the lens. With practice, you will be able to adjust for this slight difference.

The reflex type of camera has a view finder that is used in focusing as well as in composing pictures. This type of adjustable view finder is discussed in the following section.

Focusing. When you focus a telescope, pair of binoculars, or a microscope, what are you doing? You are adjusting the lens system within the instrument so that you see a clear image. Some cameras are made with ground-glass plates on which the image is focused. After focusing the image on the ground-glass plate, the glass plate is displaced or replaced by a photographic plate or cut film. A photograph taken in this way with direct focusing should be in perfect focus.

The reflex type of camera has a mirror in front of the film but behind the lens. The exact scene or subject is reflected onto a ground-glass plate at the top of the camera. Since the mirror is behind the lens, the photographer can focus as well as compose the image on the glass plate. What he sees is exactly what will be shown on the film when it is exposed. When the release lever is pressed, the mirror is raised and the shutter released exposing the film.

Some of the more expensive miniature cameras have a combined range finder–view finder. This combined range finder–view finder would have the same advantages as the reflex type of camera.

Focusing with most other types of cameras is done indirectly. The manufacturer's instructions for distance from subject, for aperture, or stop opening, and for shutter speed should be followed carefully. If you use the recommended stop opening, or aperture, objects in front of and beyond the subject being photographed will appear sharper. This is called *depth of field*. Figure 77-6 shows the same picture taken at (*a*) the correct distance but with the wrong stop opening and (*b*) the correct distance and recommended stop opening.

The film. The film in your camera is a flexible, transparent base coated with a thin layer of gelatin containing silver salts. This fine gelatin mixture is called an *emulsion*. The emulsion is very sensitive to light. When a picture is taken, the light reaching the emulsion causes a change to begin in the silver salts. The change is directly proportional to the

Fig. 77-6. Depth of field. These two pictures show how the depth of field changes as you change the lens opening. In (*a*) the camera was focused on the ball and a large lens opening was used. Notice that the nearest and farthest dominoes are out of focus. In (*b*) the camera was still focused on the ball but a small lens opening was used. Notice that all the dominoes, near and far, are clearer.

(*a*)   (*b*)

light that strikes it. In other words, the more light that hits the film the greater the change. This change cannot be seen until it is completed during the developing process. Because the picture cannot be seen on the film until the film is developed, it is called a *latent image*. When an exposed film is developed, a bright sky or surface appears dark on the negative. Areas of dark shadows leave a film almost unaffected. You will see this for yourself when you develop your own film (Unit 78).

Some film emulsions are more sensitive to light than others. Your choice of films will depend on your camera and the type of pictures you are going to take. Some films are prepared for outdoor daylight and for ordinary photoflash shots. The type of film that is most sensitive to light is called a *high-speed* film. Special films are available for taking pictures in color—one type for indoor and one for outdoor color pictures.

Check with the instructions that came with the camera that you are using for the types of films recommended. Decide on the type of pictures you wish to take and select the best film for that purpose.

Your choice of subject will depend in part upon the camera that you are

FIG. 77-7. Three general types of camera: (*a*) box; (*b*) folding; and (*c*) reflex.

(*a*)

(*b*)

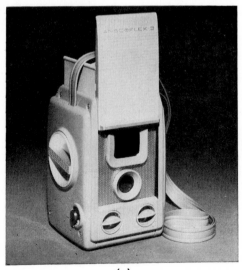

(*c*)

using. The three general types of cameras used by amateur photographers are the box camera, the small folding camera, and the reflex camera (Fig. 77-7). Other kinds of cameras are usually modifications of these three basic types.

Whether you are using your own camera or one provided by your school, you should read carefully the instruction manual that the manufacturer prepared to go with it. This manual will tell you:

1. The names of the parts.

2. What size of film and what type of film to use for different purposes.

3. How to put the film into the camera. This is called *loading* the camera.

4. How to set and use the stop, or diaphragm, openings.

5. How to set and use the shutter.

6. How to use the view finder.

7. How to use the range finder if the camera has one.

8. At what distance to take pictures and how to adjust the focal length of the camera.

9. How to take instantaneous and time exposures.

10. How to take flash pictures if the camera has a flash attachment.

11. How to remove the film after exposure.

12. How to take care of the camera.

You should be well acquainted with the camera before you take your first picture. Review with the instructor all the names of the parts of the camera and how it works. Ask the instructor to watch you load the camera the first time. The camera should be loaded indoors or in a shaded place.

After you have loaded your camera, turn the film so that the film is in the correct position for the first picture, or exposure. The film should be turned immediately to the next position after each picture is taken. If this is not done, the next picture will be taken on top of the last picture. This is called a *double exposure*. When this happens, both pictures are spoiled.

Before taking each picture, be sure that the lens of your camera is clean. A fingerprint or a piece of dirt on the lens may spoil the picture. Clean the lens with a clean, unstarched handkerchief or lint-free cloth.

SELECTING THE SUBJECT

This is the first and most important step in taking a good picture. A picture that tells a story, such as the one shown in Fig. 77-8, is usually the most interesting. It is natural and unposed. Pets make very good subjects for such pictures.

If you are interested in architecture, you might select a building or house that

FIG. 77-8. A story-telling picture—"Left behind."

Fig. 77-9. The same scene taken at (*a*) mid-morning, (*b*) midafternoon, and (*c*) sunset.

(*a*)

you like particularly as the subject for one or more pictures. A doorway of unusual design if taken when the light is just right makes a good subject.

Lighting

The light of midmorning and midafternoon is more pleasing and less glaring than that at midday. In very bright sunlight there is more contrast between the light and shadows on an object, and important details may not show up in a picture. At the same time the pattern of shadows and light might make an unusual and interesting picture. On a gray, overcast day, there may be very little shadow at all. It is, therefore, important to select the time of day and the kind of light that will give you the details that you wish to show in your picture. Figure 77-9 shows the same scene taken in mid-

(*b*)

(*c*)

(a)

(b)

Fig. 77-10. Silhouetting a subject: (a) light objects against a dark background or (b) dark objects against a light background.

morning, in midafternoon, and at sunset. Which is the most interesting?

Look beyond the subject that you have selected for the best possible background. Silhouetting a subject will make it stand out. This means either that a light object is shown against a dark background (Fig. 77-10a) or that a dark object is shown against a light background (Fig. 77-10b). This may be done by carefully selecting the position or angle from which the subject is photographed (Fig. 77-10b). It may also be done by illumination, as shown in Fig. 77-10a.

In selecting your position for taking a picture, *never* have the light shining directly into the front of the camera. If it is necessary to face the light source, the front of your camera should be shaded. A hat, a newspaper, a person's hand, or a special lens shade may be used for this purpose. Be sure that the object used for

casting the shadow is not in the field of the picture being taken.

The human eye adjusts itself automatically to changing light conditions. One can see an object very clearly in an evening light that is not bright enough to photograph the object. The amount of reflected light from an overcast sky is often difficult to determine. Furthermore, the reaction of the eye to certain colors is not the same as the reaction of the film. To determine more accurately the amount of reflected light coming from the subject being photographed, exposure meters are used (Fig. 77-11).

The manufacturer's instructions that come with each exposure meter tell you how to use it correctly. The photoelectric type of meter is the most accurate. With this type of meter, you set the speed of the film being used in the camera over the number that the meter indicates as the amount of light coming

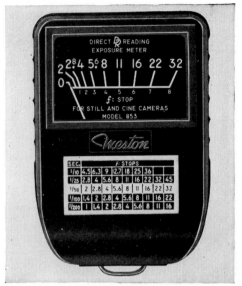

Fɪɢ. 77-11. Exposure meters. The exposure meters shown here give you the camera settings, or *f* stops and shutter speeds, directly. First set the film speed on the meter. Then aim the meter at the scene or subject being photographed and note the *f* stop indicated.

from the subject. Then you read off directly the proper *f* stop and shutter speed to use. If properly used, this type of meter will give almost 100 percent correct exposure. The visual type of exposure meter is much less expensive and may be found helpful to the beginning photographer. This type of meter has a series of translucent squares of different density. Each square has an opaque number. The subject to be photographed is viewed through this meter. The number visible on the darkest square indicates the amount of reflected light coming from the subject. This number and the type of film being used are located on the table provided with the meter. The table indicates the correct exposure for these conditions. But because of the different sensitivity to light of the eyes of different persons, each user gets different results. For this

reason, this type of exposure meter is not very accurate.

Taking the Picture

Now that you have selected your subject and determined the best lighting and position, or angle, from which to take the picture, you are ready to use the camera.

Procedure

1. Check your camera to be sure that it is properly loaded and the film is in position for exposure.

2. Clean off the lens carefully.

3. Locate the subject in the view finder. Be sure that you have the whole subject. It may be necessary for you to move a little forward or backward to get the details selected or the whole subject in the picture.

4. Check the light on the subject with an exposure meter if you have one. If you do not have an exposure meter, decide yourself if it is a bright, dull, or cloudy day.

5. Set your lens opening and shutter speed according to the manufacturer's instructions for the light, subject, and film.

6. Take the picture by slowly pushing the exposure lever down as far as it will go. A quick motion may jar the camera and spoil the picture.

7. Turn the film to the next number.

8. Take two or three more pictures of the same subject from different positions, or angles, and distances and at a different time of day if possible. Turn the film after each picture is taken.

9. Select one or more other subjects and take additional pictures until the film is used up. The film is now called an *exposed film.* How many pictures can you take on the film in the camera you are using?

10. Roll the exposed film until it is all on one reel. Turn the winder a couple more times. The film for certain types of cameras is enclosed in a cartridge. This type of film must be re-wound into the cartridge before it is removed from the camera.

11. Remove the exposed film from the camera. Check the manufacturer's instructions for removing the exposed film from the camera. Ask the instructor to watch you the first time you remove an exposed film from the camera.

12. Wrap the roll of exposed film up in the paper and put it in the box in which it came. Put your name and the date on the box and give it to the instructor.

In the next unit you will learn how to develop and print the pictures that you have taken.

Discussion Topics

1. What size and type of film did you use in the camera?
2. Name three important things to consider before taking a picture.
3. When is the best daylight for taking pictures?
4. Why is the selection of a proper background important?
5. What would happen if the light were shining into the front of the camera when you were taking a picture?
6. What is a double exposure?
7. What is an exposed film? An unexposed film?
8. What is the first thing to do after taking a picture?

Some Uses of the Photographic Process

Since its discovery about 115 years ago, the photographic process has steadily increased in importance as more and more uses for it have been found. Today it is used in science, industry, medicine, and business, as well as for an enjoyable hobby.

As you learned earlier in this course, the photographic process is used in photoengraving and for the preparation of certain types of stencils in the silk-screen process, in photo-offset printing, and for setting type by the Photon, Monophoto, Fotosetter, and Hadego machines. X-ray pictures are developed in a similar way to that you will use to develop your exposed film in the next unit. Cameras are used with electron microscopes in research laboratories and with large telescopes by astronomers. Cameras are used to take aerial photographs, motion pictures, and family portraits. The pictures taken may be used as photomurals, in advertising, and as illustrations in newspapers, magazines, and books.

Photocopying, that is, making a copy photographically, is widely used today in business and industry. Three such processes in common use are the microfilm, the photostat, and the Ozalid.

Microfilm. By the use of the microfilm process of photocopying, whole newspapers, rare books, and valuable manuscripts can be photographed page for page. The film, which occupies only a small fraction of the space of the original, can then be stored in a safe place. A special machine is needed to read the microfilm. This machine enlarges the material to about the same size as the original and projects it on a screen or ground-glass plate.

Photostat. In this process of photocopying, the negative is made on paper instead of on a film. (In Units 78 and 79 you will learn more about negatives and positives.) This negative is used to make as many positives as are desired. A photostat negative of this page would have white letters on a black background and could be read just as easily as you are reading it now.

One advantage of the photostat process is that an enlarged or reduced copy of the original material can be made as easily as a copy of the same size. One disadvantage of the process is that each photostat copy must be developed and dried.

Ozalid. By the Ozalid process copies can be made quickly of letters, engineers' or architects' drawings, graphs, charts, and so on, printed on one side of a piece of paper that allows light to pass through. It takes less than a minute's time to make each copy. The paper used to make the copy has been prepared with special Ozalid dyes. The original material that is to be copied is placed on top of Ozalid sensitized paper, and both are fed into a special machine. Inside the machine an ultraviolet light shines through the original and onto the sensitized paper. The light inactivates all the Ozalid dye on the paper that is not protected by the opaque image of the original. The Ozalid paper is then exposed to ammonia vapor inside the machine. These vapors make the image on the Ozalid paper permanent. By using different types of Ozalid paper the following combination of colors can be produced: black on green, black on blue, black on white, red on white, blue on yellow, blue on white, or black on pink.

Black-and-white photographs can be produced by the Ozalid Dryphoto process. A special diazo paper is needed for this purpose. By the Ozachrome process, natural-color prints can be made.

Because of the wide and varied applications of the photographic process, it will be helpful to you to understand something about it. Such an understanding can be arrived at through not only taking pictures but also developing the film and making prints and enlargements. An introduction to these last three steps in photography is given in the next three units.

Unit 78. Developing Film

Developing and printing your own pictures offers you an opportunity to make good prints of the pictures you have taken. You will be able to bring out the details you wish and, by blocking off parts of the negative, improve the composition and balance of a picture as you print it. In this and the following units you will be given the basic principles and steps in developing and printing your own pictures.

As mentioned in Unit 77, the photographic film is a transparent material coated on one side with a thin layer of a light-sensitive *emulsion*. This emulsion is made up of fine particles of silver salts suspended in gelatin. When you clicked the camera, the brightest part of the subject you were taking had the greatest effect on the film, and the darkest part of the subject had the least effect on the film. If the whole film were exposed to light before it was properly developed, it would all be affected equally and no pictures would show on it. For this reason it is very important to use a darkroom for the developing process. If possible, it is desirable to have running water in the darkroom.

Six Basic Steps

Developing is the process by which an exposed film is prepared for printing. There are six basic steps in the developing process: (1) wetting the film, (2) the developer, (3) the rinse or stop bath, (4) fix, (5) wash, and (6) dry. Films may be developed by either of two methods: the developing-tank method or the tray method. In both methods all six steps are used. Therefore, it is important to understand the purpose of each step. The first four steps should be carried out in a darkroom under a safelight.

1. *Wetting the film.* This is done with clear water. It helps to ensure even developing in the next step.

2. *Developer.* The developer solution completes the changes in the light-sensitive layer that were started by exposing the film. Black particles of silver are left in proportion to the amount of light that reached the film when exposed. The darkest areas on the film are those that were exposed to the strongest light. For example, a bright sky in a picture is the darkest area on the film. For the same reason, a dark shadow or black object in a picture is the lightest area on the film. The developer should be 68°F (degrees Fahrenheit).

3. *Rinse or stop bath.* Some photographers use a water rinse for this step; others prefer a special solution called the *stop bath*. The purpose of both is the same, namely, (a) to stop further development of the film and (b) to prevent excess developer from being carried into the fixing bath.

4. *Fix.* In the fixing bath, the unchanged silver salts in the emulsion are dissolved and washed away. The film loses its milky appearance, and the latent negative picture appears. After the film has fixed for about 3 minutes, room

---

* Originally sodium hyposulfite was used in the fixing solution. For this reason, many photographers call this solution *hypo*. Today, although sodium thiosulfate has replaced sodium hyposulfite, the nickname of hypo is still in common use.

lights can be used without damage to the film.

5. *Wash.* The film should be thoroughly washed. Running water or six changes of water in a large, clean container may be used. If the latter method is used, allow the film to remain at least 5 minutes in each change of water. During the washing process, occasionally stir the water gently. If a film is not fixed and washed thoroughly, it may fade or develop stains later. After the film is thoroughly washed, a few drops of suitable wetting agent may be added to the wash water. This will cause the water to drain off evenly as the film is removed from the wash water.

6. *Dry.* A clip (film clip or wooden spring-type clothespin) is attached to one end of the film and the film hung up by the clip on a line or the edge of a shelf to dry (Fig. 78-4). A second clip is attached to the other end of the film to prevent it from curling as it dries.

After the developing process described above is completed, the exposed film is called a *negative.* When the film is dry, it may be cut with scissors. Each negative should be stored in a separate envelope to protect it from dust and to prevent possible damage by scratching. Always handle negatives by their edges. A fingerprint on a negative will show up when the picture is printed.

PREPARING SOLUTIONS

It is recommended that you use the developer, stop bath (if used), and fixing solutions prepared by the manufacturer of the film you are developing. Some manufacturers specify that these solutions be made up first as concentrated *stock solutions.* These stock solutions are then diluted with water in the proportions specified by the manufacturer before using. The diluted solutions are called *working solutions.* Prepare these stock solutions first and store each in tightly capped glass bottles. Each bottle should be carefully labeled (Fig. 78-1) with the name of the solution (Developer, Stop Bath, Fixer), the words "Stock Solution for Films" and "Dilute before Using" and the proportions for diluting given, the number of minutes the diluted solution is to be used, the date the stock solution was prepared, and the initials or name of the

FIG. 78-1. Labels for stock solutions. The dilutions and times should be those recommended by the manufacturer.

Stock Solution for FILMS Dilute before using 1 to_____ Time: DEVELOPER Date: Prepared by:	Stock Solution for FILMS Dilute before using 1 to_____ Time: STOP BATH Date: Prepared by:	Stock Solution for FILMS Dilute before using 1 to_____ Time: FIXER Date: Prepared by:

one who prepared it. The date is important. Stock solutions should *not* be used after 6 to 8 weeks.

The diluted, or working, solutions should never be poured back into the stock-solution bottles. The developer solution can be used for developing several films before it is discarded. The fixing solution can also be used for several films.

TANK DEVELOPING

This method of developing films has the advantage of requiring a darkroom for only two steps—the removing of the film from the camera and the putting of the film into the developing tank. All other steps may be done in normal room light. In both methods of developing, running water is desirable but not essential.

The roll-film developing tank (Fig. 78-3) consists of a reel in which the film is threaded. Some tanks have a handle by which the reel may be turned from the outside of the tank, and a lighttight cover. The cover is so designed that the developer, stop-bath, and fixing solutions can be poured in and out of the tank without removing the cover. In this way no light can get inside the tank to spoil the film during the developing process.

Procedure

1. Prepare a Record Card (Fig. 78-2). This card should have your name; the date; the type of film; the time recommended for developer, stop bath, fix, and wash; and the dilutions of stock solutions used and date stock solutions are prepared. After the film has

been developed and dried, you may have other notes to add.

2. Assemble the following equipment:

A roll-film developing tank
A safelight
An 8-ounce graduate
Thermometer (Fahrenheit)
Stirring rod (glass)
Funnel (glass or plastic)
Developer
Stop bath
Fixer
3 tightly capped glass bottles
3 labels
An interval timer or watch with
   second hand
Wetting agent
2 film clips
A pair of scissors
Envelopes for negatives

3. Prepare the developer, stop-bath, and fixing solutions that you will need. Read the instructions on the packages or stock-solution bottles before preparing the solutions and follow them exactly. If stock solutions are to be prepared first, label each bottle (Fig. 78-1). The developing solution should be 68°F. Set the bottle or graduate containing the developer in a pan or basin of warm or cool water until the thermometer in the developer reads 68°F. Do not allow any water to get into the developing solution. Why? The stop-bath and fixing solutions should be about the same temperature (65 to 70°F).

4. Get your exposed film from the instructor and examine the box in which it came. If the words "Develop in Total Darkness" appear on the box, no safelight will be really safe. Such a film must

Name: _____		Date: _____	
Type of film:			
Solution	Time for:	Stock-solution dilutions	Date prepared:
Developer			
Stop bath			
Fixing			
Washing			
Notes:			

Fig. 78-2. Record Card for film developing.

Fig. 78-3. Equipment necessary for roll-film tank developing.

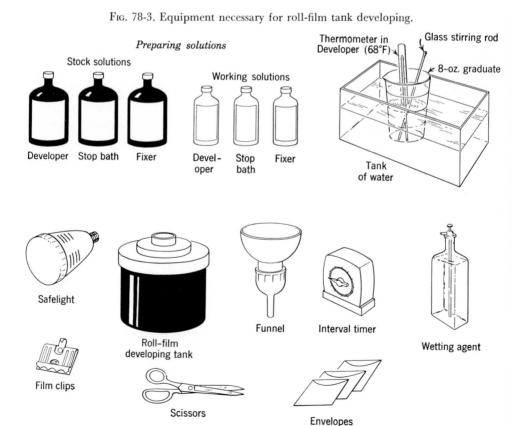

Preparing solutions

Stock solutions

Working solutions

Developer   Stop bath   Fixer

Devel-oper   Stop bath   Fixer

Thermometer in Developer (68°F)

Glass stirring rod

8-oz. graduate

Tank of water

Safelight

Film clips

Roll-film developing tank

Scissors

Funnel

Interval timer

Envelopes

Wetting agent

be unwound and placed in the developing tank in total darkness.

5. Wash your hands with soap and warm water, rinse thoroughly, and dry.

Darkroom Safelight

6. Ask the instructor to show you how to unwind your exposed film, to remove the backing paper, and to load the reel of the developing tank that you are going to use. There are several types of developing tanks. Some are loaded beginning at the center of the reel; some begin at the outside. If you are using your own tank, read carefully the instructions that came with it. Always handle the film by the edges. Keep your fingers off the picture area.

7. Place the loaded reel in the tank and put the lighttight cover over it.

Normal Room Light

8. Check the temperature of the developing solution that you prepared in step 3. Is it 68°F? Adjust the temperature if necessary. If too cool, place container of developing solution in a pan of warm water. If too hot, place container of developing solution in a pan of cool water. Stir constantly until proper temperature (68°) is reached.

9. Check your Record Card for the recommended number of minutes for each solution.

10. Using a funnel, fill the developing tank with water. Leave for about 3 minutes. Twirl the reel or move the tank with a circular motion to ensure complete and even wetting of the film. (Dry the funnel.)

11. Ask the instructor if the devel-oper, stop-bath, and fixing solutions are to be saved or thrown away after you have used them.

12. Pour out the water.

13. Set the interval timer for the exact number of minutes required for the developer, or watch the time on a watch.

14. Using a funnel, fill the tank with developer (68°F).

15. Gently twirl the reel or move the tank with a circular motion to be sure that the developer works evenly on the film. Repeat every 2 minutes until the time is up.

16. Rinse the funnel used in step 14 and dry.

17. Pour out the developer.

18. Using a funnel, fill the tank with water or stop-bath solution.

19. Gently twirl the reel or move the tank with a circular motion a few times.

20. Rinse and dry funnel used in step 18.

21. Pour out the water or stop bath.

22. Set the interval timer for 10 minutes or watch the time on a watch.

23. Using a funnel, fill the tank with fixing solution.

24. Gently twirl the reel or move the tank with a circular motion every 2 minutes until the time is up.

25. Rinse the funnel used in step 23 and dry.

26. Pour out the fixing solution.

27. Take off the developing-tank cover and set the tank in a sink under a stream of running water. The water should be about 65 to 70°F. Every 5 minutes, pour out the water and put the tank back under the stream. Continue for about 30 minutes.

28. Add a few drops of wetting agent and gently twirl the reel a few seconds.

29. Pour off the wash water.

30. Remove the reel from the developing tank.

31. Gently remove the film from reel. Handle the film by its edges. The wet film is soft and can be easily damaged.

32. Attach a film clip to one end of the film and hang it up to dry (Fig. 78-4).

33. Attach another film clip to the other end of the film to prevent it from curling as it dries.

34. Wash all equipment thoroughly. Dry with a clean towel and return it to its proper place. Leave the darkroom clean and neat.

35. When the film is thoroughly dry, cut it into separate negatives. Always handle the film by its edges.

Fig. 78-4. Film clips or clothespins may be used to hang film up to dry.

36. Store each negative in a separate envelope.

Tray Developing

This method of developing requires a darkroom throughout most of the procedure. In tray developing, each solution is held in a separate tray (Fig. 78-5). After the film is unwound and the paper backing removed, the film is passed through each tray of solution in a seesaw manner (Fig. 78-6) as follows:

1. A film clip is attached to each end of the film.

2. A clip is held in each hand.

3. The film is bent into a U shape.

4. The right hand is then lowered and the left hand raised.

5. The film near the right hand is dipped into the solution.

6. The right hand is raised and the left hand lowered until the entire film has passed through the solution.

7. With part of the film still in the solution, the left hand is raised and the right hand lowered.

This seesawing is continued until the time for the particular development is up. With practice you will be able to do this smoothly. If one part of the film remains in the developer longer than an-

Fig. 78-5. Equipment necessary for roll-film tray developing.

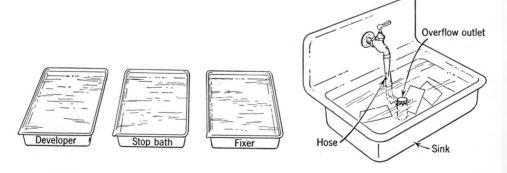

other part of the film, the development will be uneven. Avoid rubbing the film on the edge of the tray. This might scratch the film.

Procedure

1. Prepare a Record Card (Fig. 78-2). This card should have your name; the date; the type of film; the time recommended for developer, stop bath, fix, and wash; and the dilutions of stock solutions used. After the film has been developed and dried, you may have other notes to add.

2. Assemble the following equipment:

> A safelight
> 4 developing trays (5 by 7 inches labeled Water, Developer, Stop Bath, Fixing Bath)
> An 8-ounce graduate
> Thermometer (Fahrenheit)
> Glass stirring rod
> Funnel (glass or plastic)
> Developer
> Stop bath (if used)
> Fixer
> 3 tightly capped glass bottles
> 3 labels
> An interval timer or watch with second hand
> Wetting agent
> 2 film clips
> A pair of scissors
> Envelopes for negatives

If running water is not available, fill a large clean container with fresh water in which to rinse film after developing is complete.

3. Place the four developing trays in a row in the following order from left to

Fig. 78-6. Hold film by film clips and pass film through each solution in a steady seesaw manner.

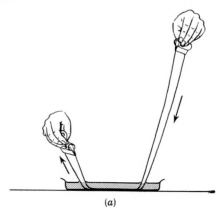

(a)

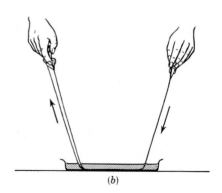

(b)

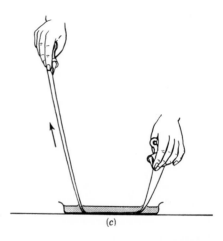

(c)

right: water, developer, stop bath, and fixing bath.

4. Prepare the developer, stop-bath, and fixing solutions that you will need. Read the instructions on the packages or on the label of the stock-solution bottles before preparing the solutions and follow them exactly. If fresh stock solutions are to be prepared first, label each bottle carefully (Fig. 78-1). The developing solution should be 68°F. Set the graduate or tray of developer in a pan or basin of warm or cool water until the thermometer in the developer reads 68°F. Do not allow any water to get into the developer.

The stop-bath and fixing solutions and the water used in the first tray and for washing should be about the same temperature (65 to 70°F).

5. Fill the four trays. Wash out the graduate thoroughly after preparing each solution.

6. Get your exposed film from the instructor and examine the box in which it came. If the words "Develop in Total Darkness" appear on the box, no safelight will be really safe. Such a film must be developed in total darkness.

7. Wash your hands with soap and warm water, rinse thoroughly, and dry.

Darkroom Safelight

8. Ask the instructor to watch you as you unwind your exposed film. Holding the spool between the thumb and forefinger of one hand and holding the paper backing of the film with the thumb and forefinger of the other hand, gently unroll the film. Handle the film by its edges.

9. Attach a film clip to one end of the film and hang the clip on a hook or nail

so that the dull, concave (emulsion) side of the film faces away from you.

10. Tear off the gummed tape.

11. Attach another film clip to the other end of the film.

12. Hold the film by the clips with the dull (emulsion) side facing down.

13. Bend the film into a U shape and slowly pass the film back and forth through the water in the first tray with the seesaw motion described on page 242 and shown in Fig. 78-6.

14. Remove the film from the water and turn it over so that the dull (emulsion) side is facing up.

15. Set the interval timer for the number of minutes required by the developer you are using.

16. Pass the film slowly and continuously through the developer. Be sure that the ends of the film are dipped in the developer. Continue until the time required is up.

17. Remove the film from the developer and pass it through the stop bath or water in the next tray for 15 seconds. Rinse the clips in this bath.

18. Set the interval timer for 10 minutes.

19. Pass the film through the fixing bath in the same way until the 10 minutes is up. You will see the film lose its milky appearance and become clear.

Normal Room Light

20. Wash the film in a sink or tray of slowly running water. If running water is not available, place film in the clean container of wash water. Stir gently every 2 or 3 minutes. Replace water every 5 minutes. This step should be continued for 30 minutes.

21. Add a few drops of wetting agent to the wash water and gently stir.

22. Remove the film from the wash water and hang it up by one clip to dry (Fig. 78-4). The weight of the bottom clip should keep the film from curling while drying.

23. If the working solutions used above are to be saved (check this with the instructor), return each to its proper bottle. Be sure to wash and dry the funnel you use after each solution.

24. Wash all equipment thoroughly. Dry with a clean towel and return it to its proper place. Leave the darkroom clean and neat.

25. When the film is thoroughly dry, cut it into separate negatives.

26. Store each negative in a separate envelope to protect it from dust and to prevent possible damage by scratching.

Discussion Topics

1. What are the six steps in the developing process? Explain the purpose of each.
2. What are the two methods by which exposed films may be developed?
3. Why is a developed film called a *negative?*
4. Why should all solutions be prepared before you start developing a film?
5. What should appear on each label?
6. What is a stock solution?
7. What is a working solution?
8. In tank developing, why is the reel twirled or the tank moved with a circular motion every 2 or 3 minutes during the developing process?
9. In tray developing, why is it important to seesaw the film through each solution smoothly and evenly?
10. What should be the temperature of the developing solution when used?
11. What should be the temperature of other solutions and water used during the developing process?
12. Why is cleanliness of hands and equipment so important in developing films?
13. Why should the film be handled by its edges?
14. Why should each negative be kept in a separate envelope?

Blueprints

Blueprints are the copies of architects', engineers', designers', and draftsmen's drawings and specifications that are used by the men who supervise or do the job. Blueprinting is a type of contact printing. You will learn more about contact printing in the next unit.

There are three speeds of blueprint paper: Standard, Rapid, and Electric-Rapid. The light-sensitive coating of the three types of blueprint paper dissolves in water unless it is set by exposure to light.

The original drawings may be made in pencil or india ink on paper or cloth that allow light to pass through. A piece of light-sensitive blueprint paper is placed under the drawing. Then both are placed in a printing frame (see Fig. 78-7). The drawing and paper are exposed to a bright light for a few minutes. The light strikes the blueprint

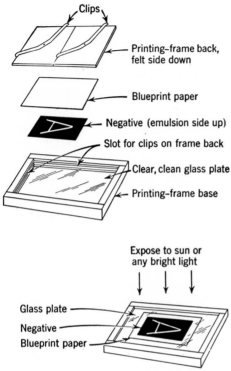

Clips

Printing-frame back, felt side down

Blueprint paper

Negative (emulsion side up)

Slot for clips on frame back

Clear, clean glass plate

Printing-frame base

Expose to sun or any bright light

Glass plate

Negative

Blueprint paper

FIG. 78-7. Using a printing frame for making blueprints.

paper that is not protected by the lines of the drawing. This sets the light-sensitive coating, and it will no longer dissolve in water as mentioned before. After exposure, the blueprint paper is removed from the printing frame and washed off in pure water. The coating that was protected by the lines of the drawing dissolves in the water and is washed away. This leaves white lines on blue paper. When dry, the blueprint is ready to be used.

The blue of the blueprint paper may be intensified by passing the paper through a solution of potassium dichromate in water (1 tablespoon of potassium dichromate in 1 quart of water).

The intensifier should be thoroughly washed off the print with clear water.

This is a very simple, direct method of contact printing. It can be easily done without a darkroom. Normal indoor light will not ruin the blueprint paper unless it is exposed for a long time. You can print some of your own negatives in this way. However, the prints will not be so permanent as those you will prepare in the next unit by the regular photographic process. Blueprints usually fade in time.

To make a blueprint from one of the negatives you have just prepared, you will need a printing frame and fresh blueprint paper. Place the negative in the printing frame with the dull (emulsion) side up. To find the proper exposure time, take a 2-inch strip of blueprint paper and place it on top of the negative. The light-sensitive side of the paper should be face down. Hold the negative and blueprint paper in place with one hand as you insert the back of the printing frame. Fasten the back in place securely. Expose to a bright light —sunlight will do—for 10 seconds. Remove the strip of paper from the frame and wash under running water. If the image is not clear enough, repeat and double the exposure time. It may take 30 seconds to 2 minutes, depending on the density of the negative and the sensitivity, or speed, of the blueprint paper being used. After the proper exposure time has been determined, print the whole picture. To do this, use a piece of blueprint paper slightly larger than the negative being printed. After exposure and washing, let the print dry face up on a clean towel or blotter.

Unit 79. Contact Printing

In contact printing the picture is placed in direct contact with a specially prepared paper coated with a light-sensitive emulsion containing silver salts. The negative and paper are held firmly together—emulsion to emulsion—and exposed to a white light. The light passing through the negative exposes the light-sensitive printing paper. Dark areas of the negative permit little or no light to reach the printing paper. Very light areas of the negative permit most of the light to reach the paper. When developed, those areas of the printing paper that received little or no light will be light, or clear. Areas that received varying degrees of light will be different shades of gray to black. The darkest areas are those that received the most light (Fig. 79-1).

After exposure, the printing paper is developed and fixed by a method similar to that used for the developing of the film. In the developing solution the picture appears in black, white, and shades of gray. The silver salts in the emulsion are changed into black particles of metallic silver by the developer. The stop bath halts this action. The fixing bath dissolves the salts that were not turned into metallic silver. Final washing removes all chemicals from the print.

The length of time the negative and light-sensitive printing paper are exposed to a bright light will depend on (1) the brightness and distance of the light from the negative and paper, (2) the density of the negative, and (3) the degree of light sensitivity of the paper used. You will need to experiment a little with the equipment and the various types of light-sensitive papers available

FIG. 79-1. The negative (a) and positive (b) of the same picture.

(a)   (b)

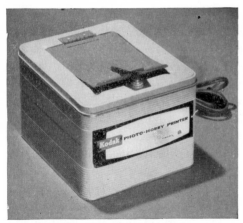

Fig. 79-2. Printing box.

other papers may prove to be more suitable. You will find that shorter exposure times are needed for the higher-contrast papers than for the lower-contrast papers. Can you think of a good reason why this is true? Why is the correct exposure time different for different negatives with the same type of printing paper?

If a printing box is used, the light will always be of the same brightness and distance from your negative and printing paper.

Contact printing may be done under a fairly bright safelight in a darkroom. Printing papers are less sensitive to light than are films.

PRINTING FRAME OR BOX

For contact printing you will need either a printing box (Fig. 79-2) or a printing frame (Fig. 79-3) to hold the negative and printing paper together during exposure. Printing frames come in different sizes. Select the proper size for the negative from which you are going to print.

If a ready-made printing box is not available, you can make one for yourself to fit your printing frame (Fig. 79-4a). The width of the box will be the width of the printing frame. The length of the box should be 4 to 5 inches longer than the frame. The box should be high enough so that a light bulb in a socket attached inside the box will be at least 1½ inches from the bottom of the printing frame. Figure 79-4 shows the printing box and wiring. The wiring permits the safelight to remain on as long as the box is plugged into a wall outlet. The switch in front of the box controls the

to determine the best paper to use for a particular negative and the length of time to expose it to the light. The final print should approximate the range of contrast from the brightest highlight to the darkest shadow of the subject photographed. For example, on a sunny day the range is wider than on an overcast day. The brightest highlight in your final print should be almost the color of the printing paper used. The darkest shadow in your print should be the darkest shade possible with the printing paper used.

Different papers have different ranges of contrast to match the range of contrast in negatives. To find out the ranges of contrast of the printing paper available to you, do the following: (1) Determine the best exposure time for one good negative on one type of printing paper. (2) Using the same negative and exposure time, make a print on each of the other types of printing paper available. (3) Compare your results. Is one of the other papers more suitable for the contrast range of your negative? By altering the exposure time, one of the

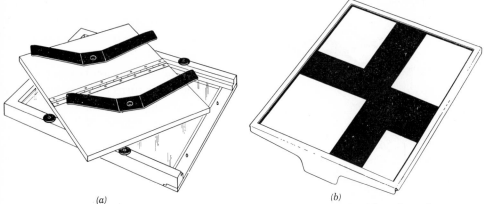

(a)   (b)

Fig. 79-3. (a) Printing frame. (b) A steel-frame printing mask with a glass plate.

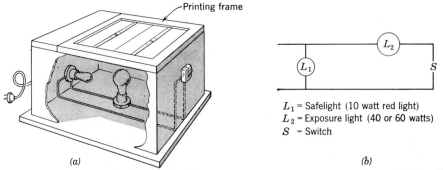

L_1 = Safelight (10 watt red light)
L_2 = Exposure light (40 or 60 watts)
S = Switch

(a)   (b)

Fig. 79-4. (a) Homemade printing box with one side removed to show position of light. (b) Wiring diagram.

white light used for exposure. Measure and cut the six pieces you will need for your box. Drill the holes in the front and back needed to put the wires through to the switch and safelight. Install and wire the switch and both sockets. Then assemble the box. Ask the instructor to examine the wiring before you try it out yourself.

With the safelight turned on, you can see the negative through the contact printing paper. This will help you to place the printing paper squarely over the negative. If the frame or printing box is equipped with adjustable metal

masks, you can readily frame the negative so that you print just that part of the picture that you wish.

You can make a printing mask of any size or shape by cutting it out of a piece of black or opaque paper. Remember that it's the opening that you print through. The mask is placed between the negative and the printing paper (Fig. 79-5). The outside dimension of the mask should be at least as large as the piece of printing paper being used. With proper masking you can improve the composition and balance of the picture you are printing. If you did not

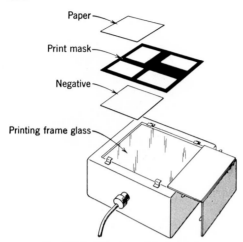

Paper

Print mask

Negative

Printing frame glass

Fig. 79-5. Printing with a mask.

hold the camera straight when you took the picture, you can mask it so that the print will appear to be straight.

SIX BASIC STEPS

Figure 79-6 shows the six basic steps in contact printing: (1) exposure, (2) developing, (3) acid stop bath, (4) fixing, (5) washing, (6) drying. The first four steps are carried out in a darkroom under a safelight. Steps 5 and 6 may be done in normal room light.

1. *Exposure* (emulsion to emulsion). The negative is placed on the glass of the printing box or frame with the dull (emulsion) side up. The mask is placed over the negative so that the part of the negative to be printed shows through the mask opening. The light-sensitive printing paper is placed shiny (emulsion) side down on top of the mask and negative. The rule to remember is *emulsion to emulsion*. (Be sure that all other light-sensitive papers are in their packages.) Hold the printing paper, mask, and

negative in place with one hand and carefully insert and fasten the back of the printing frame in place. If a printing box is used, lower the cover gently. In some types of printing boxes, the closing of the cover turns on the white light; in others the light must be turned on by hand. For size of light, distance of light from frame, and time of exposure, check the manufacturer's specifications for the light-sensitive printing paper that you are using.

2. *Developer.* After exposure, the printing paper is placed in a tray of developer. Be sure that the paper is completely covered by the developer. The action of the developer turns the silver salts in emulsion on the paper to black metallic silver where the light has reached it through the negative. Soon the picture begins to appear. Rock the tray gently and continuously to keep the developer solution in motion. This prevents air bubbles from sticking to the surface of the paper. This will ensure even development of the print. For the proper length of time the print should remain in the developer, check the manufacturer's specifications for paper and solution used. Remove the print from the developer by holding one corner. If you do not have a separate pair of tongs for each tray, a toothpick for each tray may be used to raise a corner of the print. This will help you to remove the print from a tray without getting your hands into the solution. Keep your fingers off the picture. Hold the picture with one corner down and allow it to drain into the developer for the last few seconds.

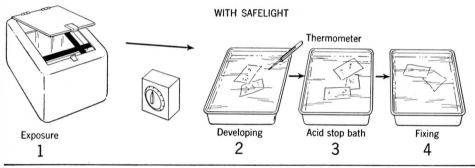

WITH SAFELIGHT

Thermometer

Exposure
1

Developing
2

Acid stop bath
3

Fixing
4

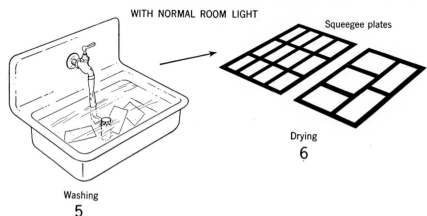

WITH NORMAL ROOM LIGHT

Squeegee plates

Drying
6

Washing
5

FIG. 79-6. The six basic steps in contact printing.

3. *Stop bath.* This stops the action of the developer on the print immediately. The stop bath is a weak mixture of acetic acid and water. Rock the tray gently to ensure even action of the solution on the print.

4. *Fixing.* This step fixes the print. After the print has been in this solution about 1 minute, you may examine the print by normal room light without damaging it. If the print is *too dark,* it may be caused by one or more of the following things: (1) The print has been overexposed in the printing frame or box. (2) The print has been left in the developer too long. (3) The negative used is not dense enough. If the print is *too light,* it may be caused by one or more of the following things: (1) The print has not been exposed long enough in the printing frame or box. (2) The print has not been left in the developer long enough. (3) The negative used is too dense. If either condition of the print exists, wash and dry your hands and prepare to make another print.

First re-examine the negative that you are using. Decide whether the negative will take a little more or a little less exposure time. Watch the print closely in the developer and remove it as soon as the desired detail shows clearly. Keep a record of the timing of each step for each print.

It takes a little experimenting and

practice to become familiar with the equipment, solutions, and paper that you are using. You may need to make three or four prints of each negative before you are satisfied with the results. Leave each print in the fixing bath 5 to 10 minutes. After you have examined a print under normal room light, it should be returned to the fixing bath.

5. *Washing.* It is very important to wash away all traces of the fixing-bath solution from the prints. Otherwise they may turn brown and eventually fade. If running water is available, place the prints face down in a tray or basin of water and let the water run into the tray or basin for 1 hour. The water should be 65 to 70°F. Separate the prints from time to time. If running water is not available, place prints in a tray of water face down and change the water every 5 minutes until the hour is up. Drain off excess water from each print before drying.

6. *Drying.* There are two methods of drying: (*a*) on a chromium squeegee plate, which gives the prints a high, glossy finish, and (*b*) on a blotter or clean lint-free towel, which gives the prints a dull finish.

a. Chromium squeegee plate and roller. This is a highly polished metal plate. It should be thoroughly cleaned before using to prevent the prints from sticking to it. After the prints have been washed off and drained, they are placed face down on the wet squeegee plate in rows. A lint-free blotter is placed over the prints, and the roller is gently run over the blotter a few times. Then it is rolled harder.

The blotter is removed, and the squeegee plate placed on edge. The prints fall off as they dry.

b. Blotter or towel. This method is used for drying prints on mat-surface paper. It is important that the blotter or towel used for drying prints be free of lint and dust. Special blotter rolls are made for the purpose. Lay the prints on the blotter or towel with the picture (emulsion) side up. Gently wipe off drops of water with a slightly damp viscose sponge.

After the prints are dry, they should be trimmed so that their margins are even all around. Flatten by putting prints of the same size face to face and placing them under a weight for a day or so. They are now ready to be mounted.

PREPARING SOLUTIONS

It is recommended that you use the developer, stop-bath, and fixing solutions prepared by the manufacturer of the light-sensitive printing paper that you are going to use. These solutions are sometimes made up first as concentrated stock solutions and diluted (working solutions) when used. Prepare these stock solutions first and store each in a tightly capped glass bottle. Each bottle should be carefully labeled (Fig. 79-7). For best uniform printing results the stock solutions should be made up fresh every 6 to 8 weeks.

The diluted, or working, solutions should not be poured back into the stock-solution bottles. Ask the instructor whether you should keep or throw out the working solutions that you have

Stock Solution for PRINTS Dilute before using 1 to_____ Time: DEVELOPER Date: Prepared by:	Stock Solution for PRINTS Dilute before using 1 to_____ Time: STOP BATH Date: Prepared by:	Stock Solution for PRINTS Dilute before using 1 to_____ Time: FIXER Date: Prepared by:

Fig. 79-7. Labels used for solutions in contact printing. The dilutions and times should be those recommended by the manufacturer.

been using. If they are to be saved, each solution should be stored in a tightly capped glass bottle and each bottle carefully labeled with the name of the solution (Developer, Stop Bath, Fixer), the words "Working Solution for Prints," and the number of seconds or minutes it is to be used on each print.

If you are making prints less than 2½ inches wide, small, screw-topped jam or peanut-butter jars are very useful for this purpose. After exposure, the prints can be dipped directly into these jars of solutions for the developing process. Clothespins may be used to move the prints up and down during the developing process to ensure even action of the solutions and to remove the prints from the jars. A separate clothespin should be used for each jar. The jar tops and clothespins should be labeled as well as the jars.

NOTE: If the film and the light-sensitive paper that you use are produced by the *same* manufacturer, the same stock solutions of developer and fixer may be used for both film and prints. However, if you save the working solutions after using them, the fixer solution for films

and that for prints should be kept in separate, well-labeled bottles.

CONTACT PRINTING

Since you will be using the same darkroom with other people, be considerate. You will make more and better prints in less time if you go about it quietly. If you spill some solution or water, wipe it up immediately. Before you leave the darkroom, clean up after yourself. Be sure to put the materials and equipment that you have used back in their proper places.

Procedure

1. Prepare a Record Card (Fig. 79-8). This card should have your name; the date; the type of paper used; and the recommended time for exposure, developer, stop bath, fixing bath, and washing. If your negatives are numbered, the same card may be used for several of them by placing the negative numbers at the top of a column. Leave enough space in each column so that you may add the two or three different timings that you used on each negative. Circle the timing that gives the best results in each case.

	Time recommended	Time used; negative number							
		1	2	3	4	5	6	7	8
Exposure									
Developer									
Stop bath									
Fixing									
Washing									

Name: _____ Date: _____
Type of paper used: _____

Fig. 79-8. Record Card used in contact printing.

2. Assemble the following equipment (Fig. 79-9):

> Printing box or printing frame
> Masks
> 3 trays (5 by 7 inches labeled Developer, Stop Bath, Fixer)
> 3 print tongs
> A large tray or basin for washing prints
> Tray thermometer (Fahrenheit)
> Interval timer or watch with second hand
> Safelight with 10-watt bulb and greenish-yellow filter
> Exposure light if printing frame used (60 watt)
> Contact printing paper
> For dull-surface prints on mat-surface paper:
> 1 viscose sponge
> Blotter, towel, or blotter roll (lint-free)
> For glossy prints:
> Chromium squeegee plate
> Blotter (lint-free)
> Print roller
> 8-ounce graduate
> Developer
> Stop bath (28 percent acetic acid)
> Fixer
> A pair of scissors

If the contact printing paper is not exactly the right size for the negatives from which you are making prints, cut it carefully before using it. Do not waste printing paper.

3. Line up the three printing trays. Are they clean and dry?

4. Prepare the developer, stop-bath, and fixing solutions that you will need. Read the instructions on the packages or stock-solution bottles carefully before preparing each solution.

5. Check the temperature of the developer with a tray thermometer. It should be 68°F. If it is not, set the tray in a pan of warm or cold water as required. Do not allow any water to splash into the developer.

6. Rinse the thermometer in water. Use running water if available.

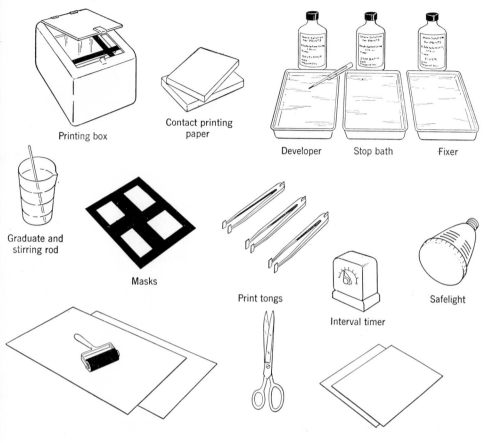

Fɪɢ. 79-9. Equipment necessary for contact printing.

Darkroom Safelight

7. Select your favorite negative and place it on the glass of your printing frame or box with the dull (emulsion) side up.

8. Place a suitable mask over the negative.

9. Place a sheet of light-sensitive paper that is slightly larger than the negative over the mask shiny (emulsion) side down. (*Emulsion to emulsion;* remember this rule.) Center the paper over the mask and negative.

10. Holding the paper, mask, and

negative in position, insert the back of the printing frame. Fasten the back in place by both spring catches. If a printing box is used, lower the top slowly.

11. Be sure that all light-sensitive papers are in their packages.

12. Turn on the white light and expose the paper the specified time. Consult your Record Card for timing.

13. Turn off the white light and remove the exposed paper from the frame.

14. Hold the paper by one edge shiny side down for a few seconds in the developer to ensure complete and even contact. After a few seconds turn

shiny side up. Check your time. Rock the tray gently to ensure even action of the developer. The picture should begin to appear. When the time is up, remove the print with the right hand. Hold it carefully by the edge.

15. Drain off the developer from the print into the developer tray (Fig. 79-10).

16. Slip the print into the stop bath. Check your Record Card for timing. Rock the tray gently. Remove the print and drain as before.

17. Slip the print into the fixing bath. Check your Record Card for timing (5 to 10 minutes). Rock the tray gently. Wash and dry your hands. Remove the print from this bath and examine it in normal room light. If too light, add 1 second to your exposure time. If too dark, subtract 1 second from your exposure time. Note this on your Record Card. Return the print to fixing bath. Wash and dry your hands.

18. Make another print from the same negative with a new exposure time. Repeat steps 10 to 17.

19. Make as many prints as time will permit.

Normal Room Light

20. Remove prints from fixing bath and place them face down in a tray of water (65 to 70°F). If running water is available, let water run into the tray for 1 hour. If running water is not available, change the water in the tray every 5 minutes for 1 hour. Separate the prints from time to time.

21. While the prints are being ⌐ed, clean up the trays that you have ⌐ing. If the working solutions are

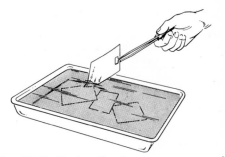

Fig. 79-10. Drain off print as you remove it from each solution.

to be saved, return each to its proper bottle. Wash the trays thoroughly and dry with a clean towel.

22. Return the trays, printing frame or box, masks, printing paper, and solutions to their proper places.

23. Prepare for drying of the prints. (*a*) If a glossy-finish paper has been used, get out a squeegee plate, roller, and lint-free blotter. Is the plate clean? (*b*) If a mat-surface paper has been used, get out a viscose sponge and lint-free blotter, towel, or blotter roller.

24. After washing is complete, drain each print and dry by either of the following methods:

a. *For glossy finish.* Lay each print face down on the wet, clean squeegee plate. Arrange the prints in rows. Place lint-free blotter over the prints and gently run the roller over the blotter a few times. Then roll harder. Remove the blotter and stand the plate on edge. The prints fall off as they dry.

b. *For a dull finish on mat-surface paper.* Place each print face up on a lint-free blotter or towel or on a blotter roll made for this purpose. Wipe off drops of water from the prints with a slightly damp viscose sponge.

25. When dry, trim the prints so that the margins are even all around.

26. Flatten prints by putting prints of the same size face to face and placing them under a weight for a day or two.

If this is the first time you have made prints, you should keep the time schedule, the negative, and the prints made from the same negative together for future reference. In this way you will begin to see for yourself the relationship between density of the negative and time of exposure when the same type of light-sensitive paper is used. Then you can begin to experiment with other types of light-sensitive papers using the same negative.

Discussion Topics

1. What is contact printing?
2. Which side of the negative is placed next to the glass of the printing frame or box?
3. What are printing masks? How are they used?
4. Why should the back of the printing frame be securely fastened?
5. What determines the exposure time?
6. What does the developer do?
7. What does the stop bath do?
8. What does the fixing bath do?
9. Why should each tray be rocked when a print is in it?
10. What should go on the label of each bottle of stock solution? Each bottle of working solution?
11. How long can stock solutions be kept?
12. Examine the pictures you have taken and printed yourself and check the following questions:

   a. Were any of them double-exposed?
   b. Are they all in focus?
   c. Is your shadow in any of them?
   d. Was the light too bright? Not bright enough?
   e. Did you hold your camera straight and steady when taking all the pictures?
   f. Is the composition of each picture well balanced?
   g. Which picture would you like to enlarge?

CARE AND USE OF PRINTS AND NEGATIVES

Now that you are learning how to develop your own films and to print your own pictures, what are you going to do with them? As suggested in Unit 77, you may wish to start a picture album. If this is of interest to you, you should decide now what type of album or albums you wish to have.

Albums. You might start an experimental album in which you could keep the different prints made from the same negative with different exposure times and with different types of printing paper. Each print should be carefully labeled with all important information (paper, exposure time, and so on) so that you can use your experimental album for reference purposes.

Family albums may be kept chronologically, that is, adding the prints as they are taken, or they may be classified. If classified, separate albums may be made for each member of the family, for special occasions, such as vacations and holidays, and for the general family history.

Pictorial records. If your family is going to build a house, a boat, or make a garden, you could take a series of pictures that would make a permanent record of the event.

Pictorial records of other hobbies or collections are fun to have in years to come.

Greeting and post cards. You might use some of your pictures to make family Christmas or birthday cards. Family post cards may be made from pictures in and around your home, of your school, of the family pet, or of members of the family.

Camera club. If your school does not already have a camera club, you and your friends may wish to start one. It will give you experience in preparing your pictures for exhibition. Some day you might have a picture that you would like to enter in a state or national prize contest.

Mounting. Mounting pictures whether in an album or for an exhibition should be done carefully. Rubber cement may be used, but a special rapid-drying mounting cement, which is made for mounting prints, is better. A dry mounting tissue that requires heat is particularly good for mounting large prints. Whatever system is used, the corners and edges should be firmly held down. Otherwise, the prints may curl and become torn. In mounting, care should be taken not to leave fingerprints on the picture area. Placing a piece of clean paper over the print when you are pressing it down will prevent this. If you do get a fingerprint on a picture, wipe off the picture gently with a soft paper tissue.

Negative file. Your negatives are an important part of your picture collection. Each negative should be filed and indexed. The entry number placed next to the print in the album will help you locate the negative quickly.

Unit 80. Projection Printing

In contact printing the negative and the printing paper were in direct contact with each other. In *projection printing* the image on the negative is *projected* onto the printing paper. In projection printing a lens is placed between the negative and the printing paper (Fig. 80-1). As the light shines through the negative and then through the lens, the image is made larger or smaller. The beginning photographer will find the en-

largement type of projection printing most useful. This type of projection printing is, therefore, described here.

All or part of the image on a negative may be enlarged and printed. By projection printing it is possible to make a 11- by 14-inch, or larger, print from a 1- by 1½-inch negative. The amount by which a picture can be enlarged depends on the quality of both the negative and the lens used. A good negative

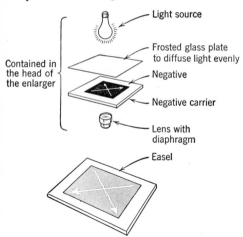

FIG. 80-1. Projection printing. Note the name and position of each part.

with clear, sharp detail can be enlarged more than the negative in which there are no clear, sharp details.

For projection printing, you will need two special pieces of equipment known as an *enlarger* and an *easel* (Fig. 80-2).

The so-called *head* of the enlarger contains the projection light, one or more frosted plates of glass to diffuse the light evenly, a holding device for the negative called the *negative carrier,* and a *lens.* The lens is used to focus the projected image of the negative. The head is attached to the vertical supporting post, which is fastened to the base. The size of the projected image is controlled by moving the head of the enlarger up and down. By moving the head down, a smaller image is produced. By moving the head up, a larger image is produced. When the size of the projected image is satisfactory, it is brought into focus by adjusting the lens.

FIG. 80-2. (*a*) Enlarger and easel showing projected image properly focused and centered. (*b*) An enlarger made by high school students.

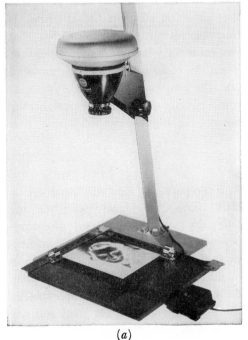

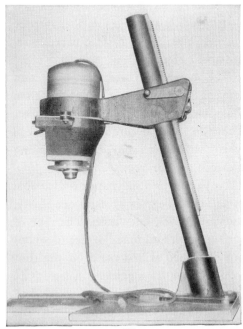

(*a*)   (*b*)

Fig. 80-3. Adjustable easel used in projection printing.

An *easel*, although not essential, is a very useful piece of equipment to have. It is used to hold the printing paper flat and steady during the exposure. Two types of easels are available: (1) the nonadjustable easels that hold standard sizes of paper (4 by 5, 5 by 7, and 8 by 10 inches) and (2) the adjustable easels that have adjustable guides that may be moved, or adjusted, to fit different sizes of paper (Fig. 80-3).

The emulsions used for projection printing paper are more sensitive than those used on contact printing paper. Therefore, special care should be taken when handling projection printing paper in the darkroom.

Projection printing paper is available in different degrees of light sensitivity, contrast grades, and finish. The type of surface finish and tone (degree of whiteness) selected will depend on the subject. The contrast grade and sensitivity selected will depend on the range and degree of contrast appearing in the negative. Only by experimentation and

experience will you be able to select the best paper for a negative.

The size of the enlargements that you make will determine the size of the trays you will need. In the beginning it is recommended that you limit the size of your enlargements to 4 by 5 inches. It takes practice and some experimenting to become familiar with the equipment and procedure of projection printing.

For developing your enlarged prints, you will need the same solutions as those used for developing contact prints. If you used 5- by 7-inch trays for your contact prints, the same trays may be used for the 4- by 5-inch enlargements.

Now you are ready to enlarge some of those pictures that you have taken. Select a good negative for which you have made a contact print. You may enlarge and print the whole image of the negative or select a part of it that you wish to enlarge. In either case, you place the whole negative in the enlarger. If time permits, it is recommended that you print the whole enlarged image first. Then, by re-adjusting the enlarger head and the position of the easel, you may print the most interesting part of the image (Fig. 80-6c, page 265).

Procedure

1. Prepare a Record Card (Fig. 80-4). This should have your name; the date; the type of paper used; the number of the negative or some identification of the negative used; the recommended time for the developer, stop bath, and fixing bath; and the exposure times you use on the test print you will make in step 24 below.

		Test print	Final prints					
			1	2	3	4	5	6
Exposure	Whole–10 sec.							
	¼ –20 sec.							
	½ –40 sec.							
	¾ –80 sec.							
	Suggested times:							
Developer								
Stop bath								
Fixing								
Washing								

Name: _____ Date: _____
Negative enlarged: _____
Type of paper used: Time recommended:

FIG. 80-4. Record Card for projection printing.

2. Assemble the following equipment:

Enlarger and easel
3 trays (5 by 7 inches labeled Developer, Stop Bath, Fixer)
A large tray or basin for washing prints
Developer
Stop bath (28 percent acetic acid)
Fixer
8-ounce graduate
Tray thermometer (Fahrenheit)
Safelight with 10-watt bulb and greenish-yellow filter
Interval timer or watch with a second hand
Projection print scale (if available —not essential, Fig. 80-5*b*)
For dull-surface prints on mat-surface paper:
1 viscose sponge
Blotter or towel (lint-free)
For glossy prints:
Chromium squeegee plate
Blotter (lint-free)
Print roller

Projection printing paper
1 piece of plain white paper the same size as the printing paper to be used
1 piece of cardboard slightly larger than the print you are going to make
A pair of scissors

3. Prepare working solutions of developer, stop bath, and fixer as indicated on the stock-solution bottles.

4. Set up wash tray of fresh water. A tray siphon is particularly handy for washing large prints. It is fastened to the edge of the tray and is connected to a faucet. The heavier-than-water fixing solution tends to collect at the bottom of the wash tray. A tray siphon draws off this fixing-solution layer and circulates fresh water.

5. If the negative carrier you are using has glass plates, wash and dry these plates carefully. Use lens tissue or a lint-free towel for drying.

(a)

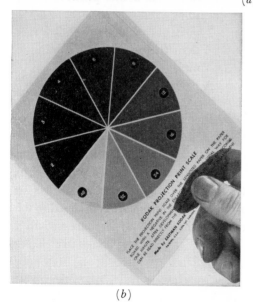

(b)

Fig. 80-5. Two methods of determining the correct print exposure: (a) test print and (b) projection print scale. (a) This test print was prepared to show the effect of a wider than usual range of exposure times. The darkest strip was exposed 100 seconds; the next darkest, 70 seconds; the third, 50 seconds; and the lightest, 15 seconds. The time selected for the final picture (c) was 45 seconds.

6. Hold the negative by its edges. Place it in the carrier with the dull (emulsion) side down.

7. Place the negative carrier in the enlarger.

8. Set the easel guides to the size of the paper to be printed. Allow for a ¼-inch margin around the print.

9. Place the plain white sheet of paper under the easel guides.

(*c*)

10. Open the lens diaphragm as far as it will go.

11. Turn on the safelight.

12. Turn on the enlarger light.

13. Turn off the white room light.

Darkroom Safelight

14. Adjust the size of the projected image:

    a. If it is too small, raise the enlarger head.

    b. If it is too large, lower the enlarger head.

15. Move the easel until the part of the enlarged image you wish to print is centered on the white paper.

16. Sharpen the focus of the image by moving the lens slowly up and down until the image is clear and bright. Do not move the enlarger head.

17. Adjust the lens diaphragm as recommended by the manufacturer of the enlarger. This will ensure the sharpness of the image at the corners and in the center.

18. Turn off the enlarger light.

19. Check the temperature of the developer. It should be 68°F.

20. Ask the instructor to help you select the proper enlarging paper for the negative you are using.

21. Make a note on your Record Card of the paper used. With experience you will be able to make this selection yourself.

22. Remove one sheet of enlarging paper from the package. Be sure that all the rest of the printing paper is in its original package and completely covered.

23. Without moving the easel, replace the plain white paper with the printing paper. The printing paper

should be placed under the guides with the shiny (emulsion) side up.

24. Make a *test print* as follows:

Method I (Fig. 80-5a)

a. Expose the entire print for 10 seconds.

b. Cover one-quarter of the print and expose for 10 seconds more. Use a piece of cardboard to cover the print.

c. Cover one-half of the print and expose for 20 seconds more.

d. Cover three-quarters of the print and expose for 40 seconds more.

(a)

Fig. 80-6. An enlargement of the whole negative or of just a part of a negative may be made. Here we have a contact print (a), an enlargement of the whole negative (b), and an enlargement of just a part of the negative at (c).

(b)

(c)

e. Turn off the enlarger.

Each quarter has been exposed a different length of time: 10, 20, 40, and 80 seconds.

Method II (Fig. 80-5*b*)

a. Place the projection print scale on top of the printing paper. Be sure that the numbers in each pie-shaped part read correctly. If they read backward, turn the scale over.

b. Expose the paper for 1 minute and turn off the enlarger.

25. Remove the test print from the easel. Be careful not to move the easel.

26. Check your Record Card and set the timer. Slide the test print into the developer, shiny side up. Move the print back and forth with your hand to be sure that no air bubbles stick to the surface of the print.

27. Rock the developer tray constantly during developing time to ensure even action of the developer on the print.

28. Holding the print by one corner, drain the print for the last 5 seconds of developing time.

29. Slip the print into the stop bath, picture side up, for about 5 seconds and drain for 5 seconds.

30. Slip the print into the fixing bath, picture side up. Rock tray for 5 seconds; then turn the print face down in fixing bath. Leave the print in the fixing bath for about 2 minutes longer.

Normal Room Light

31. Remove the test print and examine it under normal room light. Which exposure time has given clear white in the highlights and good blacks in the shadows? Make a note of all exposure times on your Record Card. Circle the best one. If a projection print scale was used (Method II), select the pie-shaped part that shows normal density. The number in this section is the correct exposure.

32. Return the test print to the fixing solution for 10 minutes.

33. Slip the test print into the wash tray, picture side down.

34. Wash your hands thoroughly and dry them on a clean towel.

Darkroom Safelight

35. Make a print using the best exposure time indicated by your test print.

36. Use the same time for developer and stop bath as you did for the test print.

37. Leave this print in the fixing bath about 10 minutes.

Normal Room Light

38. Remove the negative from the carrier. Be sure that the projection light of the enlarger is turned off.

39. Slip the print into the wash tray, picture side down. Wash the print, and any others that you make, for 1 hour in running water. If running water is not available, change water every 5 minutes.

40. Dry the prints by using (*a*) the squeegee plate and roller, or (*b*) the towel method if a mat-surface paper has been used for printing.

> *a.* If a glossy print is slightly wavy after drying thoroughly, place it between two pieces of cardboard and put a weight on top of it.
>
> *b.* If a mat-surface print is slightly wavy, rub the back of it with a piece of slightly damp cotton. Then place print between two pieces of cardboard and put a weight on top of it. Books make good weights.

41. Return working solutions to their proper bottles. Wash trays, put all equipment away, and clean up the darkroom before you leave it.

Discussion Topics

1. Why should the negative carrier glass plates be clean and free from dust?
2. Why do you put the negative in the carrier with the dull (emulsion) side facing down? What would happen if the dull side were facing up?
3. Why should all printing paper not being used be returned to the original package?
4. Why should the easel not be moved after the focusing of the image?
5. Why make a test print?
6. How long was each of the four exposures of the test print? Did you make a record of this on your Record Card?
7. If an air bubble remained on the surface of the print during developing, what would happen?
8. Why should you save your test print and Record Card?

LET THE END BE THE BEGINNING

Now that you have come to the end of this book, it is hoped that you may have found at least one phase of the graphic arts with which you wish to continue. Printing, bookbinding, linoleum block, silk screen, and photography all have vocational as well as avocational possibilities. Some of the vocational opportunities have already been suggested; more are given on the following pages.

The purpose of this book has been to introduce printing and the other graphic arts to you and to give you guidance in gaining experience in each. You will find additional information in the books listed on pages 271–276.

Let the end of this course be the beginning of your search for further knowledge, experience, and pleasure in the graphic arts. It is up to you.

Occupations in the Graphic-arts Industry*

The purpose of this book and the course for which it was written is to give you an introduction to and a working knowledge of the mechanics of printing and an appreciation of the graphic-arts industry as a whole. It is hoped that through them you will become a more intelligent user and buyer of the products of the graphic-arts industry.

If you have discovered that you really like this kind of work, you may have an aptitude for it and desire vocational instruction in any one or more of the graphic arts. If so, you will be interested in the information about the industry given below. Also, you may wish to reread the brief description on Job, or Commercial, Printing, pages 48–49; Newspaper Printing, pages 51–53; and Machine Composition, pages 56–59.

PRINTING INDUSTRY

1. The printing and publishing industry is one of the nation's largest industries. It employs about 802,000 people. Less than half of these are office personnel (executives, editors, salesmen, etc), and over half of them are production workers—craftsmen and apprentice craftsmen.

2. Generally, the printing industry is divided into the following divisions:

Job, or commercial, printing
Book printing and publishing
Newspaper and magazine printing and publishing
Offset lithography
Photoengraving
Bookbinding
Steel and copper plate engraving
Stereotyping
Electrotyping
Gravure printing
Layout and design artists

3. Printing requires seven major types of workers:

Composing-room workers (the largest group)
Pressroom workers
Bindery workers
Electrotypers
Stereotypers
Photoengravers
Lithographic workers

Most of the printing workers are skilled. The main exceptions are the press assistants and most of the bindery workers, who are semiskilled. Practically all the workers in the skilled occupations are men. Many of the semiskilled workers, especially in the binderies, are women.

---

* For further occupational information on the printing industry, write to the Government Printing Office, Washington 25, D.C., for BLS Bulletin No. 1126, and to the Educational Council of the Graphic Arts Industry, Inc., 718 15th Street, N.W., Washington 5, D.C., for *Career Opportunities in the Printing Industry.*

4. Printing workers tend to have higher earnings than those in most other industries because of the large number of skilled workers employed, the strong influence of the printing unions, and other factors. Earnings vary considerably from one occupation to another, from city to city, and sometimes among employees in the same city.

5. Generally throughout the nation, workers in the printing industry enjoy good working conditions and excellent wages and work an average of forty hours a week. The printing plants are kept clean, well lighted, and properly ventilated. Many are now air-conditioned. There are no occupational diseases in the industry. Printers lose little time because of illness.

6. Apprentices or trainees spend from four to six years (depending on the branch of the industry) learning to become craftsmen. To be eligible for an apprenticeship, the applicant is generally required to have a high school education. A thorough knowledge of spelling, punctuation, and grammar is essential for most trades in the printing industry. Apprentices receive good wages while they are learning and generally receive pay increases as they display new skills.

7. Employment in the printing industry is continuous and not seasonal. Its people receive paid vacations, paid holidays, and extra pay for overtime work.

8. Each year large numbers of young people enter the printing industry to make it their life work. A good education will assist you in becoming a better craftsman.

SILK SCREEN

The recent development of automatic silk-screen presses, the new photofilm used to prepare silk-screen stencils, and the new process of setting type photographically (see pages 67–71) together indicate a definite future use of the silk-screen process on a large commercial scale never before possible.

PHOTOGRAPHY

1. Although there is keen competition for jobs in the field of photography, the long-run employment trend has been slowly upward.

2. There are four major divisions in photography: portrait, commercial, news, and aerial work.

3. A photographer must be able to use cameras, lenses, filters, and other equipment.

4. A photographer must have a knowledge of good picture composition and lighting and artistic ability.

5. A photographer must be able to develop, finish, print, enlarge, and retouch pictures. This part of the work requires a knowledge of the use of chemicals and the ability to apply this knowledge skillfully.

6. Most photographers are employed in studios handling portrait or commercial work; others are employed by newspapers and magazine publishers, advertising agencies, and manufacturing plants.

7. A high school education with emphasis on chemistry, physics, and art is recommended for all prospective photographers.

8. On-the-job training is the usual method of entering the field of professional photography. This type of training takes two or three years and covers all phases of photography. Some employers have formal apprenticeship programs.

9. Portrait photographers have rush seasons and may work long hours at such times. Commercial and news photographers often work nights and Sundays.

It is recommended that you visit some of the printing and silk-screen plants and photographic studios in your community and talk with people who are profitably employed in the graphic-arts industry. If you decide to take vocational training in any one phase of the graphic-arts industry, apply yourself to that training. With hard work you should become a good printer, craftsman, or photographer.

For Further Reading and Additional Information

There is always more to learn. Some people are interested in history and stories; others are interested in facts and details. From the carefully selected list of books given below, you may find a few that will be of special interest and assistance to you.

PRINTING

Layout and Design

The Art of Printing, Stanley Morison, Diamant Typographic Service, Inc., New York, 1945.

Basic Lessons in Printing Layout, R. Randolph Karch, The Bruce Publishing Company, Milwaukee, Wis., 1952.

Design with Type, Carl Dair, George J. McLeod, Ltd., Toronto, 1952.

Designing Books, Jan Tschichold, Wittenborn & Company, New York, 1951.

Designing for Printing, John Brinkley, Chas. A. Bennett Company, Inc., Peoria, Ill., 1949.

Designs, Borders, Backgrounds, Tints, and Patterns, Harry B. Coffin (ed.), The Studio Publications, Inc., New York, 1951. Distributed by Thomas Y. Crowell Company.

Graphic Design: Lettering, Typography, Illustration, John N. C. Lewis and John Brinkley, The British Book Centre, Inc., New York, 1954.

How to Recognize Type Faces, R. Randolph Karch, McKnight & McKnight Publishing Company, Bloomington, Ill., 1952.

The Index of American Design, Erwin O. Christensen, The Macmillan Company, New York, 1950.

Introduction to Typography, Oliver Simon, Penguin Books, Inc., Baltimore, Md., 1955.

Modern Book Design, Ruari McLean, Longmans, Green & Co., Inc., New York, 1951.

Newspaper Designing, John E. Allen, Harper & Brothers, New York, 1947.

Printing Types and How to Use Them, Stanley C. Hlasta, Rutgers University Press, New Brunswick, N.J., 1950.

Printing Types: Their History, Forms and Use, 2 vols., 2d ed., Daniel Berkeley Updike, Harvard University Press, Cambridge, Mass., 1951.

Specimens of Type Faces, Superintendent of Documents, Government Printing Office, Washington, D.C., 1954.

The 26 Letters, Oscar Ogg, Thomas Y. Crowell Company, New York, 1948.

Type and Typography, Gilbert P. Farrar, International Textbook Company, Scranton, Pa., 1949.

Typography for Community Journalism, William F. Swindler, Burgess Publishing Company, Minneapolis, Minn., 1950.

Typography and Newspaper Makeup, Albert A. Harum, William C. Brown Company, Dubuque, Iowa, 1951.

The Use of Type: The Practice of Typography, John R. Biggs, Pitman Publishing Corporation, New York, 1954.

Composition

Applied Course for Student Printers, Merle A. Clark, Chas. A. Bennett Company, Inc., Peoria, Ill., 1949.

A.T.A. Advertising Production Hand Book, Donald Herold, Advertising Typographers Association of America, Inc., New York, 1954.

Career Opportunities in the Printing Industry, Educational Services Department, American Type Founders, Inc., Elizabeth, N.J., 1954.

Composition and Proofreading, International Textbook Company, Scranton, Pa., 1947.

General Printing, Glen U. Cleeton and Charles W. Pitkin, McKnight & McKnight Publishing Company, Bloomington, Ill., 1953.

Haberule Visual Copy-caster, The Haberule Co., Wilton, Conn., 1954.

Hand Composition, Hugo Jahn, John Wiley & Sons, Inc., New York, 1947.

The Practice of Printing, Ralph W. Polk, Chas. A. Bennett Company, Inc., Peoria, Ill., 1952.

A Primer of Engraving and Printing, Harry A. Groesbeck, Jr., Colton Press, Inc., New York, 1950.

Printing and the Allied Trades, 3d ed., R. Randolph Karch, Pitman Publishing Corporation, New York, 1954.

Printing for Pleasure, John Ryder, Charles T. Branford Company, Boston, 1955.

Printing for the Schools, C. W. Hague, The Bruce Publishing Company, Milwaukee, Wis., 1943.

Theory and Practice of Composition, Government Printing Office, Washington, D.C., 1950.

Presswork

Care and Use of Printers' Rollers, Research and Education Council of the Graphic Arts Industry, Washington, D.C., 1953.

Platen Press Operation, George J. Mills, Carnegie Institute of Technology, Pittsburgh, Pa., 1953.

Printing Presswork Related Instruction, John C. Heinike and George W. Mullenhoff, The University of the State of New York, Albany, N.Y., 1949.

Theory and Practice of Presswork, Government Printing Office, Washington, D.C., 1948.

History

Adventures of a Tramp Printer, 1880–1890, John Edwards Hicks, Mid-Americana Press, Kansas City, Mo., 1950.

American Album of Incidental Printers, Hortense Mendel and Robert L. Leslie (eds.), The Composing Room, Inc., New York, 1948.

American Journalism: A History of Newspapers in the United States

Through 260 Years, 1690 to 1950, rev. ed., Frank D. Mott, The Macmillan Company, New York, 1950.

Chronology of Books and Printing, rev. ed., David Greenwood and Helen Gentry, The Macmillan Company, New York, 1936.

The Colonial Craftsman, Carl Bridenbaugh, New York University Press, New York, 1950.

Eight Hundred Years of Fine Printing, 1146–1946, Carl J. Weber (comp.), Colby College Press, Waterville, Me., 1946.

Goudy, Master of Letters, Vrest Orton, Black Cat Press, Chicago, 1939.

The Invention of Printing in China and Its Spread Westward, 2d ed., Thomas Francis Carter and Carrington Goodrich, The Ronald Press Company, New York, 1955.

John Baskerville, Type-founder and Printer, 1706–1775, Josiah Henry Benton, Southworth Press, Portland, Me., 1944.

The Origin and Progress of Printing, Henry G. Bohn, Diamant Typographic Service, Inc., New York, 1946.

The Origins of Printing and Engraving, Andre Blum, Charles Scribner's Sons, New York, 1940.

Printers as Men of the World, Evelyn Harter, Peter Pauper Press, Mount Vernon, N.Y., 1947.

Printing Types: Their Origin and Development, Sol Hess, Diamant Typographic Service, Inc., New York, 1947.

Samuel Richardson: Master Printer, William M. Sale, Jr., Cornell University Press, Ithaca, N.Y., 1950.

The Shaping of Our Alphabet, Frank Denam, Alfred A. Knopf, Inc., New York, 1955.

Story of the Book, Agnes Allen, The Macmillan Company, New York, 1953.

Tramp Printer, Harry J. Muntz, Pageant Press, New York, 1953.

Updike: American Printer and His Merrymount Press, Peter Beilenson, American Institute of Graphic Arts, New York, 1947.

Wings for Words, Douglas C. McMurtrie, Rand McNally & Company, Chicago, 1940.

Style and Reference Books

Arithmetic for Printers, 2d ed., J. Woodard Auble, Chas. A. Bennett Company, Inc., Peoria, Ill., 1954.

Copy Editing Workbook, Vernon R. Frost and L. L. Jermain, Appleton-Century-Crofts, Inc., New York, 1952.

A Manual of Style, 11th ed., The University of Chicago Press, Chicago, 1949.

Printing and Promotion Handbook, 2d ed., Daniel Melcher and Nancy Larrick, McGraw-Hill Book Company, Inc., New York, 1956.

Safety Manual for the Graphic Arts Industry, L. Stemp, National Safety Council, Inc., Chicago, 1954.

United States Government Printing Office Style Manual, rev. ed., Government Printing Office, Washington, D.C., 1953.

Webster's New Collegiate Dictionary, G. & C. Merriam Company, Springfield, Mass., 1953.

Webster's New International Dictionary

of the English Language, G. & C. Merriam Company, Springfield, Mass., 1954.

BOOKBINDING

Basic Bookbinding, Arthur W. Lewis, The British Book Centre, Inc., New York, 1953.

Bookbinding and the Care of Books, 5th ed., Douglas Cockerell, Pitman Publishing Corporation, New York, 1954.

Bookbinding by Hand for Students and Craftsmen, Laurence Town, Pitman Publishing Corporation, New York, 1951.

Bookbinding at Home, Sidney Le Vine, Victor Press, New York, 1953.

Bookbinding for Schools, 6th ed., J. S. Hewitt-Bates, Chas. A. Bennett Company, Inc., Peoria, Ill., 1954.

General Bookbinding, rev. ed., Chris H. Groneman, McKnight & McKnight Publishing Company, Bloomington, Ill., 1946.

Lectures on Bookbinding for Hobbyists, Manly M. Banister, M. M. Banister, Kansas City, Mo., 1949.

Let's Bind a Book, Guy A. Pratt, The Bruce Publishing Company, Milwaukee, Wis., 1948.

Library Binding Manual, Louis N. Feipel and E. W. Browning, American Library Association, Chicago, 1951.

Theory and Practice of Bookbinding, Government Printing Office, Washington, D.C., 1950.

BLOCK PRINTING

Block Printing Designs, William S. Rice, The Bruce Publishing Company, Milwaukee, Wis., 1947.

Block Printing on Fabrics (wood), Florence H. Pettit, Hastings House, Publishers, Inc., New York, 1953.

Block Printing with Linoleum, Henry Frankenfield, C. H. Hunt Pen Company, Camden, N.J., 1949.

Essentials of Linoleum Block Printing, Ralph W. Polk, Chas. A. Bennett Company, Inc., Peoria, Ill.

Linoleum Block Printing, Francis J. Kafka, McKnight & McKnight Publishing Company, Bloomington, Ill., 1955.

Making Linoleum Cuts, Samuel Greenberg, Stephen Daye Press, New York, 1947.

SILK SCREEN

Handbook of the Silk Screen Printing Process, Harry Summer and Ralph M. Audrieth, Arthur Brown & Bro., Inc., New York, 1946.

Mitography: The Art and Craft of Screen Process Printing, Albert Kosloff, The Bruce Publishing Company, Milwaukee, Wis., 1952.

Modern Silk Screen, Victor Strauss, Pied Piper Press, New York, 1950.

Silk Screen Color Printing, H. Sternberg, McGraw-Hill Book Company, Inc., New York, 1942.

Silk Screen Printing, James Eisenberg, McKnight & McKnight Publishing Company, Bloomington, Ill., 1952.

Silk Screen Stencil Craft as a Hobby, J. I. Biegeleisen, Harper & Brothers, New York, 1939.

PAPERMAKING

From Trees to Paper: The Story of Newsprint, Henry B. Lent, The Macmillan Company, New York, 1952.

Guide to Career Opportunities in the Paper Industry, Beloit College, Beloit, Wis., 1954.

Paper and Its Uses, 4th ed., Edward A. Dawe, Anglobooks, New York, 1953.

Paper Making, 2d ed., Dard Hunter, Alfred A. Knopf, Inc., New York, 1947.

Paper Making in Pioneer America, Dard Hunter, University of Pennsylvania Press, Philadelphia, 1952.

Paper and Paper Making, F. H. Norris, Oxford University Press, New York, 1952.

Paper for Printing, Today and Tomorrow, U.N. Educational Scientific and Cultural Organization, Columbia University Press, New York, 1953.

Pulp and Paper Industry in the U.S.A., Organization for European Economic Cooperation, Columbia University Press, New York, 1951.

The Story of Papermaking, Edwin Sutermeister, R. R. Bowker Company, New York, 1954.

GRAPHIC ARTS

Books and Printing, Paul A. Bennett, The World Publishing Company, Cleveland, Ohio, 1951.

Craftsmen in the Graphic Arts, Florence E. Clark, International Textbook Company, Scranton, Pa., 1950.

Exploring the Graphic Arts, Anthony Marinaccio and Burl Neff Osburn, D. Van Nostrand Company, Inc., Princeton, N.J., 1942.

First Year Graphic Arts, Otis H. Chidester, Otis H. Chidester, Tucson, Ariz., 1949.

The Graphic Arts, William H. Johnson and L. V. Newkirk, The Macmillan Company, New York, 1942.

Graphic Arts Procedures, R. Randolph Karch, American Technical Society, Chicago, 1949.

Kodak Graphic Arts Handbook, Eastman Kodak Company, Rochester, N.Y., 1955.

The Printed Book, Harry G. Aldis, revised by John Carter and Brooke Crutchley, Cambridge University Press, New York, 1951.

PHOTOGRAPHY

Amateur Photographer's Handbook, 3d rev. ed., Aaron Sussman, Thomas Y. Crowell Company, New York, 1955.

Beginner's Book of Photography, rev. ed., Wallace E. Dobbs, Crown Publishers, Inc., New York, 1953.

Better Prints, The Camera Magazine, Baltimore, Md., 1950.

Bigger and Better: The Book of Enlarging, Don D. Nibbelink, Garden City Books, New York, 1952.

Careers in Photography, Carroll B. Neblette, Ziff-Davis Publishing Company, Chicago, 1946.

Complete Introduction to Photography, rev. ed., J. Harris Gable, Harper & Brothers, New York, 1948.

Develop, Print, and Enlarge Your Own Pictures, Jack O. Flynn, Albert J. Rosenberg, and Alan Kellock, McGraw-Hill Book Company, Inc., New York, 1952.

Developing, Printing, and Enlarging with Kodak Materials, Eastman Kodak Company, Rochester, N.Y.

Developing and Printing Made Easy, Ansco, Binghamton, N.Y.

The First Book of Photography, John Hoke, Franklin Watts, Inc., New York, 1954.

History of Photography from 1839 to the Present Day, Beaumont Newhall, Museum of Modern Art, New York, 1950.

How to Make Good Pictures, Guide for the Amateur Photographer, 29th ed., Eastman Kodak Company, Rochester, N.Y., 1951.

How to Take Better Photographs, B. M. Kanameisha (ed.), Popular Mechanics Press, Chicago, 1954.

How to Take Better Pictures, Arthur A. Goldsmith, The Bobbs-Merrill Company, Inc., Indianapolis, Ind., 1955.

How to Use Colour Film, Leslie C. Thomson, Focal Press, Inc., New York, 1950.

The Kodak Color Handbook, Eastman Kodak Company, Rochester, N.Y.

Kodak Master Photoguide, Eastman Kodak Company, Rochester, N.Y.

The Kodak Reference Handbook, Eastman Kodak Company, Rochester, N.Y.

Modern Color Photograph, rev. ed., William P. Durning, Crown Publishers, Inc., New York, 1954.

My Hobby Is Photography, Don Langer, Hart Publishing Co., Inc., New York, 1955.

New Guide to Better Photography, rev. ed., Berenice Abbott, Crown Publishers, Inc., New York, 1953.

Photo Darkroom Guide, Robert E. Hertzberg, Greenberg, Publisher, Inc., New York, 1954.

Photography, William Gottlieb, Alfred A. Knopf, Inc., New York, 1953.

Photography Handbook, Arco Publishing Company, New York, 1955.

Practical Photography, Benjamin K. Johnson, Longmans, Green & Co., Inc., New York, 1954.

Practical Photography, Robert A. McCoy, McKnight & McKnight Publishing Company, Bloomington, Ill., 1950.

Short Cut to Photography, Godfrey Frankel, Sterling Publishing Company, Inc., New York, 1954.

Toward Better Photography, Vincent McGarrett, American Photographic Publishing Company, New York, 1947.

What's Wrong with This Picture? Charles Abel, Greenberg, Publisher, Inc., New York, 1950.

Correlated List of Visual Aids

The films listed below and on the following pages can be used to illustrate and supplement much of the material in this book. For the convenience of users, they are grouped under three general headings—films of general interest, films depicting various printing processes, and films on photography. Both motion pictures and filmstrips are included, the character of each being indicated by the self-explanatory abbreviations "MP" and "FS." Immediately following this identification is the name of the main source (or sources) of the film. Abbreviations are used for these names and are identified in the list of sources at the end of the bibliography. Unless otherwise indicated, the motion pictures are 16mm sound black-and-white films and the filmstrips are 35mm black-and-white and silent. The length of motion pictures is given in minutes (min), of filmstrips in frames (fr).

Most of the films can be borrowed or rented from state and local film libraries, and users should consult *A Directory of 3,300 16mm Film Libraries,* available from the Government Printing Office, Washington 25, D.C.

Although this bibliography is a selective one, film users should also examine the latest annual editions and supplements of *Educational Film Guide* and *Filmstrip Guide,* published by The H. W. Wilson Company, New York. These *Guides,* standard reference books, are available in most school, college, and public libraries.

GENERAL-INTEREST FILMS

Colonial Printer (MP CWF 25min color). An account of eighteenth-century printing in America. Shows the methods employed to produce books, newspapers, and other printed materials. Emphasizes the importance of newspapers and of freedom of the press.

Democracy's Diary (MP McGraw 16min). Story of modern journalism, using *The New York Times* as an example. Includes scenes of the printing of the newspaper. Produced by RKO in *This Is America* series.

In Black and White (MP BIS 20-min). An explanation of and a tribute to the traditions of British printing. Dramatized sequences portray the discoveries through the ages that have led to improvements in printing processes. Surveys the status (1952) and future of the British publishing industry.

Love of Books (MP BIS 11min). Presents books as "things of paper, ink, leather, and glue" and shows that, while the printing press has outmoded handwork, British artists and artisans are carrying on the traditions of bookmaking. Produced by the Crown Film Unit for the British Board of Trade.

Printing (MP VGF 11min). A

vocational guidance film reviewing the printing industry and occupations. Shows hand composition, machine composition, proofreading, make-up, lockup, make-ready, and presswork (on platen, flat-bed, rotary, hand-fed, and machine-fed presses).

Printing thru the Ages (MP EBF 13min). Traces the story of printing from ancient times, including Gutenberg's contributions, evolution of modern type faces, impact of the industrial revolution, and modern book and newspaper printing operations. Produced for the British Ministry of Education by Films of Fact.

Printing Trades (FS SVE 47fr). Points out the various kinds of jobs available, the required qualifications, and the advantages and disadvantages of the different occupations.

Story of Printing (MP EBF 40-min). Reviews the progressive developments in printing from an early Babylonian seal being impressed on clay to the operations of modern printing presses. Produced for the British Ministry of Education by Films of Fact.

Printing Processes

Block Cutting and Printing (MP EFLA 13min color). Shows how to cut and print a two-color design, including details of transferring the design, cutting, proofing, correcting, registering for color, and printing the blocks by three different methods. Produced by the Stout Institute.

Five Centuries of Type Founding (FS Am Type 71fr with disc 30min). Traces the development of type from Jensen in 1470 to Caslon in 1720 and

gives illustrations of today's types derived from sources in that period.

Hasty Sign Making (MP USA/ UWF 21min). Demonstrates procedures to be followed, using an Army kit of materials, in making signs by the silk-screen process.

How to Build a Silk Screen Frame (FS Syracuse U 47fr). Describes the materials needed and the techniques used in building a printing frame and assembling the squeegee.

How to Make a Good Impression (MP Harris 21min color). Explains offset lithography through picturing a pamphlet from rough layout to the finished product. Includes explanations on making a halftone, color separations, stripping in, platemaking, multicolor runs, deep etch, and use of the four-color process.

How to Make Linoleum Block Prints (MP Bailey 10min color or b&w). Demonstrates different methods of printing with mounted and unmounted linoleum blocks on cloth and paper.

Kodak Ektagraph Process (MP Kodak 8min color). Demonstrates the Ektagraph process of making silk-screen stencils, including the types of copy that can be used, procedures for processing, and examples of silk-screen prints.

Of the People for the People (MP FON 14min). Explains and illustrates the steps in the silk-screen process.

Putting a Job on a Platen Press (MP Bailey 11min). Shows the operations of inking the press, putting in heavy and light forms, preparing a simple packing, marking and inserting guides, pulling and checking a proof, making necessary adjustments, sealing and tapping the guides, and placing grippers to cover the margins.

Rainbows to Order (MP Interchem 21min color). Explains and illustrates the processes used in manufacturing printing inks. Discusses the characteristics of different kinds of inks.

Silk Screen Textiles Printing (MP Bailey 11min color). Explains the basic silk-screen process and shows its use in cards, place mats, and dress and drapery textiles.

Type and Its Origin (FS Monsen 96fr color with disk 16min). Describes the development of the printed word from crude markings on cave walls up through modern typography.

Type Speaks (MP Am Type 25-min color). Reviews the history of foundry type and shows a type designer at work on his original drawings. These drawings are copied before pattern drawings are made, pattern plates cut, and matrices made in different sizes.

PHOTOGRAPHY

Action of Lenses and Shutters (MP OSU 12min). Illustrates the action of air-operated, spring-driven, and gear-driven shutters and gives the purpose and function of the leaf-type aperture in controlling depth of field.

Fundamentals of Photography (MP series USN/UWF). Five films with the following definitive titles: *The Basic Camera* (15min); *Elementary Optics in Photography* (19min); *Light-sensitive Materials* (22min color); *Developing the Negative* (16min); *Printing the Positive* (19min).

The Photographer (MP UWF 30min). Personality, philosophy, techniques, and artistry of Edward Weston, a contemporary American photographer, are illustrated through exhibitions of his portraits and through scenes of Weston at his home in California and on location, working and talking with his students. Produced by U.S. Information Agency for overseas use.

Photographic Darkroom Procedures (FS series McGraw). Two sets of filmstrips with the following titles: Set One—*Developing Roll Film* (62fr); *Developing Sheet Film and Film Packs* (46fr); *Contact Printing* (67fr); *Projection Printing* (86fr); *Spot Printing and Dodging* (42fr). Set Two—*Advanced Projection Control* (50fr); *Quality Control in Negatives* (126fr); *Print Contrast Control* (58fr); *Composition in Printing* (54fr); *Spotting of Prints* (58fr); *Print Presentation* (50-fr).

SOURCES OF FILMS LISTED

Am Type—American Type Founders, Inc., 200 Elmora Ave., Elizabeth, N.J.

Bailey—Bailey Films, 6509 De Longpre Ave., Hollywood 28, Calif.

BIS—British Information Services, 30 Rockefeller Plaza, New York 20, N.Y.

CWF—Colonial Williamsburg Films, Williamsburg, Va.

EBF—Encyclopaedia Britannica Films, Inc., 1150 Wilmette Ave., Wilmette, Ill.

EFLA—Educational Film Library Association, 250 West 57th St., New York 19, N.Y.

FON—Films of the Nations, 62 West 45th St., New York 36, N.Y.

Harris—Harris-Seybold Company, 4510 East 71st St., Cleveland 5, Ohio.

Interchem—Interchemical Corporation, Printing Ink Division, 67 West 44th St., New York 18, N.Y.

Kodak—Eastman Kodak Company, 343 State St., Rochester 4, N.Y.

McGraw—McGraw-Hill Book Company, Inc., Text-Film Department, 330 West 42d St., New York 36, N.Y.

Monsen—Monsen, Inc., 22 East Illinois St., Chicago 11, Ill.

OSU—Ohio State University, Teaching Aids Laboratory, Columbus 10, Ohio.

SVE—Society for Visual Education, Inc., 1345 West Diversey Parkway, Chicago 14, Ill.

Syracuse U.—Syracuse University, Audio-Visual Center, Syracuse 10, N.Y.

USA—U.S. Department of the Army, Washington 25, D.C.

USN—U.S. Department of the Navy, Washington 25, D.C.

UWF—United World Films, Inc., 1445 Park Ave., New York 29, N.Y.

VGF—Vocational Guidance Films, 215 East 3d St., Des Moines 9, Iowa.

Index